Electrical Coils
and Conductors

*Their Electrical
Characteristics
and Theory*

*This book is produced in full compliance
with the government's regulations for con-
serving paper and other essential materials.*

Electrical Coils and Conductors

Their Electrical Characteristics and Theory

BY

HERBERT BRISTOL DWIGHT

Professor of Electrical Machinery
Massachusetts Institute of Technology

First Edition

New York   *London*

McGRAW-HILL BOOK COMPANY, INC.

1945

ELECTRICAL COILS AND CONDUCTORS

THE MAPLE PRESS COMPANY, YORK, PA.

Preface

Cylindrical coils without iron cores frequently occur in electrical engineering work as reactance coils. They are used also for many purposes in physical laboratories. The collection of formulas in Chaps. 26 to 34 includes most of those needed for practical cases. Especial care has been employed to take account of the thickness of winding of such coils, because it is important in many cases.

The formulas for skin effect and eddy-current loss in transformer, generator, and motor windings and in bus bars, cables, and other heavy conductors, given in this book, have many practical applications.

Many numerical problems, based on practical cases, are given throughout the book.

Although some of the characteristics of apparatus are presented in the form of curves and can be read directly without trouble, for most of the calculations a knowledge of the principles of operation of the different types of electrical apparatus and a working knowledge of elementary integral calculus are assumed.

Many of the chapters in this book have been used as class notes on the subject of electrical machinery.

Acknowledgments are made to the following publications for permission to use articles or portions of articles, including figures, as mentioned by footnote or otherwise throughout the text: *Transactions of the American Institute of Electrical Engineers; Bulletin of the Bureau of Standards*, Washington; *Electric Journal; Electrical World; General Electric Review; Journal of Mathematics and Physics; Physics;* and "Standard Handbook for Electrical Engineers."

Thanks are due also to the following coauthors of papers: E. G. Allen, G. W. Andrew, M. M. Bagai, S. H. Chen, L. S. Dzung, Professor F. W. Grover, T. Y. Lu, R. W. Purssell, P. W. Sayles, H. W. Tileston, Jr., and T. K. Wang.

HERBERT B. DWIGHT.

CAMBRIDGE, MASS.,
April, 1945.

Contents

vii

ELECTRICAL COILS AND CONDUCTORS

CHAPTER 1

REACTANCE OF CONCENTRIC CORE-TYPE TRANSFORMERS

Concentric core-type transformers are a commonly used type of medium- and large-power transformers. The geometric shape of the copper coils and the pattern of the flux paths are simple so that with this type of transformer the computation of leakage reactance is comparatively straightforward and is quite precise.

The coils of concentric core-type transformers are circular cylinders surrounding the vertical parts of the laminated steel core. The core is rectangular and similar in shape to a heavy picture frame or window frame. The opening through the core is often called the "window." Each low-voltage coil is a cylinder close to the core. Surrounding each low-voltage coil, concentric with it and of the same length, is a high-voltage cylinder.

In single-phase transformers of this type, a series connection is usually made between the two low-voltage coils which are on different parts of the core; and a series connection is made also between the two corresponding high-voltage coils.

In three-phase transformers, there is a coil for each phase. A low-voltage cylinder with its concentric high-voltage cylinder is called a "leg" of the transformer.

Let the two rectangles in Fig. 1 be the cross section of the low-voltage and high-voltage coils of one leg of a concentric core-type transformer.

The flux density in the space of width g (Fig. 1) may be found by applying the fundamental law that, if a unit magnetic pole is carried completely around a current of I amperes, the work done in absolute electromagnetic units is $4\pi I/10$. This may be expressed by the equation

$$\oint H\,ds = \frac{4\pi I}{10} \qquad (1)$$

where the integral sign represents integration along a path that returns to the starting point, ds being an element of the path,

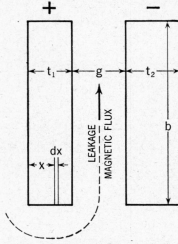

FIG. 1.—Section of transformer winding.

measured in centimeters, and H being the component of magnetic force along ds.

When one of the windings of the transformer is short-circuited and magnetizing current is taken to be negligible, as in calculating the leakage reactance of a transformer, then the ampere-turns applied to magnetizing the iron core are taken as zero and the ampere-turns of the high- and low-voltage windings are equal and opposite. The path along which the unit magnetic pole is carried surrounds one of the rectangles in Fig. 1, as is partly indicated by the dotted line. The leakage flux density may be taken as constant for the distance b, and the magneto-motive force (mmf) as zero for the remaining part of the way. This assumption is found, by measurement of the reactance, to give a good approximation.

The flux density in electromagnetic units is

$$B = H = \frac{4\pi N \times 2.54^2}{10 \times 2.54b} = 3.19\,\frac{N}{b} \qquad \text{lines/sq in.} \quad (2)$$

where dimensions are in inches, where N is the number of turns on one leg of the transformer represented in Fig. 1, in the winding which is taken to carry 1 ampere, and where the root-mean-square value of the alternating flux is given.

Let m be the length in inches of the circle that goes around the core through the middle of the insulation space g. The area of the ring of width g is gm and the leakage flux in the space of width g between the two windings is

$$\frac{3.19Ngm}{b} \qquad \text{lines}$$

The voltage drop in one leg caused by this alternating leakage flux, for 1 ampere, is

$$\frac{3.19N^2gm}{b} \times 2\pi f \times 10^{-8} = \frac{20N^2gmf}{b} 10^{-8} \qquad \text{volts}$$

This is equal in value to the reactance of one leg in ohms, due to flux in the space g, referred to the winding which has N turns per leg.

Effect of Flux in the Copper.   By carrying a unit pole along dx and returning on the outside to the left of the section (Fig. 1), it is seen that the flux in dx has a density x/t_1 times the density in g. It is linked with only x/t_1 of the turns of the winding marked $+$ and induces voltage in that part of the turns. The area of width dx has therefore x^2/t_1^2 times as much effect in producing voltage drop as a similar portion of g.

To find the thickness to which t_1 is equivalent, which may be added to g, integrate $\dfrac{x^2}{t_1^2} \, dx$ from $x = 0$ to t_1, giving

$$\frac{t_1^3}{3t_1^2} = \frac{t_1}{3}$$

Similarly, $t_2/3$ is also to be added to g.

The reactance of one leg of the transformer is

$$X = \frac{20N^2mf10^{-8}}{b}\left(g + \frac{t_1}{3} + \frac{t_2}{3}\right) \qquad \text{ohms} \quad (3)$$

where dimensions are in inches and N is the number of turns per leg. It may be noted that, for this approximate calculation, the same mean turn m is assumed for the three portions of leakage flux.

In most single-phase concentric core-type transformers, equation (3) must be multiplied by 2 to give the reactance of the complete transformer, since there are usually two legs in a single-phase power transformer.

Since the reactance varies as the square of the number of turns, a design may be changed so as to have lower reactance by increasing the section of iron and decreasing the number of turns. The reactance of transformers must usually be predetermined quite exactly, so as to obtain good parallel operation with transformers already installed.

The well-known equation (3) is found to agree quite well with tests for concentric core-type transformers with circular coils uniformly distributed along the stack, whose length is large compared with the distance between the high- and low-voltage windings.

An example of the computation of the leakage reactance of an untapped core-type transformer may be found in the computation of X_c in Example 2, Chap. 2.

CHAPTER 2

INTERLEAVED COMPONENT OF TRANSFORMERS

The reactance of a power transformer is materially changed when connection is made to taps of different voltages. This can be computed for concentric core-type transformers by dividing the winding into a concentric component and an interleaved component according to the method of H. O. Stephens.[1] In this chapter an algebraic formula for this change in reactance is derived.[2]

The concentric component is an assumed transformer winding in which the secondary ampere-turns are equal and opposite to the primary ampere-turns for each centimeter along the axis. The cylinder of winding of the actual transformer which has no part tapped out, is taken as one of the windings of the concentric component. The other winding of the concentric component matches the first exactly in ampere-turns per centimeter along the axis, magnetizing current being left out of consideration.

The interleaved component of winding is what is needed to be added to the concentric component to make the total equal to the actual transformer for the particular connection considered. Nothing needs to be added to the cylinder which has no part tapped out, and so the interleaved component is a single cylinder. Its positive and negative ampere-turns are equal and opposite. See Fig. 1 and the descriptions referred to in footnote 1.

It is evident, from the simple rules just given by which the interleaved component is defined, that the number of ampere-turns of the parts of the interleaved component of winding, and their location, can be easily determined without any special formulas. Examples are clearly illustrated in footnote 1. See also Example 1 of this chapter.

---

[1] Transformer Reactance and Losses with Non-uniform Windings, by H. O. Stephens, *Trans. A.I.E.E.*, Vol. 53, p. 346, 1934.
[2] A Formula for the Reactance of the Interleaved Component of Transformers, by H. B. Dwight and L. S. Dzung, *Trans. A.I.E.E.*, 1937, p. 1368.

When a terminal of a transformer is connected to one end of a high-voltage cylinder, additional insulation is put on the turns nearest the terminal, so as to withstand voltages due to lightning. When it is desired to operate on a lower tap, these turns should not be cut out. It is, therefore, a common practice to have the tapped-out turns near the center of the cylinder. Thus, in the right-hand rectangle of Fig. 1a, 10 per cent of the turns in the middle of the rectangle are by-passed by a connector so that these turns are not connected to anything and do not carry any

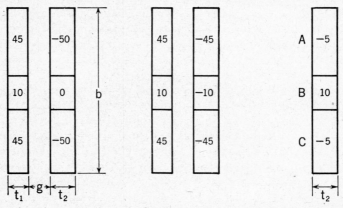

a. Actual transformer   b. Concentric component   c. Interleaved component

FIG. 1.—Transformer winding and winding components. The numbers represent ampere-turns. Rectangles vertically above one another, with numbers of the same sign, are connected in series.

current. Note that the numbers in Fig. 1 represent ampere-turns rather than turns.

The leakage reactance X of a transformer when expressed in ohms is referred to either the primary or the secondary side. This is the same as finding the leakage reactance in ohms of a one-to-one ratio transformer. If I is the current of the side taken, the stored energy of the leakage magnetic field is proportional to I^2X and is equal to the summation of $B^2/(8\pi)$ for every cubic centimeter of the leakage magnetic field in nonmagnetic regions. Magnetizing current is taken equal to zero or, in other words, the iron is assumed to have zero reluctance so far as the computation of leakage reactance is concerned.

If the primary and secondary of the one-to-one ratio transformer are connected in series and the current I is sent through them in the proper directions, the magnetic field will be the same as the leakage magnetic field, because it is produced by the same currents. The stored energy $B^2/(8\pi)$ will be the same and I^2X will be the same as in the transformer operation. But X is now $2\pi f L$ where L is the self-inductance of the complete circuit. This provides a method for computing X.

Since the ampere-turns of the concentric and interleaved components are together equal to the ampere-turns of the actual transformer, the summation of $B^2/(8\pi)$ when both are carrying current gives I^2X for the transformer. The magnetic field of the concentric component is chiefly axial where the density is greatest and the most energy is stored, and the densest parts of the field of the interleaved component are radial (see Figs. 2 and 3, footnote 1). The fields of the two components are chiefly at right angles.

In any cubic centimeter in nonmagnetic regions, the stored energy of two fields B_1 and B_2, which are at right angles, is $(B_1^2 + B_2^2)/(8\pi)$. As a consequence, the reactances of the concentric and interleaved components may be computed separately and added together to give, very nearly, the reactance of the tapped-out transformer. See the discussion by A. Boyajian, *Trans. A.I.E.E.*, 1934, p. 1318. This has been shown to be a close approximation, by comparing the result with the transformer reactance computed by methods not involving the division into concentric and interleaved components. Tests on practical transformers also have shown the accuracy of the method. See the discussion by A. N. Garin, *Trans, A.I.E.E.*, 1934, p. 1319.

The study of interleaved components has shown that when transformers are operating on voltage taps the reactance can be reduced and the eddy-current losses in the copper can be minimized, by thinning out the turns in one winding opposite the tapped-out section of the other winding.

For instance, if "thinning out" were to be applied to the transformer in Fig. 1, the center rectangle of thickness t_1 (Fig. 1a) would be given 5 per cent of the turns instead of 10 per cent. This would be done by spacing the disk coils twice as far apart in that section. The rectangles in the left-hand part of Fig. 1a and in Fig. 1b would be marked 47.5, 5, and 47.5. This would result in the ampere-turns for c being -2.5, 5, and -2.5. The radial flux or "cross flux" for the 10 per cent tap connection would be only one-half as great as if thinning out were not used. See footnote 1 and Example 1 of this chapter.

The definition of interleaved component which has been given applies quite well to the case of thinned-out transformer windings; therefore no special arrangements are necessary in the computation. All that is needed is to find the ampere-turns of the interleaved component and then the reactance of the two components of winding.

The leakage reactance of one leg of a concentric core-type transformer without tapped-out sections is given very closely by the following well-known formula, the dimensions being in centimeters and the letters referring to the same parts as in Chap. 1:

$$X_c = \frac{8\pi^2 N^2 fm 10^{-9}}{b} \left(g + \frac{t_1}{3} + \frac{t_2}{3} \right) \qquad \text{ohms} \quad (1)$$

See Fig. 1 and equation (3) of Chap. 1, to which this equation is equivalent. Note that $8\pi^2 \times 2.54 = 20$, the numerical constant in equation (3), Chap. 1. The dimension m is the length of mean turn for the transformer.

For the interleaved component of one leg of a core-type transformer which has one central tapped-out section, as shown in Fig. 1, find T, the number of turns in the tapped-out section in the interleaved component. The interleaved component has the same number of positive as negative ampere-turns. Assuming that the windings of the three rectangles A, B, and C (Fig. 1) are connected in series,

$$L_i = 2L_A + L_B - 4M_{AB} + 2M_{AC} \qquad (2)$$

since A and C are of the same size and their current is opposite in direction to that of B.

Let $L_{AB}{}^{(B)}$ equal self-inductance of A and B connected in series but with current direction and winding density in turns per square centimeter in both the same as in B. Let k be the ratio of winding density of B to that of A.

$$L_{AB}{}^{(B)} = L_A{}^{(B)} + L_B + 2M_{AB}{}^{(B)} \qquad (3)$$

since the entire inductive voltage drop in AB is made up of drop in A caused by its own current plus the drop in B caused by its own current, plus the drop in A caused by current in B, plus the drop in B caused by current in A.

$$2M_{AB}{}^{(B)} = 2kM_{AB} = L_{AB}{}^{(B)} - k^2L_A - L_B \qquad (4)$$

$$2M_{AB} = \frac{1}{k}L_{AB}{}^{(B)} - kL_A - \frac{1}{k}L_B \qquad (5)$$

$$L_{ABC}{}^{(B)} = 2L_A{}^{(B)} + L_B + 4M_{AB}{}^{(B)} + 2M_{AC}{}^{(B)}$$
$$= 2L_A{}^{(B)} + L_B + 2M_{AC}{}^{(B)} + 2L_{AB}{}^{(B)} - 2L_A{}^{(B)} - 2L_B$$
$$\text{from} \quad (3)$$

$$= 2L_{AB}{}^{(B)} - L_B + 2M_{AC}{}^{(B)}$$

$$2M_{AC} = \frac{2}{k^2}M_{AC}{}^{(B)} = \frac{1}{k^2}L_{ABC}{}^{(B)} - \frac{2}{k^2}L_{AB}{}^{(B)} + \frac{1}{k^2}L_B \qquad (6)$$

From (2), (5), and (6),

$$L_i = 2L_A + L_B - \frac{2}{k}L_{AB}{}^{(B)} + 2kL_A + \frac{2}{k}L_B + \frac{1}{k^2}L_{ABC}{}^{(B)}$$
$$- \frac{2}{k^2}L_{AB}{}^{(B)} + \frac{1}{k^2}L_B$$

$$L_i = 2(1+k)L_A + \left(1 + \frac{2}{k} + \frac{1}{k^2}\right)L_B + \frac{1}{k^2}L_{ABC}{}^{(B)}$$
$$- \frac{2}{k}\left(1 + \frac{1}{k}\right)L_{AB}{}^{(B)} \qquad (7)$$

Turns in $B = T$.
Turns in $A = T/2$.
Turns in $AB^{(B)} = T + k(T/2)$.
Turns in $ABC^{(B)} = T + kT$.

Assuming that the inductance of the windings per centimeter is the same as if they were straight,

$$L_A = 2p\,\frac{T^2}{4}\,\text{logn}\,\frac{u}{G_A} \qquad \text{abhenries}$$

$$L_B = 2pT^2\,\text{logn}\,\frac{u}{G_B} \qquad \text{abhenries}$$

$$L_{AB}{}^{(B)} = pT\,\frac{(2+k)^2}{2}\,\text{logn}\,\frac{u}{G_{AB}} \qquad \text{abhenries}$$

$$L_{ABC}{}^{(B)} = 2pT^2(1+k)^2\,\text{logn}\,\frac{u}{G_{ABC}} \qquad \text{abhenries}$$

where p is the mean turn in centimeters of the interleaved component, logn denotes natural logarithm, u is a certain large distance to which flux is counted and which cancels out later, and where G_A is the self geometric mean distance, or GMD, of the rectangle A, and similarly for the other rectangles. This type of computation, which applies quite well for transformer reactance, deals with the reactance per centimeter of the circuit made up of the primary and secondary windings, and it is assumed that the effect of their curvature is negligible.

The logarithm of the geometric mean distance, or GMD, between two areas is defined as the average of the logarithms of all possible distances from points on one area to those on the other, and the logarithm of the self GMD is the average of the logarithms of all possible distances between two points on the area. See Maxwell, "Electricity and Magnetism," Par. 691.

From (7), $L_i = pT^2 (1 + k) \operatorname{logn} \dfrac{u}{G_A} + 2pT^2 \left(1 + \dfrac{1}{k}\right)^2 \operatorname{logn} \dfrac{u}{G_B}$

$$+ 2pT^2 \left(1 + \frac{1}{k}\right)^2 \operatorname{logn} \frac{u}{G_{ABC}} - pT^2 \left(\frac{2 + k}{k}\right)^2 (1 + k) \operatorname{logn} \frac{u}{G_{AB}}$$
$$(8)$$

From the fact that the total turns in A, B, and C of the interleaved component are zero, and putting a = ratio of the axial length of rectangle B to the length of the complete rectangle ABC,

$$ka - (1 - a) = 0$$
$$k = \frac{1 - a}{a}$$
$$1 + k = \frac{1}{a}$$
$$1 + \frac{1}{k} = \frac{1}{1 - a}$$
$$\left(\frac{2 + k}{k}\right)^2 (1 + k) = \frac{(1 + a)^2}{a^2} \frac{a^2}{(1 - a)^2} \frac{1}{a} = \frac{(1 + a)^2}{a(1 - a)^2}$$

A very close approximation[3] to the self GMD of a rectangular area is $0.2235 \times$ (length + breadth). If this is used in (8), the following is obtained:

$$L_i = \frac{2.303pT^2}{a(1 - a)^2} [(1 + a)^2 \log_{10} S_{AB} - (1 - a)^2 \log_{10} S_A$$
$$- 2a \log_{10} S_B - 2a \log_{10} S_{ABC}] \quad (9)$$

[3] Formulas and Tables for Mutual and Self-inductance, by E. B. Rosa, and F. W. Grover, *Bur. Standards Sci. Paper* 169, equation (128), p. 167 (also published as *Bur. Standards Bull.*, Vol. 8, No. 1).

where S denotes (length + breadth) of the rectangle indicated.

The coefficient of logn u in (8) is

$$1 + 2a + a^2 - (1 - 2a + a^2) - 4a$$

which is equal to 0, and so u cancels out. In the same way, 0.2235 cancels out and does not appear in the final formula.

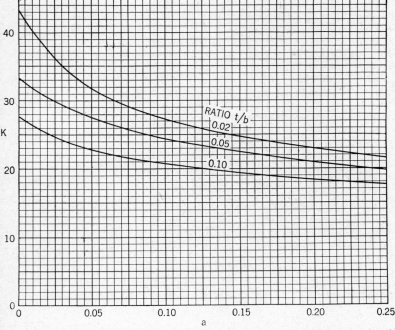

Fig. 2.—Curves for reactance of interleaved component: a, ratio of height of middle rectangle, to b; b, height of stack; t, thickness of interleaved component; f, frequency; p, mean turn of interleaved component, in centimeters; T, turns of interleaved component.

$X_i = KfpT^2\,10^{-9}$ ohms per leg.

Also, if S_{AB}, etc., are given in inches, their multipliers 2.54 cancel out, but this does not apply to the dimension p which must always be changed to centimeters.

From (9), $X_i = \dfrac{4.605\pi fp T^2 10^{-9}}{a(1 - a)^2} \left[(1 + a)^2 \log_{10} S_{AB} \right.$

$$- (1 - a)^2 \log_{10} S_A - 2a \log_{10} S_B - 2a \log_{10} S_{ABC_3}$$

$$\text{ohms per leg} \quad (10)$$

Curves are given in Fig. 2 by which most of the computation of equation (10) may be avoided.

Example 1.   A transformer has a tapped-out portion in the middle of each stack equal to 20% of the secondary turns of each stack.   Opposite this part, the primary winding has only 10% of its turns, the winding being thinned out by spacing the inividual coils farther apart.   If N is the number of turns in one cylinder of the secondary winding when not tapped, then T for equation (10) is 0.1 N when operating on the 80% tap.   When the transformer is operating on the 100% tap, the numerical value of T is also 0.1 N.

If the primary winding were not thinned out, then for operation on the 80% tap the value of T would be 0.2 N, and the increase in reactance would be about 4 times as great, since it varies as T^2.

Example 2.   Rating of transformer, 500 kva, 2,200/11,000 volts, single phase, 60 cycle, core type.   The l-v winding does not have taps and is not thinned out.   Taps to remove 20% of the turns of each h-v stack are provided, near the middle of the stack.

Axial length of stacks is 18.8 in.

Mean turn is h-v, 43 in.; l-v, 31.5 in.

Thickness of winding is h-v, 1.16 in.; l-v, 0.82 in.

Insulation space between high and low windings is 0.85 in.

The lengths of rectangles A, B, and C (Fig. 1c) are 7.5, 3.75, and 7.5 in. and their width is 1.16 in.

The number of turns per stack in the untapped h-v winding is 457.

The reactance X_c of the concentric component is computed by (1).   It is the same in this case as the reactance of the transformer when it is operated on the 100% tap.

$$\text{Mean turn for h-v and l-v} = \frac{43 + 31.5}{2} = 37.25$$

Let ohms per leg $= X_c$.

$$X_c = 8\pi^2 \times 457^2 \times 60 \times 37.25 \times 2.54 \times 10^{-9}$$
$$\times \frac{1}{18.8} \left(0.85 + \frac{0.82}{3} + \frac{1.16}{3} \right)$$

7.52 ohms per leg, referred to the h-v side.

$$\text{Per cent } X_c \text{ drop} = \frac{7.52 \times 45.45 \times 100}{5,500} = 6.21\%$$

The reactance X_i of the interleaved component is given by (10), the value of T being $457 \times 0.2 = 91$.

$$\log_{10} S_{AB} = \log_{10} (7.5 + 3.75 + 1.16) = \log_{10} 12.41 = 1.09377$$

Inch dimensions are permissible for S_{AB}, etc., as described following equation (9).

$$\log_{10} S_A = \log_{10} (7.5 + 1.16) = 0.93752$$
$$\log_{10} S_B = \log_{10} (3.75 + 1.16) = 0.69108$$
$$\log_{10} S_{ABC} = \log_{10} 19.91 = 1.29907$$
$$a = 0.2$$

$$X_i = \frac{4.605\pi \times 60 \times 43 \times 2.54 \times 91^2 \times 10^{-9}}{0.2 \times 0.64} [1.44 \times 1.09377$$

$$- 0.64 \times 0.93752 - 0.4 \times 0.69108 - 0.4 \times 1.29907] = 1.10 \quad \text{ohms per leg}$$

$$\text{Per cent } X_i \text{ drop} = \frac{1.10 \times 45.45 \times 100}{5,500} = 0.91\%$$

Reactance of the tapped transformer $= 6.21 + 0.91 = 7.12\%$

Thus, the reactance is increased about one-seventh by tapping out the section.

The rated input to the tapped transformer is taken to be 500 kva at 2,200 volts, the same as for the untapped transformer, neglecting magnetizing current.

The way in which N and T are used and the way in which reactance ohms are converted to percentages in the example should be noted, as the definitions for these items perhaps may be taken most easily from the example.

In order to make an approximate check of the calculations, a quarter-size model of the transformer coils of Example 2 was made. The reactance of the coils was measured without any iron core. In order to have the reactance larger than the resistance, a higher frequency current was used and the reactance then was corrected for 60-cycle current and for size. The result was 6.3 per cent for the tapped transformer, to compare with 7.12 per cent computed.

A quarter-size model of the interleaved component of the windings also was made and tested. Its reactance was 1.0 per cent, to compare with 0.91 per cent computed.

The result for Example 2 can be obtained from the curves of Fig. 2, putting $a = 0.2$ and $t/b = 0.062$. Then K from the curves is 20.4.

$$X_i = 20.4 \times 60 \times 43 \times 2.54 \times 91^2 \times 10^{-9}$$
$$= 1.11 \qquad \text{ohms per leg}$$

CHAPTER 3

CROSS SECTION OF TRANSFORMER CORES[1]

Core-type transformers of moderately large size have round, cylindrical coils. It is desirable to get as much iron as possible in the circular opening without undue complication, and this means, in practice, without having too many notches in the

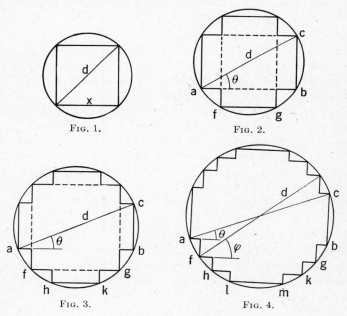

Fig. 1.

Fig. 2.

Fig. 3.

Fig. 4.

corners of the core with a correspondingly large number of different sizes of punchings.

In small transformers, a square core can be used, as in Fig. 1. For somewhat larger sizes, one notch can be used as in Fig. 2, and for still larger sizes, it will be economical to use the more complicated sections shown in Fig. 3, 4, or 5. For each of these

[1] The Cross Section of Transformer Cores, by H. B. Dwight, *Gen. Elec. Rev.*, February, 1935, p. 92.

there is a certain shape having the maximum amount of iron, the specification for which is given in Table I.   There does not seem to be any reason regarding cost or convenience in manufacture why the shape giving maximum section should not be used.

It can be stated that, from symmetry, if no notches are to be used, the section should be a square as in Fig. 1.   To verify this, take a rectangle of side x and area $x \sqrt{d^2 - x^2}$, where d is the

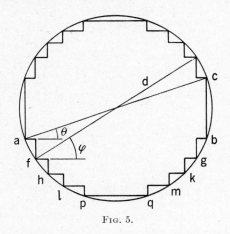

Fig. 5.

diameter of the given circle.   Differentiating the area with respect to x and equating to zero, we obtain

$$d^2 - x^2 = x^2$$

That is, $x^2 = d^2/2$, $x = d/\sqrt{2}$, and the figure is a square.

The space factor for gross iron is the ratio of the core section assembly to the area of the circle.   When there are no notches, it is

$$\frac{d^2}{2} \times \frac{4}{\pi d^2} = \frac{2}{\pi} = 0.6366$$

In the case of the other figures, it can also be stated that, from symmetry, the sections should be symmetrical about a 45-deg line.

If there is one notch per corner as in Fig. 2, the area of the dotted square is

$$d^2 \sin^2 \theta$$

and the area of the section is

$$A = d^2 \sin^2 \theta + 2d^2 \sin \theta(\cos \theta - \sin \theta)$$
$$= d^2(\sin 2\theta - \sin^2\theta) \tag{1}$$
$$\frac{\partial A}{\partial \theta} = d^2(2 \cos 2\theta - 2 \sin \theta \cos \theta)$$
$$= 0 \qquad \text{for maximum area}$$

Therefore, $\qquad 2 \cos 2\theta = \sin 2\theta$
$$\tan 2\theta = 2 \tag{2}$$
$$2\theta = 63°26', \qquad \theta = 31°43' \tag{3}$$
Then in Fig. 2, $ab = d \cos \theta = 0.8507d \tag{4}$
$$fg = bc = d \sin \theta = 0.5257d \tag{5}$$

The space factor, for one notch per corner, is

$$\frac{4}{\pi}\left(\sin 63°26' + \frac{1}{2}\cos 63°26' - \frac{1}{2}\right) \qquad \text{from} \quad (1)$$
$$= 0.7869 \qquad \text{See Table I}$$

When there are three notches per corner there are two angles φ and θ to be found. If Fig. 4 shows the maximum area for the given circle of diameter d, then any change will decrease the area. For instance, if φ is kept constant and θ is increased or decreased, the area will be decreased in either case. This is expressed by

$$\frac{\partial A}{\partial \theta} = 0$$

Similarly, $\qquad\qquad \dfrac{\partial A}{\partial \varphi} = 0 \qquad\qquad$ for maximum area

$$A = d^2 \sin^2 \varphi + 2d^2 \sin \varphi(\cos \varphi - \sin \varphi)$$
$$+ 2d^2 \sin \theta(\cos \theta - \cos \varphi)$$
$$= d^2(\sin 2\varphi + \tfrac{1}{2}\cos 2\varphi + \sin 2\theta - 2 \sin \theta \cos \varphi - \tfrac{1}{2}) \tag{6}$$

For maximum area,

$$\frac{\partial A}{\partial \theta} = d^2(2 \cos 2\theta - 2 \cos \theta \cos \varphi) = 0 \tag{7}$$

$$\frac{\partial A}{\partial \varphi} = d^2(2 \cos 2\varphi - \sin 2\varphi + 2 \sin \theta \sin \varphi) = 0 \tag{8}$$

$$\cos \varphi = \frac{\cos 2\theta}{\cos \theta} \qquad \text{from} \quad (7)$$

Let $\cos \varphi = x$ and let $\sin \theta = y$.

$$2x^2 - 1 - x \sqrt{1 - x^2} + y \sqrt{1 - x^2} = 0 \quad \text{from} \quad (8)$$
$$4x^4 - 4x^2 + 1 = (1 - x^2)(x^2 - 2xy + y^2)$$

Rearranging, $(x^2 - 1)(5x^2 - 2xy + y^2) + 1 = 0$

Let this be $f(x,y) = 0$.

Plot $f(x,y)$ on base θ, and where the curve cuts the zero line, the value of θ for maximum area is given.

When $\theta = 21°$, $f(x,y) = +0.00127$
      $\theta = 21°10'$, $f(x,y) = -0.00328$

For maximum area, $\theta = 21°3'$
Then $\varphi = 37°20'$

The distances between corresponding faces, and the space factor, are given in Table I.

TABLE I, CHAP. 3

Notches per corner	θ	φ	Diameter across flats = ab	fg	hk	lm	pq	Space factor for gross iron
0			$0.7071d$					0.6366
1	31°43′		$0.8507d$	$0.5257d$				0.7869
2	25°5′		$0.9056d$	$0.7071d$	$0.4240d$			0.8510
3	21°3′	37°20′	$0.9333d$	$0.7951d$	$0.6065d$	$0.3591d$		0.8860
4	18°17′	32°15′	$0.9495d$	$0.8458d$	$0.7071d$	$0.5336d$	$0.3138d$	0.9079

With four notches per corner,

$$A = d^2 \left[\tfrac{1}{2} + 2 \sin \varphi \left(\cos \varphi - \frac{1}{\sqrt{2}} \right) + 2 \sin \theta (\cos \theta - \cos \varphi) \right]$$
$$= d^2 (\tfrac{1}{2} + \sin 2\varphi - \sqrt{2} \sin \varphi + \sin 2\theta - 2 \sin \theta \cos \varphi) \quad (9)$$

$$\frac{\partial A}{\partial \theta} = d^2 (2 \cos 2\theta - 2 \cos \theta \cos \varphi) = 0 \text{ for maximum area} \quad (10)$$

$$\frac{\partial A}{\partial \varphi} = d^2 (2 \cos 2\varphi - \sqrt{2} \cos \varphi + 2 \sin \theta \sin \varphi) = 0 \quad (11)$$

Let $x = \cos \varphi = \dfrac{\cos 2\theta}{\cos \theta}$ from (10), and let $y = \sin \theta$.

From (11), $(4x^2 - x \sqrt{2} - 2)^2 - 4y^2(1 - x^2) = 0 = f(x,y)$
              $\theta = 18°10'$, $f(x,y) = -0.00456$
              $\theta = 18°20'$, $f(x,y) = +0.00164$

For maximum area,

$$\theta = 18°17' \quad \text{and} \quad \varphi = 32°15'. \quad \text{See Table I.}$$

Owing to enamel, oxide, and air spaces between the punchings, the net iron in a core is generally about 10 per cent less than the gross cross section of the assembly, that is, the building factor is about 0.9. The shapes indicated in Table I give the maximum gross section and also the maximum net iron. Similarly, if ducts are provided in the core, they will have a standard size and spacing and will reduce the section by a definite percentage, with very slight variations. Accordingly, Table I will still give the shapes for maximum iron.

CHAPTER 4

OPERATION OF DELTA AND V TRANSFORMER BANKS

If one transformer of a delta bank is taken out of service, because of burnout or other cause, it is well known that the rating

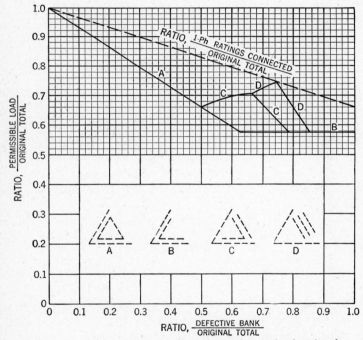

Fig. 1.—Curves of permissible loading of transformer banks after loss of a single-phase transformer. EXAMPLE: 4,500-kva and 5,500-kva delta banks connected as in A, with one 1,500-kva transformer cut out.

$$\frac{\text{Defective bank}}{\text{Original total}} = \frac{4,500}{10,000} = 0.45$$

$$\text{Permissible load, from curve,} = 0.7 \times 10,000$$
$$= 7,000 \text{ kva.}$$

of the remaining V bank is $1/\sqrt{3}$, or 58 per cent, of the rating of the complete delta bank. If, however, two unequal delta banks are in parallel and one single-phase transformer is taken out, the permissible load for the remaining transformers depends on which of the connections (A, B, C, or D) of Fig. 1 is used.

For such a case it may be assumed that the percentage impedance of the transformers is the same, since they are operating in parallel. This makes it possible to draw a simple set of curves of permissible loadings, shown in Fig. 1, which may be used instead of making calculations.[1]

To determine the currents in a delta bank, assume that a balanced three-phase load current is taken from the bank. The currents in the three lines A, B, and C may be represented as follows:

$$i_A = I$$
$$i_B = -0.5I + j\,0.866I$$
$$i_C = -0.5I - j\,0.866I$$

If j quantities are plotted at right angles to real quantities, representing 90-deg difference in phase, the above three currents will be seen to be equal in magnitude and 120 deg apart in phase.

Let the current in transformer AB, which is unknown, be

$$i_1 = i_p + ji_q$$

in the direction AB. The currents in the other transformers may be derived from i_1 and are

$$
\begin{aligned}
i_2,\text{ in direction } BC, &= i_1 - i_B \\
&= i_p + ji_q + 0.5I - j\,0.866I \\
i_3,\text{ in direction } CA, &= i_1 + iA \\
&= i_p + ji_q + I
\end{aligned}
$$

If the resistance and reactance of the transformers are inversely proportional to the transformer ratings, the impedance of the first transformer can be written

$$\frac{R}{K_1} + j\,\frac{X}{K_1}$$

where K_1 is the kilovolt-ampere rating of side AB of the delta. The units for R and X do not matter since R and X will cancel

[1] Transformer Bank Capacity, by H. B. Dwight and E. G. Allen, *Elec. World*, Sept. 15, 1928, p. 504.

out of the final expressions. Using similar expressions for the other sides of the delta, the impedance drops in the transformers are

$$\text{Drop in } AB = (i_p + ji_q)\left(\frac{R}{K_1} + j\frac{X}{K_1}\right)$$

$$\text{Drop in } BC = (i_p + ji_q + 0.5I - j\,0.866I)\left(\frac{R}{K_2} + j\frac{X}{K_2}\right)$$

$$\text{Drop in } CA = (i_p + ji_q + I)\left(\frac{R}{K_3} + j\frac{X}{K_3}\right)$$

Since these transformers are connected in delta and are assumed to have balanced voltages impressed on them, the sum of the above three parts is zero; that is, the sums of the real and imaginary parts are each equal to zero. Therefore,

$$i_pR\left(\frac{1}{K_1} + \frac{1}{K_2} + \frac{1}{K_3}\right) - i_qX\left(\frac{1}{K_1} + \frac{1}{K_2} + \frac{1}{K_3}\right)$$
$$= -I\left(\frac{0.5R}{K_2} + \frac{R}{K_3} + \frac{0.866X}{K_2}\right) \quad (1)$$

$$i_pX\left(\frac{1}{K_1} + \frac{1}{K_2} + \frac{1}{K_3}\right) + i_qR\left(\frac{1}{K_1} + \frac{1}{K_2} + \frac{1}{K_3}\right)$$
$$= -I\left(\frac{0.5X}{K_2} + \frac{X}{K_3} - \frac{0.866R}{K_2}\right) \quad (2)$$

Eliminate i_q and also R and X by multiplying (1) by R and (2) by X and dividing by $R^2 + X^2$.

$$i_p\left(\frac{1}{K_1} + \frac{1}{K_2} + \frac{1}{K_3}\right) = -I\left(\frac{0.5}{K_2} + \frac{1}{K_3}\right)$$

Similarly, $$i_q\left(\frac{1}{K_1} + \frac{1}{K_2} + \frac{1}{K_3}\right) = I\frac{0.866}{K_2}$$

Let AB be the first side of the delta to reach its rated load.

Then, $$i_p{}^2 + i_q{}^2 = \frac{K_1{}^2}{E^2}$$

where E is the rated voltage in kilovolts.

Let the permissible load on the bank be K_0 in kilovolt-amperes.

Then,
$$I = \frac{K_0}{E\sqrt{3}}$$

$$\frac{K_0^2}{3E^2}\left(\frac{0.25}{K_2^2} + \frac{1}{K_2 K_3} + \frac{1}{K_3^2} + \frac{0.75}{K_2^2}\right) = \frac{K_1^2}{E^2}\left(\frac{1}{K_1} + \frac{1}{K_2} + \frac{1}{K_3}\right)^2$$

$$\frac{K_0^2(K_2^2 + K_2 K_3 + K_3^2)}{K_2^2 K_3^2} = 3K_1^2 \frac{(K_1 K_2 + K_2 K_3 + K_3 K_1)^2}{K_1^2 K_2^2 K_3^2}$$

$$K_0 = \frac{1.732(K_1 K_2 + K_2 K_3 + K_3 K_1)}{\sqrt{K_2^2 + K_2 K_3 + K_3^2}} \tag{3}$$

It is seen that the side K_1, which first reaches its rated load as the load on the bank is increased, will be the smallest of the three kilovolt-ampere ratings K_1, K_2, and K_3, since this will give the largest possible value of the denominator of (3) and therefore the smallest value of K_0. The value of the numerator is the same no matter which side is at its rated load.

An example of the use of equation (3) may be taken from diagram A of Fig. 1, taking the capacity of the delta bank in A as $0.55Q$ where Q is the rating of the original total when both delta banks were complete. Then, $K_1 = 0.55Q/3$, $K_2 = Q/3$, and $K_3 = Q/3$, these being single-phase ratings. Then,

$$K_0 = \frac{1.732(0.55 + 1.0 + 0.55)Q}{3\sqrt{1 + 1 + 1}} = 0.70Q$$

See the example under Fig. 1.

K_0, K_1, etc., can be expressed in actual kilovolt-amperes or in ratios of the original total kilovolt-amperes, as desired. Their values can be written by inspection of diagram A, B, C, or D.

In explanation of the curves, the straight line A gives the permissible load that may be carried without overloading any part when one single-phase transformer has been removed, leaving the remainder connected as in diagram A. The delta part of diagram A may be made up of two or more delta banks in parallel. Thus, Fig. 1 applies to several banks of transformers in parallel and not merely to two.

For diagram A, the permissible load is equal to the rating of the complete delta bank plus the rating of one single-phase transformer of the V bank. If the defective bank, however, is

more than 63 per cent of the total, it is better not to use diagram
A, since it results in less than 58 per cent of the total rating.

Diagram B can always be used, as it involves merely disconnecting the remaining transformers of one phase, giving a
straight V connection.

Diagram C involves special wiring outside of the transformers,
or it involves wheeling the defective transformer out of its place
and wheeling one of the other transformers into the vacant place.

Diagram D involves special wiring. If the large transformers
of diagram D have three times the rating of the small ones, the
permissible load is equal to the sum of the ratings of the single-
phase transformers, thus giving 100 per cent "apparatus effi-
ciency." Except for this one case, this does not occur with any
of the diagrams (see Fig. 1).

The short curves C and D of Fig. 1 are parts of longer curves or
lines. Thus, the left-hand part of D curves downward so as to
pass through the point (0, 0) and the right-hand part of D is a
line passing through the point (1, 0.33). Only those parts of
the lines have been drawn which would probably be used in
practical operation of transformer banks.

A matter not illustrated in Fig. 1 is the permissible load of a
delta bank with a spare single-phase transformer connected
across one of the phases. The permissible load is 109 per cent
of the rating of the delta bank, when the four transformers are
duplicates and the spare transformer is connected in parallel
with one phase of the delta. If the four transformers are connected in double V—that is, with two V's in parallel—the permissible load is 115 per cent of the rating of the delta bank. The
latter arrangement would give a somewhat more unbalanced
voltage than the former.

When a delta bank becomes overloaded and a spare transformer is available, it may sometimes be good engineering to
use the spare to relieve the overload, increasing the rating of the
bank as just described. The reserve capacity of the spare
transformer is not sacrificed by doing this, for trouble usually
happens to only one single-phase transformer at a time.

CHAPTER 5

STANDARD SIZES FOR RECTANGULAR WIRE

For medium and large transformers and rotating machines, rectangular copper wire is usually used rather than round wire. By this means a greater cross section of copper can be put in a given space and the heat conductivity through the copper coil is improved, thus allowing a higher current density for a given temperature rise of the insulation.

Instead of allowing a list of standard sizes to grow up in a haphazard manner, it is better engineering to adopt a systematic list of standard sizes. A very successful list of this kind is made by using the simple rule that all widths and thicknesses are to be taken from the list of diameters of round copper wires of the American Wire Gauge. In this way the designer is assured that, within the limit of gauge sizes of 0.46 in. or a few sizes larger, there is always a size of rectangular copper about 12 per cent thinner or thicker, narrower or wider, than any given size.

The standard sizes just described are used to some extent in practice. They are the basis for the table of rectangular copper wire in the appendix of "Design of Electrical Apparatus," by J. H. Kuhlmann.

The basis by which the numbers are derived is that the diameter of No. 0000 round wire is given as exactly 0.46 in. and that

AMERICAN STANDARD COPPER WIRE SIZES, IN INCHES

0.460	0.129	0.0359
0.410	0.114	0.0320
0.365	0.102	0.0285
0.325	0.091	0.0253
0.289	0.081	0.0226
0.258	0.072	0.0201
0.229	0.064	0.0179
0.204	0.057	0.0159
0.182	0.051	0.0142
0.162	0.045	0.0126
0.144	0.040	0.0113
		0.0100

of No. 36 as exactly 0.005 in. The 39 intervals between them are made equal by ratio. The resulting values are specified to the nearest mil (0.001 in.) or $\frac{1}{10}$ mil, as desired, and the list of permissible dimensions in inches is obtained as shown on p. 24.

For an example, one of the standard sizes of rectangular copper according to this system is 0.064 by 0.325 in.

The increase of one number above the next is not exactly 12 per cent. Theoretically it is 12.293 per cent, since

$$\sqrt[39]{\frac{0.4600}{0.005}} = 1.12293$$

This exact ratio, of course, does not obtain between dimensions that are given to the nearest mil.

Another noticeable ratio is that 6 places above any number in the list there is another number that is almost exactly twice as great, or sometimes it will be just twice as great when the dimensions are given to the nearest mil.

Example 1.   Use logarithms to find to 5 significant figures the value of the dimension which is given in the list as 0.325 in.

Example 2.   Find the ratio, to 5 decimal places, of the precise values of two dimensions which are 6 places apart in the list of standard sizes.

CHAPTER 6

EDDY-CURRENT LOSS IN TRANSFORMER WINDINGS

For a concentric core-type transformer it may be assumed, as in calculating transformer reactance, that the leakage flux is in straight lines and that the reluctance for the leakage flux is equal to that of a path of length s, the length of the stack of coils. The cross section of one leg of a transformer is shown in Fig. 1, where the rectangles, which in most transformers are in a vertical position, are shown in a horizontal position.

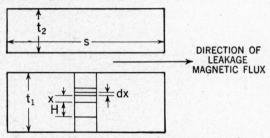

FIG. 1.—Section of core-type transformer winding.

To find the eddy-current loss in the pth conductor from the bottom in Fig. 1, in the winding of thickness t_1, first assume uniform current density of i amp per sq cm in the copper, as in the paper by H. W. Taylor.[1] Let all dimensions be in centimeters. Let there be q rectangular conductors one above the other connected in series, each of height H cm. In Fig. 1, $q = 4$ and $p = 3$. Let s be the length of the coils in the direction of the leakage magnetic flux (s is the same as b of Chaps. 1 and 2). Let the net amount of copper in the direction of s be W cm.

Current below $dx = iWx + (p - 1)iWH$, where x is measured from the bottom of the pth conductor.

[1] *Jour. I.E.E.* (England), Vol. 58, p. 279, 1920. In connection with Chaps. 6 and 7, see also Heat Losses in Conductors, by W. V. Lyon, *Trans. A.I.E.E.*, 1921, p. 1361, and "Standard Handbook for Electrical Engineers," 7th ed., Sec. 2, Par. 103.

Mmf due to this current $= \dfrac{4\pi i W x}{10} + \dfrac{4\pi i W H}{10}(p - 1)$

Flux density at $dx = \dfrac{4\pi i W x}{10s} + \dfrac{4\pi i W H}{10s}(p - 1)$ (rms value)

Only flux in the copper of the pth conductor produces eddy currents in that conductor, in this case where the conductors are all in series.

Multiply by dx and integrate from x to H. Flux above dx, between x and H, per centimeter along the conductors, is

$$\frac{4\pi i W}{10s}\left[\frac{H^2}{2} - \frac{x^2}{2} + H(p - 1)(H - x)\right]$$

Multiply by $j\omega 10^{-8}$ where $\omega = 2\pi f$ and $f = $ frequency.
Reactive voltage drop at dx due to this flux is equal to

$$j\,\frac{\omega 4\pi i W}{s10^9}\left[\frac{H^2}{2} - \frac{x^2}{2} + H(p - 1)(H - x)\right]\quad\text{volts/cm}$$

Let an eddy current of density i_1 flow, whose sum is zero when integrated over the section and whose resistance drop makes the voltage drop for all values of x uniform, as calculated so far. The resistance drop due to i_1 for any portion of cross section A of the conductor is

$$i_1 A\,\frac{\rho_1}{A} = i_1\rho_1 \quad\text{volts/cm}$$

where ρ_1 is the resistance in ohms of a centimeter cube of copper. Then

$$i_1\rho_1 + j\,\frac{\omega 4\pi i W}{s10^9}\left[\frac{H^2}{2} - \frac{x^2}{2} + H(p - 1)(H - x)\right] = \text{constant}$$

$$i_1 = j\,\frac{\omega 4\pi i W}{\rho_1 s10^9}\left[\frac{x^2}{2} + H(p - 1)x + K\right]$$

where K is a constant.

Now i_1 when integrated over the section of the pth conductor has zero total. Multiply i_1 by dx and integrate from $x = 0$ to H.

$$j\,\frac{\omega 4\pi i W}{\rho_1 s10^9}\left[\frac{x^3}{6} + H(p - 1)\frac{x^2}{2} + K x\right]_{x=0}^{H} = 0$$

$$\frac{H^3}{6} + \frac{(p - 1)H^3}{2} + KH = 0$$

$$K = \frac{H^2}{3} - \frac{pH^2}{2}$$

$$i_1 = j \frac{\omega 2\pi i W}{\rho_1 s 10^9} \left[x^2 + 2H(p-1)x + \frac{2H^2}{3} - pH^2 \right]$$

This is in quadrature with i as shown by the letter j and so the extra resistance loss due to the eddy current i_1 can be calculated separately.

The extra loss in the element of thickness dx whose section is $W\,dx$ and resistance $\rho_1/(W\,dx)$ is equal to

$$\left(\frac{\omega 2\pi i W}{\rho_1 s 10^9} \right)^2 [x^4 + 4x^3 H(p-1) + \tfrac{4}{3}H^2 x^2 - 2pH^2 x^2$$
$$+ 4H^2(p-1)^2 x^2 + 4H(p-1)x(\tfrac{2}{3}H^2 - pH^2)$$
$$+ \tfrac{4}{9}H^4 - \tfrac{4}{3}pH^4 + p^2 H^4]\,(W\,dx)^2 \frac{\rho_1}{W\,dx}$$

Integrate from $x = 0$ to H. Loss in the pth conductor is

$$\left(\frac{\omega 2\pi i W}{\rho_1 s 10^9} \right)^2 rwH^5 \left[\tfrac{1}{5} + (p-1) + \tfrac{4}{9} - \tfrac{2}{3}p + \tfrac{4}{3}(p^2 - 2p + 1) \right.$$
$$\left. + 2(p-1)(\tfrac{2}{3} - p) + \tfrac{4}{9} - \tfrac{4}{3}p + p^2 \right]$$

Divide by $i^2 \rho_1 W H$, the loss per centimeter due to the total main current of density i. Fractional extra loss due to eddy current i_1 is

$$\left(\frac{\omega 2\pi W}{\rho_1 s 10^9} \right)^2 H^4 \left(\frac{p^2}{3} - \frac{p}{3} + \frac{4}{45} \right) \tag{1}$$

It is desired to find the average value of (1) for q conductors. Note that

$$1 + 2 + 3 + \cdots + q = \frac{q(q+1)}{2}$$

and the average value is $(q+1)/2$.

$$1^2 + 2^2 + 3^2 + \cdots + q^2 = \frac{2q^3 + 3q^2 + q}{6}$$

and the average value is $\dfrac{q^2}{3} + \dfrac{q}{2} + \dfrac{1}{6}$.

The fractional extra loss for the q conductors is equal to

$$\left(\frac{\omega 2\pi W}{\rho_1 s 10^9} \right)^2 H^4 \left(\frac{q^2}{9} + \frac{q}{6} + \frac{1}{18} - \frac{q}{6} - \frac{1}{6} + \frac{4}{45} \right)$$
$$= \left(\frac{\omega 2\pi W}{\rho_1 s 10^9} \right)^2 H^4 \left(\frac{q^2}{9} - \frac{1}{45} \right) \tag{2}$$

Since this ratio is independent of the amount of the main current, it can be called a fractional increase in *resistance*. It is then equal to $(R_{ac} - R_{dc})/R_{dc}$.

Let the coefficient of $\left(\dfrac{q^2}{9} - \dfrac{1}{45}\right)$ in (2) be D and let h be height of the individual section of copper in inches, measured at right angles to the direction of leakage magnetic flux. Then, for copper at 75°C,

$$D = \frac{h^4 f^2 W^2 (4\pi^2)^2 \times 6.45^2}{1{,}724^2 \times 1.216^2 s^2} = \frac{h^4 f^2 W^2}{68 s^2} \tag{3}$$

The number 1.216 is the ratio for changing the resistivity from 20 to 75°C. It is

$$\frac{234.5 + 75}{234.5 + 20} = \frac{309.5}{254.5} = 1.216$$

Calling the numerator, $234.5 + 75$, the temperature factor for 75°C, then for other copper temperatures, the number 68 can be changed in proportion to the square of the temperature factor.

For slide-rule work, it is advantageous to compute

$$\sqrt{D} = \frac{h^2 f W}{8.23 s} \qquad \text{(for 75°C)} \tag{4}$$

and then square it to obtain D. For other temperatures, the number 8.23 should be changed in proportion to the temperature factor.

Conductors in Series. If there are q rectangular conductors one above the other, counted across the direction of leakage flux, for the primary or secondary separately, each conductor being of height h in. and all connected in series, then the average extra loss is given by the ratio

$$\frac{R_{ac} - R_{dc}}{R_{dc}} = D\left(\frac{q^2}{9} - \frac{1}{45}\right) \tag{5}$$

where D is computed by (4) [see equation (2)]. Note that the insulation between the q conductors does not affect the extra loss in this case. It is sometimes convenient to write $1/45$ as $0.2/9$.

The eddy-current loss ratio for the primary and secondary of a transformer should be computed separately, using, in general, different values of h and q in (3) and (5).

To find the eddy-current loss ratio of the complete transformer, the ratios for the primary and secondary should be averaged on the basis of the d-c loss to which each ratio applies. For example, if the primary has a d-c loss of 100 kw with 4 per cent eddy-current loss and the secondary has a d-c loss of 150 kw with 6 per cent eddy-current loss, the total eddy-current loss is $4 + 9 = 13$ kw and the total d-c loss is 250 kw. The eddy-current loss ratio for the transformer is then $\frac{13}{250} = 0.052$ or 5.2 per cent.

Laminated Conductors, Transposed. When the laminations are so transposed that they all have equal currents, the magnetic-flux density at every point and the crowding of current across the copper, that is, the eddy currents, are the same as if the laminations were in series, and equation (5) should be used. The dimension h is the thickness of one lamination and q is the number of laminations counted across the leakage flux from zero flux density to maximum in either the primary or secondary, whichever is being considered. It is usual to transpose the laminations of a transformer so that they have equal currents.

It is seen from equations (3) and (4) that the eddy-current loss is proportional to the fourth power of the dimension of the copper lamination, measured across the leakage flux. Since the axial dimension of the copper is often $\frac{1}{4}$ to $\frac{3}{8}$ in., while the radial dimension is usually less than $\frac{1}{8}$ in., a small component of leakage flux in a radial direction can produce a relatively large amount of eddy-current loss, as mentioned in Chap. 2.

Effect of Additional Calculated Terms. The eddy current i_1 was computed from the magnetic field caused by the uniform current density i. But a magnetic field is also caused by the current i_1 and produces an eddy current of density i_2. The values of the currents i, i_1, i_2, etc., form a series which, when the eddy-current loss is not excessive, is so rapidly convergent that the current i_2 can be neglected.

This can be shown from the solution of this problem obtained from a differential equation, as given by W. V. Lyon in the paper referred to at the beginning of this chapter. This gives (see case 3, p. 1378, of his paper) for nonlaminated conductors in series

$$\frac{R_{ac}}{R_{dc}} = M_r + \frac{q^2 - 1}{3} N_r$$

$$= \text{real part of } \left[\alpha d \coth \alpha d + \frac{q^2 - 1}{3} 2\alpha d \tanh \frac{\alpha d}{2} \right] \tag{6}$$

where $\alpha^2 = j \dfrac{8\pi^2 f W}{\rho_1 s 10^9},$ $\tag{7}$

d = thickness of one copper strap, cm, the same as H, equation (1).

Replacing the hyperbolic functions by their series, there is obtained

$$\frac{R_{ac}}{R_{dc}} = \text{real part of } \left[1 + \frac{1}{3}(\alpha d)^2 - \frac{1}{45}(\alpha d)^4 + \frac{2}{945}(\alpha d)^6 \right.$$
$$- \frac{1}{4,725}(\alpha d)^8 + \cdots + \left(\frac{q^2 - 1}{3} \right) 4 \left\{ \left(\frac{\alpha d}{2} \right)^2 - \frac{1}{3}\left(\frac{\alpha d}{2} \right)^4 \right.$$
$$\left. \left. + \frac{2}{15}\left(\frac{\alpha d}{2} \right)^6 - \frac{17}{315}\left(\frac{\alpha d}{2} \right)^8 + \frac{62}{2,835}\left(\frac{\alpha d}{2} \right)^{10} - \cdots \right\} \right]$$

The quantity $(\alpha d)^2$ contains j and is unreal. The quantities $(\alpha d)^4$ and $(\alpha d)^8$ are real.

$$\frac{R_{ac} - R_{dc}}{R_{dc}} = -\frac{1}{45}(\alpha d)^4 - \frac{1}{4,725}(\alpha d)^8 - \cdots$$
$$-\frac{4}{9}(q^2 - 1)\left[\left(\frac{\alpha d}{2} \right)^4 + \frac{17}{105}\left(\frac{\alpha d}{2} \right)^8 + \cdots \right]$$

Note that $\qquad -\dfrac{1}{45} + \dfrac{1}{36} = \dfrac{1}{4 \times 45}$

and

$$\frac{17}{945 \times 64} - \frac{1}{4,725} = \frac{85 - 64}{4,725 \times 64} = \frac{1}{225 \times 64} = \frac{1}{4 \times 3,600}$$

$$\frac{R_{ac} - R_{dc}}{R_{dc}} = -\frac{q^2}{4}\left[\frac{1}{9}(\alpha d)^4 + \frac{17}{945 \times 16}(\alpha d)^8 \cdots \right]$$
$$+ \frac{1}{4}\left[\frac{1}{45}(\alpha d)^4 + \frac{1}{3,600}(\alpha d)^8 \cdots \right]$$

Now, from equation (2), $\sqrt{D} = \dfrac{4\pi^2 f W H^2}{\rho_1 s 10^9} = \dfrac{\alpha^2 d^2}{2j}$

where $H = d$ is height of one rectangular copper wire in centimeters.

Then,
$$D = -\frac{\alpha^4 d^4}{4}$$

$$\frac{R_{ac} - R_{dc}}{R_{dc}} = q^2 \left[\frac{1}{9} D - \frac{17}{3,780} D^2 \cdots \right] - \frac{1}{45} D + \frac{1}{900} D^2 \cdots \quad (8)$$

This checks with (5) and shows further terms of the series.

Example. The h-v winding of a 60-cycle concentric core-type transformer consists of 40 disk-shaped coils in each stack. The laminated copper conductor has 3 laminations in parallel, each 0.102×0.365 in., and each disk-shaped coil has 9 turns of the laminated conductor, the laminations being completely transposed. The 0.102-in. dimension is in a radial direction. The space between disk coils is 0.41 in., copper to copper.

Find the ratio of eddy-current loss of the h-v winding at 75°C, assuming that the leakage magnetic flux is in straight lines parallel to the axis. Find also the effect of the terms involving D^2.

$$q = 9 \times 3 = 27$$

$$\sqrt{D} = \frac{0.102^2 \times 60 \times 0.365 \times 40}{8.23(0.365 \times 40 + 0.41 \times 39)} = 0.0361$$

$$D = 0.00131$$

$$\frac{R_{ac} - R_{dc}}{R_{dc}} = 0.00131 \left(\frac{27^2 - 0.2}{9} \right) = 0.106, \qquad \text{or } 10.6\%$$

$$\text{Term in } q^2 D^2 = -\frac{17}{3,780} \times 27^2 \times 0.00131^2 = 4.3 \times 10^{-6}$$

$$\text{Term in } D^2 = \tfrac{1}{900} \times 0.00131^2 = 1.9 \times 10^{-9}$$

These are negligible compared with 0.106.

CHAPTER 7

EDDY-CURRENT LOSS IN ARMATURE COILS

The formulas for eddy-current loss in armature coils are similar to those for eddy currents in transformer coils. Each formula is the first term of a convergent series. The succeeding terms, that is, the terms in D^2 and higher powers, are negligible if the calcuated increase in loss due to eddy currents is comparatively small, which is the case in most practical designing.

As in equation (3), Chap. 6, let

$$D = \frac{h^4 f^2 W^2}{68 s^2}$$

where h = height, in., of one of the rectangular copper wires or laminations making up the coil, measured perpendicularly to the leakage flux, which is taken to go horizontally across the slot when the slot is pointing vertically upward.

f = cycles/sec.

W = net amount of copper measured horizontally across the slot.

s = width of slot.

The number 68 corresponds to copper at 75°C.

As in the case of transformers [see equation (4), Chap. 6], it is more convenient for slide-rule work to compute the value of

$$\sqrt{D} = \frac{h^2 f W}{8.23 s} \tag{1}$$

and then square it to obtain D. The number 8.23 contains the factor $234.5 + 75 = 309.5$, which is the temperature factor for copper at 75°C. For copper at other temperatures, the number 8.23 should be changed in proportion to the temperature factor.

1. All Rectangular Wires in Series. Extra-loss factor for lower half of slot, embedded part of coil,

$$\frac{R_{ac} - R_{dc}}{R_{dc}} = D\left(\frac{q^2}{9} - \frac{1}{45}\right) \tag{2}$$

where q indicates the number of wires of height h in the *half* slot, one above the other.

Extra-loss factor for upper half of slot, embedded part of coil,

$$\frac{R_{ac} - R_{dc}}{R_{dc}} = D\left(\frac{7}{9}q^2 - \frac{1}{45} - \frac{2}{3}q^2\sin^2\frac{\phi}{2}\right) \qquad (3)$$

where ϕ is the phase angle between the upper and lower currents. This is usually either 0 or 60 deg in a three-phase machine

The extra-loss factor for the entire slot (embedded part of coil) is the average of (2) and (3) and is

$$\frac{R_{ac} - R_{dc}}{R_{dc}} = D\left(\frac{4}{9}q^2 - \frac{1}{45} - \frac{1}{3}q^2\sin^2\frac{\phi}{2}\right) \qquad (4)$$

q being the number of conductors in the *half* slot, one above the other.

Note that the amount of insulation between the conductors does not affect the extra loss when the rectangular wires are all in series (conductors not laminated). Terms in D^2 have been omitted. Since the magnetic flux density is weak in the parts of the coil that are not embedded in the slots, it is taken that the eddy-current loss in those parts is negligible.

2. Laminated Conductors, Thoroughly Transposed. In the Punga and Roebel types of transposed conductors, the laminations lie in inclined planes and go successively from top to bottom positions in the conductor. These are illustrated in the "Standard Handbook for Electrical Engineers," Sec. 7, Par. 25. Since all laminations have an equal exposure in the upper positions, where current density tends to be high, the result is that the amperes in all the laminations are almost exactly the same. Then magnetic flux conditions and current distribution are the same as if all the laminations were in series. Equations (1) to (4) are used, h being the height of one lamination in inches and q being the number of laminations one above the other in a half slot. This loss, which is in the embedded part, is called the "short-path eddy-current loss." The loss in the nonembedded part of the coil is taken to be negligible.

3. Laminated Conductors, Not Thoroughly Transposed. Cases will be taken up where the laminations are soldered together at the ends of each coil. Circulating currents flow along the upper laminations and return along the lower ones, producing extra copper loss in the entire coil, in both the embedded and the nonembedded parts. This extra loss is called the "long-path eddy-current loss." It is to be added to the short-path loss given by equations (1) to (4) which occurs in the embedded parts of all coils. The two types of circulating current are taken not to influence each other, which is a close approximation in practical cases.

If, with the slot pointing upward as in Fig. 1, the copper is laminated in a horizontal direction and the laminations are short-circuited together at the ends of the core, the current distribution and the loss are the same as for solid copper if the insulation between the laminations is infinitely thin. As the current flows in paths parallel to the laminations, its flow is not changed in any way by the thin insulation between the laminations.

If now, in a case of a large number of laminations in parallel, the insulation has appreciable thickness while the copper and its resistance are unchanged, then the total depth of a laminated conductor is increased in the ratio c, where c is a fraction greater than 1, equal to the gross height of a laminated conductor divided by the net height of copper in it. The amount of flux (not the density) and the reactive voltage producing i_1 are increased in the ratio c and, as the resistance is unchanged, the current i_1 is increased in the ratio c and the loss in the ratio c^2.

In a generator, the coils extend past the core, and the laminations are usually short-circuited together at the ends of the coils; therefore only the fraction b of the coil is subjected to voltage driving circulating current around the laminations, where b is the core length divided by the length of a half turn of the coil. This long-path circulating current is proportional to b as well as to c, and the loss due to it is proportional to b^2c^2. The factor b is less than 1. In the formulas the long-path eddy-current loss may be recognized by the presence of the multipliers b^2c^2.

In calculating the long-path eddy-current loss, any laminated conductor may be called right side up, ⊟, denoted by D (direct). For such a conductor, let

$$I_0 = +I_b \tag{5}$$

where I_b is the vector sum of all the current below it in the same slot.

For conductors wrong side up, ⊡, denoted by R (reversed),

$$I_0 = -I - I_b \tag{6}$$

where I is the current in the conductor considered and I_b is the vector sum of all the current below it.   That is, I_0 is always (-1) times all of the current in the slot below the double line (see Fig. 1) of the conductor considered, added vectorially.

The special twisting of the laminated conductors, by which D can be changed to R as desired, as in Fig. 1, is illustrated in Reduction of Armature Copper Losses, by I. H. Summers, *Trans.*

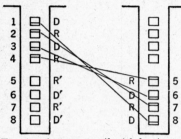

Fig. 1.—Armature coil with laminated conductors.

A.I.E.E., 1927, p. 102, and by a photograph in "Design of Electrical Apparatus," by J. H. Kuhlmann, p. 199.

a. Normal Diamond-type Coils without Special Twisting and with Upper and Lower Currents in Phase. Let there be t turns per coil, that is, t laminated conductors per half slot, one above the other.

($tn = q$ = number of laminations per half slot, one above the other.) Any normal diamond-type coil, without special twisting of the laminated conductors, is arranged $DD \cdots RR \cdots$, starting at the top.   If the currents of the upper and lower halves of the slot are in phase,

$$\text{Total } I_0 = [(2t - 1) + (2t - 2) + \cdots + (2t - t) - t$$
$$- (t - 1) - \cdots - 1]I$$
$$= \left[2t^2 - \frac{2t(t + 1)}{2} \right] I = (t^2 - t)I$$

since the sum of the first t integers is $\dfrac{t(t + 1)}{2}$.

The average value of I_0/I is

$$\frac{\text{total } I_0}{2tI} = \frac{t - 1}{2} \tag{7}$$

for a normal-type coil with the upper and lower currents in phase.

The extra-loss ratio due to long-path eddy current in a coil with any arrangement of direct and reversed laminated conductors is

$$b^2 c^2 \left[M_r - 1 + \left(\left| \frac{I_0}{I} \right|^2 + \left| \frac{I_0}{I} \right| \cos \delta \right) N_r \right] \tag{8}$$

where the notation is the same as in Chap. 6.   This result is given in Heat Losses in the Conductors of A. C. Machines, by W. V. Lyon, *Trans. A.I.E.E.*, 1921, p. 1378.   The average value of I_0/I is to be used.   The angle δ is the phase angle between I_0 and I.

As derived in Chap. 6,

$$M_r - 1 = -\frac{1}{45}(\alpha d)^4 - \frac{1}{4{,}725}(\alpha d)^8 - \cdots \qquad (9)$$

and
$$N_r = 4\left[-\frac{1}{3}\left(\frac{\alpha d}{2}\right)^4 - \frac{17}{315}\left(\frac{\alpha d}{2}\right)^8 - \cdots\right] \qquad (10)$$

where d is the net height of copper in the laminated conductor and

$$-\frac{\alpha^4 d^4}{4} = Dn^4$$

D being computed for a single lamination and n being the number of laminations per conductor.

$$M_r - 1 = \frac{4}{45}Dn^4 - \frac{16}{4{,}725}D^2 n^8 + \cdots \qquad (11)$$

$$N_r = \frac{Dn^4}{3} - \frac{17}{1{,}260}D^2 n^8 + \cdots \qquad (12)$$

The terms involving D^2 are usually negligible for practical machines, but this should not be taken for granted.   The user of the formulas should make sure whether the terms in D^2 are negligible or not.

The extra-loss ratio due to long-path eddy current in a normal diamond-type coil without special twisting of the laminated conductors, and with upper and lower currents in phase, is, from (7) and (8),

$$b^2 c^2 \left[\frac{4}{45}Dn^4 - \frac{16}{4{,}725}D^2 n^8 + \cdots + \left(\frac{t^2 - 2t + 1}{4}\right.\right.$$
$$\left.\left. + \frac{t-1}{2}\right)\left(\frac{Dn^4}{3} - \frac{17}{1{,}260}D^2 n^8 + \cdots\right)\right]$$
$$= b^2 c^2 \left[\frac{4}{45}Dn^4 - \frac{16}{4{,}725}D^2 n^8 + \cdots + \left(\frac{t^2 - 1}{4}\right)\left(\frac{Dn^4}{3}\right.\right.$$
$$\left.\left. - \frac{17}{1{,}260}D^2 n^8 + \cdots\right)\right] \qquad (13)$$

b. Normal Diamond-type Coils without Special Twisting and with Upper and Lower Currents 60 deg out of Phase. If the phase belts in a three-phase machine overlap a little, the phase angle between the upper and lower currents is 60 deg.

Using the method of W. V. Lyon's paper,

$$\text{Total } I_0 = [(t - 1) + (t - 2) + \cdots + 0$$
$$+ t^2(\cos 60° + j \sin 60°) - t - (t - 1) - \cdots - 1]I$$

$$\text{Average } \frac{I_0}{I} = \frac{\text{total } I_0}{2tI} = \frac{t}{4} - \frac{1}{2} + jt\frac{\sqrt{3}}{4}$$

$$\left|\frac{I_0}{I}\right|^2 = \left(\frac{t}{4} - \frac{1}{2}\right)^2 + \frac{3}{16}t^2 = \frac{t^2}{4} - \frac{t}{4} + \frac{1}{4}$$

$$\left|\frac{I_0}{I}\right| \cos \delta = \text{real part of } \frac{I_0}{I} = \frac{t}{4} - \frac{1}{2}$$

The extra-loss ratio due to long-path eddy current, omitting terms in D^2, is, from (8),

$$b^2c^2\left[\frac{4}{45}Dn^4 + \left(\frac{t^2}{4} - \frac{t}{4} + \frac{1}{4} + \frac{t}{4} - \frac{1}{2}\right)\frac{Dn^4}{3}\right]$$
$$= b^2c^2\left[\frac{4}{45}Dn^4 + \left(\frac{t^2 - 1}{4}\right)\frac{Dn^4}{3}\right] \quad (14)$$

This is the same expression as (13). Therefore, for normal coils without special twisting, the long-path eddy-current loss is the same whether the upper and lower currents are in phase or are 60 deg out of phase. This is not true of all types of coils. The short-path eddy-current loss, which is to be added to (13) or (14), is not the same if the phase angle ϕ between the upper and lower currents is 0 or 60 deg, as is shown by (4).

c. Diamond Coils with Twisted Conductors, with an Even Number of Turns per Coil and Upper and Lower Currents in Phase. If t is even, the recommended arrangement of twisted conductors is $DRDR \cdots RDRD \cdots$ as in Fig. 1. This can be obtained by twisting each conductor, turning it upside down, as it passes the end of the coil away from the terminals. See the paper by I. H. Summers, *Trans. A.I.E.E.*, 1927, p. 102, Fig. 3.

$$\text{Total } I_0 = [t - 1 - (t - 1) + (t - 3) - (t - 3) \cdots$$
$$+ t - t + t - t + \cdots - t + (t - 2) - (t - 2)$$
$$+ (t - 4) - (t - 4) \cdots + 2 - 2 + 0]I$$

$$\text{Average } \frac{I_0}{I} = \frac{\text{total } I_0}{2tI} = -\frac{1}{2} \quad (15)$$

The extra-loss ratio due to long-path eddy current, from (8) and (15), is

$$b^2 c^2 \left[\frac{4}{45} D n^4 - \frac{16}{4,725} D^2 n^8 + \left(\frac{1}{4} - \frac{1}{2} \right) \left(\frac{D n^4}{3} - \frac{17}{1,260} D^2 n^8 \right) \right]$$
$$= b^2 c^2 \left[\frac{D n^4}{180} - \frac{D^2 n^8}{75,600} \right] \quad (16)$$

This is very small compared with an untwisted coil. It is to be noted that twisting the conductors does not reduce the short-path eddy-current loss, which can be minimized by using a large number of thin laminations to make up the conductor.

d. Diamond Coils with Twisted Conductors, with an Even Number of Turns per Coil and with Upper and Lower Currents 60 deg out of Phase. With the same arrangement as in Case (3)

$$\text{Total } I_0 = [(t - 1) - (t - 1) + (t - 3) - (t - 3) \cdots$$
$$+ t\underline{/\phi} - t\underline{/\phi} + t\underline{/\phi} - t\underline{/\phi} \cdots - t + (t - 2) - (t - 2)$$
$$+ (t - 4) - (t - 4) \cdots + 2 - 2 + 0]I$$

where $\underline{/\phi} = \cos \phi + j \sin \phi$.

$$\text{Average } \frac{I_0}{I} = -\frac{1}{2}$$

which is the same as in (15). Equation (16), therefore, gives the long-path eddy-current loss ratio when the upper and lower currents are in phase and also 60 deg out of phase, for an even number of turns per coil.

e. Diamond Coils with Twisted Conductors, with an Odd Number of Turns per Coil and with Upper and Lower Currents in Phase. For 3 turns per coil, use *DRD, RRR,* starting at the top or open end of the slot, as in Fig. 1.

$$\text{Total } I_0 = [5 - 5 + 3 - 3 - 2 - 1]I$$
$$\text{Average } \frac{I_0}{I} = \frac{-3I}{6I} = -\frac{1}{2}$$

For 5 turns per coil, use *DRDRR, RDDDD,* starting at the top.

For 7 turns per coil, use *DRDRDRR, RDDRDDD,* starting at the top.

There is apparently no rule for the order of *D* and *R*.

In all these cases,

$$\text{Average } \frac{I_0}{I} = -\frac{1}{2}$$

and the extra-loss ratio due to long-path circulating currents with upper and lower currents in phase is given by (16.)

f. Diamond Coils with Twisted Conductors, with an Odd Number of Turns per Coil and with Upper and Lower Currents 60 deg out of Phase. The solutions are not regular but may be obtained by means of equation (8), as was done in computing (14). The loss is greater than with $\frac{I_0}{I} = -\frac{1}{2}$.

In the embedded part of the coil, the total extra-loss ratio is the sum of the short-path extra-loss ratio computed by equations (1) to (4) as if the laminations were thoroughly transposed, and the long-path extra-loss ratio. Adding the short-path and long-path losses is a close approximation in practical cases. In the nonembedded part of the coil, that is, the coil ends, the total ratio is equal to the long-path extra-loss ratio.

For an entire winding the loss may first be computed for direct current, then the watts of extra loss may be determined for the embedded parts where $\phi = 0$ and where $\phi = 60$ deg and for the coil ends. In this way the total watts of loss with alternating current may be found.

In designing a coil, if it is desired to reduce the short-path extra-loss ratio, a larger number of thinner laminations may be specified, though care should be taken not to reduce the total amount of copper so much as to increase the a-c resistance. If it is desired to reduce the long-path extra-loss ratio, the conductors may be twisted in the coil ends, if that has not already been done, or a thoroughly transposed type of conductor may be specified.

Example. Find the short-path and long-path eddy-current loss of the following 60-cycle armature coil at 75°C, for slots in which the upper and lower currents are in phase. The laminated conductors consist of 5 laminations, each 0.072 by 0.325 in., the 0.072-in. dimension being in the direction of the depth of the slot. There are 4 turns per coil and 2 coil sides per slot, that is, there are 8 laminated conductors in each slot. The slot is 0.82 in. wide. The ratio of core length to the half mean turn of the coil is 0.60. The insulation between laminations is 0.020 in. and that between the laminated conductors, that is, between the 4 turns of the coil, is 0.070 in. The coils are normal diamond-shaped coils, with no special twisting of the conductors.

$$\sqrt{D} = \frac{h^2 f W}{8.23s} = \frac{0.072^2 \times 60 \times 0.325}{8.23 \times 0.82} = 0.01495$$

$$D = 0.000224$$

For the short-path eddy-current loss, $q = 5 \times 8 = 40$.

$$0.000224 \left(\frac{40^2 - 0.2}{9}\right) = 0.040 \qquad \text{by eq. (2)}$$

Short-path eddy-current loss $= 4.0 \%$.

Gross height of laminated conductor
$$= 5 \times 0.072 + 4 \times 0.020 = 0.360 + 0.080 = 0.440$$
$$c = \frac{\text{gross height}}{\text{net height}} = \frac{0.440}{0.360} = 1.222$$
$$b = 0.60$$
$$Dn^4 = 0.000224 \times 625 = 0.140$$
$$t = 4$$

Long-path loss ratio, by eq. (13),
$$= 0.60^2 \times 1.222^2 \left[\frac{4}{45} \times 0.140 - \frac{16}{4,725} \times 0.140^2\right.$$
$$\left. + \left(\frac{16-1}{4}\right)\left(\frac{0.140}{3} - \frac{17}{1,260} \times 0.140^2\right)\right]$$
$$= 0.537 \; (0.0124 - 0.00007 + 0.175 - 0.0010)$$
$$= 0.100 \qquad \text{or } 10.0\%$$

The dimension 0.070 in. of thickness of insulation between turns does not enter into the calculation.

Total eddy-current loss of the coil $= 14.0\%$.

This could be reduced by putting a twist in the conductor in the diamond end of the coil, as described.

CHAPTER 8

CONNECTION OF ARMATURE COILS
FOR BALANCED POLYPHASE WINDINGS

In laying out the connections for a balanced three-phase armature winding, it is desirable to have a general proof that the phase angles of the vectors in the vector diagram of the winding are equally spaced, for the fundamental voltages. Such a proof is presented in this chapter.

The most common type of polyphase armature winding consists of diamond-shaped coils with two coil sides per slot. The coils are connected in groups, there being one group for each phase opposite each pole. The number of phases generally used is three.

If the number of slots per pole per phase is an integer, it is the same as the number of coils per group. In such a case the groups of a phase are alike in every way. The voltages generated in them are of the same wave shape and are equal in magnitude and phase.

If the number of slots per pole per phase is a fraction, it is equal to the average number of coils in a group. The groups will be of two different sizes, the larger with one more coil than the smaller. Such a winding adds together a comparatively large number of coil voltages which are slightly out of phase, considering their fundamentals. The higher harmonics in the coil voltages differ widely in phase and are more thoroughly canceled out, resulting in a purer sine wave of terminal voltage than when the number of slots per pole per phase is an integer.

In general, there may be several sections of the winding which are exact repetitions of each other. This is determined by writing the fraction equal to the number of slots divided by the number of poles and canceling factors as much as possible. Thus

$$\frac{\text{Slots}}{\text{Poles}} = \frac{s}{p} = \frac{r}{q}$$

where r/q is reduced to its lowest terms, that is, r and q contain no common factor. The letter r then denotes the number of slots in a repeatable section and q the number of poles in a section.

For a balanced three-phase winding, r must be divisible by 3, so that exactly $\frac{1}{3}$ of the slots in the section can be devoted to each phase. The three phases of the winding must be precisely the same except for the phase difference of 120 deg. This is the reason for the well-known rule for balanced three-phase windings, that the factor 3 must occur at least one more time in the number of slots than in the number of poles. Balanced windings are practically always required for synchronous machines and very frequently for induction motors.

Since, with the usual type of coils which are all alike, a lower coil side is always at the same phase angle from an upper coil side in the same coil, the voltages developed in all the upper coil sides may be computed first. The voltages developed in the lower coil sides will be the same and may be added on vectorially, in one step, using the usual coil pitch factor.

The position angles in electrical radians, or the phase angles of the emfs, of the upper coil sides of the first few slots of a repeatable section are

$$0, \frac{q\pi}{r}, \frac{2q\pi}{r}, \frac{3q\pi}{r}, \cdots$$

since r slots correspond to q poles and the angle of the entire section of q poles $= q\pi$. When these angles become greater than π, then a multiple of π, or π, is to be subtracted, so that the angle is measured on the nearest pole and is always less than π. In this way, the angles for the coil sides of a given phase are obtained. The coil sides are connected in series and their fundamental components of voltage aid rather directly.

An angle $\left(\dfrac{mq}{r} - 1\right)\pi$ cannot be the same as any of the preceding angles, since $mq - r - m_1 q$ or $(m - m_1)q - r$, cannot equal 0, as q is not a factor of r. Similarly for the nth pole, an angle $\left(\dfrac{mq}{r} - n\right)\pi$ cannot be the same as any of the preceding angles, since $mq - nr - (m_1 q - n_1 r)$, or $(m - m_1)q - (n - n_1)r$, cannot equal 0, because if it did, $\dfrac{r}{q}$ would equal $\dfrac{m - m_1}{n - n_1}$. But

$m - m_1$ is an integer less than r, and $n - n_1$ is an integer less than q. Therefore the fraction r/q would have been reduced to a smaller numerator and denominator, which was stated to be not possible when r and q were defined.

Since every angle is different from all the preceding angles, no two are alike. Therefore, there are r different angles, all less than one pole angle π, for the r slots of the section. They are all of the form

$$\left(\frac{mq - nr}{r}\right)\pi$$

all the letters except π being integers. There are r different numerators, all less than r and all integers, including 0, and so they must be 0, 1, 2, 3, $\cdots$, $(r - 1)$. That is, the voltage vector diagram of the slots is a fan with the vectors equally spaced at the angle π/r, the vectors being drawn from one point.

One-third of this fan, covering 60 electrical degrees, may be taken for each of the three phases. This will be the best arrangement, since it will give the largest resultant voltage. Any other arrangement, even though it might give a balanced winding, would involve using a vector more than 30 deg from the resultant, instead of one less than 30 deg from it.[1]

A usual way to lay out the connections for a balanced polyphase winding with fractional slots per pole per phase is to list the slots of a repeatable section in a column and to fill in items as in the table in Example 1, in which a repeatable section having 18 slots and 5 poles, or $1\frac{1}{5}$ slots per pole per phase, is taken.

The angle of the nth slot is $(n - 1)\alpha$. To obtain the equivalent angles, subtract multiples of 180 deg from each angle. Assign the vectors to the phases according to their equivalent angles, as follows:

$$a,\ 0 \text{ to } 59 \text{ deg;} \quad -c,\ 60 \text{ to } 119 \text{ deg;} \quad b,\ 120 \text{ to } 179 \text{ deg} \quad (1)$$

Change the sign of the letters when an odd number times 180 deg has been subtracted.

The fundamental voltage of one phase of a machine is

$$e\, Z\, k_d\, k_p \qquad (2)$$

---

[1] *Elec. Engrg.*, October, 1943, p. 468.

In (2), e is the voltage of sine wave form and fundamental frequency in one conductor which passes from the front of the machine to the back.   One turn in a coil is made up of two such conductors.   The quantity Z is the number of conductors connected in series in one phase.

The factor k_d is the distribution factor.   It is the ratio of the resultant voltage developed in the upper coil sides of a phase of the winding, to the numerical sum of the separate voltages in those conductors.   Its value is given by an expression which

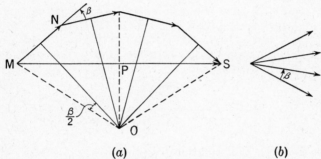

(a)   (b)

Fig. 1.—Vector diagrams of an armature winding.

may be derived directly from the vector diagram of the voltages.

Let the voltage vectors of the conductors connected in series be drawn end to end, so that the resultant voltage is MS, as in Fig. 1a of this chapter.   If the vectors were all drawn from one point as in Fig. 1b, they would form a regular fan.   The angle between any two adjacent vectors is $\beta = \pi/r$.

Draw a perpendicular from the middle of each vector in (a). They will meet in the point O which is the center of a regular polygon of which the vectors are sides.   Each half vector spans an angle $\beta/2$ at O.   The angle $MOS = n\beta$ where n is the number of vectors.

$$\text{The resultant voltage} = MS = 2\ MO \sin MOP$$
$$= 2\ MO \sin \frac{n\beta}{2}$$

The length of one vector is

$$MN = 2\ MO \sin \frac{\beta}{2}$$

and the numerical sum of the n vectors is

$$2n \, MO \sin \frac{\beta}{2}$$

The ratio gives

$$k_d = \frac{\sin \dfrac{n\beta}{2}}{n \sin \dfrac{\beta}{2}} \tag{3}$$

This expression gives the ratio of loss in voltage for any group of vectors which form a regular fan, as in Fig. 1b. If the number of slots per pole per phase is an integer, all the coil sides whose voltages make up the vector diagram of Fig. 1 lie in adjacent

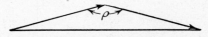

FIG. 2.—Vector diagram for coil pitch factor.

slots in one belt, and equation (3) gives the well-known breadth factor.

The factor k_p in (2) is the coil pitch factor. When the coil pitch angle ρ is specified in electrical degrees, the voltages of the two coil sides add together as in Fig. 2 and the ratio of loss of voltage due to their being out of phase is

$$k_p = \sin \frac{\rho}{2} \tag{4}$$

Example 1.   144 slots, 40 poles, 3 phases.

$$\frac{144}{40} = \frac{18}{5} = \frac{\text{slots/section}}{\text{poles/section}}$$

$$\text{Slots/pole/phase} = \tfrac{6}{5} = 1\tfrac{1}{5}$$

Angle between adjacent slots $= \alpha = \dfrac{5 \times 180°}{18} = 50°$ (electrical degrees)

Angle between vectors in diagram of winding (upper coil sides only)

$$= \beta = \frac{180°}{18} = 10°$$

Slot	Angle	Equivalent angle	Phase connection, see eq. (1)	Slots per group	Poles
1	0	0	a	2	N
2	50	50	a		
3	100	100	$-c$	1	
4	150	150	b	1	
5	200	20	$-a$	1	S
6	250	70	c	1	
7	300	120	$-b$	2	
8	350	170	$-b$		
9	400	40	a	1	N
10	450	90	$-c$	1	
11	500	140	b	1	
12	550	10	$-a$	1	S
13	600	60	c	2	
14	650	110	c		
15	700	160	$-b$	1	
16	750	30	a	1	N
17	800	80	$-c$	1	
18	850	130	b	1	

$$\text{Distribution factor} = k_d = \frac{\sin\dfrac{6 \times 10°}{2}}{6 \sin\dfrac{10°}{2}} = \frac{0.5}{6 \times 0.0872} = 0.955$$

Example 2. A slow-speed synchronous 3-phase motor has 300 slots and 140 poles. Show the layout of a repeatable section of the armature winding and indicate approximately the position of the N and S poles. Find the distribution factor k_d.

$$\frac{\text{Slots}}{\text{Poles}} = \frac{300}{140} = \frac{15}{7} = \frac{\text{slots/section}}{\text{poles/section}}$$

$$\text{Slots/pole/phase} = \tfrac{5}{7}$$

$$\text{Angle between two adjacent slots} = \alpha = \frac{180 \times 140}{300} = 84°$$

Angle between vectors in the fan diagram,

$$\beta = \frac{180°}{\text{slots/section}} = \frac{180°}{15} = 12°$$

Slot	Angle	Equivalent angle	Phase connection, see eq. (1)	Slots per group	Poles
1	0	0	a	1	N
2	84	84	$-c$	1	
3	168	168	b	1	
			$(-a)$	0	S
4	252	72	c	1	
5	336	156	$-b$	1	
			(a)	0	N
6	420	60	$-c$	1	
7	504	144	b	1	
8	588	48	$-a$	1	S
			(c)	0	
9	672	132	$-b$	1	
10	756	36	a	1	N
			$(-c)$	0	
11	840	120	b	1	
12	924	24	$-a$	1	S
13	1008	108	c	1	
			$(-b)$	0	
14	1092	12	a	1	N
15	1176	96	$-c$	1	
			(b)	0	

Number of slots of phase a in section $= n = 5$ at 0, 12, 24, 36, 48 deg.

$$\beta = 12°$$

$$k_d = \frac{\sin \dfrac{5 \times 12°}{2}}{5 \sin \dfrac{12°}{2}} = \frac{0.5}{5 \times 0.1045} = 0.957$$

A proposition similar to that in the first part of this chapter relates to plotting angles greater than 2π, on paper. If s vectors are equally spaced over a large angle $p(2\pi)$, and if the fraction s/p is reduced to the form r/q by canceling common factors as far as possible, then the angles when plotted on paper will form a uniform star all around the circle. It will be shown that the star has r branches, and the angle between any two adjacent branches is $2\pi/r$.

From the preceding paragraph, an angle $q(2\pi)$ is divided into r equal parts and q and r contain no common factor. If there has been any canceling and if q is different from p, then the angle $q(2\pi)$ is a repeating section of the original large angle $p(2\pi)$.

The position angles of the first few vectors are

$$0,\ q\,\frac{2\pi}{r},\ 2q\,\frac{2\pi}{r},\ 3q\,\frac{2\pi}{r},\ \cdots \tag{5}$$

When these angles become greater than 2π, then 2π or a multiple of 2π is subtracted, in order to give the angular position on the paper, which, of course, is always less than 2π.

Such a position angle, in general, is

$$mq\,\frac{2\pi}{r} - n2\pi \tag{6}$$

where $m < r$ and $n < q$, m and n being integers. The angle (6) cannot be the same as any of the preceding angles, since

$$mq - nr - m_1q - n_1r \qquad \text{or} \qquad (m - m_1)q - (n - n_1)r$$

cannot equal 0 because if it did, $\dfrac{r}{q}$ would equal $\dfrac{m - m_1}{n - n_1}$, which would have a smaller numerator and denominator than $\dfrac{r}{q}$. But this was stated to be not possible, when r and q were defined.

Therefore, there are r different angles all less than 2π, and all of the form

$$\left(\frac{mq - nr}{r}\right) 2\pi \qquad\qquad \text{given in} \quad (6)$$

These r different numerators, all less than r, must be

$$0,\ 1,\ 2,\ 3,\ \cdots,\ (r - 1)$$

and so the r vectors drawn on paper must be equally spaced at the angle $2\pi/r$, when the vectors are drawn from one point.

CHAPTER 9

HEAT TRANSFER

Conduction of Heat and Thermal Resistivity. When heat is conducted through a uniform body, the temperature drop is proportional to the distance along the heat flow and to the number of watts conducted across unit area of cross section. Various units are in use, depending on the application. In this chapter, use will be made principally of a unit of resistivity K, which is equal to the temperature drop in degrees centigrade for 1 watt conducted through a 1-cm cube of the material.

Some approximate values of K are given in Table I. A more complete set of values may be found in *Jour. I.E.E.*, October, 1930, p. 1313.

TABLE I, CHAP. 9

Material	Thermal Resistivity, K
Copper	0.26
Iron	1.7
Laminated steel cores, with heat flow across varnished laminations	100–150
Stoneware	50– 80
Concrete	About 110
Water at 25°C	About 150
Ice	About 180
Fiber board	300–500
Mica and paper insulation, pressed	400–600
Many kinds of compact insulation	600–800
Layers of confined air, up to about 1 cm. thick:	
At 25°C	3,830
At 75°C	3,360
At 100°C	3,180

The values for air in Table I are from Sutherland's law,

$$K = \frac{42,500(1 + 165/T)}{T^{\frac{1}{2}}} \tag{1}$$

where T is the absolute temperature of the air, that is, the temperature in degrees centigrade plus 273. Equation (1) does not include the energy radiated from the hot surface to the cold surface across the layer of air.

The value of K for hydrogen is about 500. The thermal resistivity of air and hydrogen is almost exactly constant for changes in pressure.

Many kinds of heat insulation of light weight, such as feathers, felt, and wool blankets, which consist mainly of cells of air with comparatively little solid material, have a thermal resistivity approximating 3,000, similar to air.

Radiation and Convection of Heat. Heat is dissipated from a surface exposed to free air in two ways: by radiation and by convection.

The loss of heat by radiation from a body to the walls of a room follows the Stefan-Boltzmann law:

$$W_r = 36.6 \times 10^{-12} e(T_1^4 - T_2^4)$$

or, rearranged for slide-rule work,

$$W_r = 36.6 \, e \left\{ \left(\frac{T_1}{1,000} \right)^2 + \left(\frac{T_2}{1,000} \right)^2 \right\} \left(\frac{T_1}{1,000} + \frac{T_2}{1,000} \right) \left(\frac{T_1}{1,000} - \frac{T_2}{1,000} \right) \quad \text{watts/sq in.} \quad (2)$$

where T_1 is the temperature of the small body and T_2 that of the walls, in degrees absolute, that is, the temperature in degrees centigrade plus 273. The factor e is a constant for a given surface. It is less than unity and is called the *emissivity coefficient*. Values of e can be measured with a thermopile. The absorptivity of a surface is taken equal to the emissivity e, that is, when radiation falls on a body, a fraction e of the radiation is absorbed and changed into heat, the remainder being reflected or transmitted.

Note that the term "emission" is usually taken to include the entire amount of heat escaping from a surface due to radiation, convection, and conduction, combined, while the term "emissivity" refers to radiation only.

A few approximate values of e are given in Table II.

The Stefan-Boltzmann law, equation (2), was derived for the case of a sphere at the center of a larger one whose inner walls behave like a black body and have $e = 1$. The law applies approximately to irregular objects like transformers or bus bars which are indoors and are shielded from direct sunshine.

TABLE II, CHAP. 9.—EMISSIVITY COEFFICIENT

	e
Dull, nonmetallic paint, any color	0.9–0.95
Copper or aluminum bus bars, thickly lacquered	0.8–0.9
Copper, tarnished from partial oxidation	About 0.3
Iron, oxidized	About 0.6
Aluminum paint	0.3–0.6
Insulating materials	About 0.9

In applying the law to a transformer that has thick clusters of cooling pipes or radiators around it, the number of square inches to be used is that of the "envelope area," formed by wrapping a cloth or elastic sheet around the transformer. The recesses back of the envelope surface add something to the amount of the radiation, provided the emissivity e is low; they add theoretically nothing, if $e = 1$ for all parts of the surface. Since e for transformer surfaces is usually 0.9 or higher, the envelope surface can usually be used without correction.

For built-up bus bars, made of rectangular conductors separated by air spaces about $\frac{1}{4}$ in. wide, the envelope surface may be used for computing the amount of heat radiated.

The escape of heat from a large surface by natural convection in air is given by the approximate formula:

$$W_c = 0.0014P^{0.5}\theta^{1.25} \qquad \text{watts/sq in.} \quad (3)$$

where P = air pressure in atmospheres.

= 1 at sea level and normal pressure.

θ = temperature rise of the hot body above the surrounding air, °C.

With natural convection, the air currents are merely those which are caused by the warmth of the body. With forced convection, the air is set in motion by some mechanical means such as a fan or the rotation of the body.

If the vertical dimension of the body is less than about 7 in., as in the case of a bus bar whose longitudinal axis is horizontal, the following formula for convection should be used:

$$W_c = \frac{0.0022P^{0.5}\theta^{1.25}}{h^{0.25}} \qquad \text{watts/sq in.} \quad (4)$$

where h is the vertical dimension of the body in inches.

Note that the one-fourth power of a number may be conveniently found on a slide rule by taking the square root twice in succession.

With transformers, equation (3) may generally be used with all parts of the radiators and other surfaces, since the passage of air over the surfaces is not much restricted. The envelope surface is not used for convection.

With built-up bus bars, as previously described, the envelope surface is not used for convection. For the exposed surfaces of bus bars of not more than about four straps in parallel planes, equation (4) may be used; for the surfaces in the $\frac{1}{4}$-in. air spaces, the constant 0.0022 in (4) may be changed to 0.0017.

The computations for watts loss are based on the assumption that all parts of the bus bar are at the same temperature. Where there are five or more straps in parallel planes, with alternating current, the outer straps carry a great deal more current than the inner ones owing to skin-effect action, and they attain a higher temperature than the inner straps because there is very little connection for the transfer of heat between them. Accordingly, the computations do not apply in cases of five or more straps in parallel planes.

See "Heat Transmission," by W. H. McAdams, ed. of 1942, McGraw-Hill Book Company, Inc., pp. 240 and 241, equations (16)–(19), and Temperature Rise of Bus Bars, by H. B. Dwight, G. W. Andrew, and H. W. Tileston, Jr., *Gen. Elec. Rev.*, May, 1940, p. 213.

TABLE III, CHAP. 9

Temperature rise (room temperature, 25°C)	Watts/sq in.	
	W_c by convection	W_r by radiation ($e = 0.9$)
10°C	0.025	0.037
20°C	.059	.078
30°C	.098	.122
40°C	.141	.171
50°C	.186	.225
60°C	.234	.284
70°C	.283	.348

The watts per square inch by convection and by radiation with $e = 0.9$ are shown in Table III.

When the total watts dissipated per unit length of a bus bar at a certain temperature rise have been computed, by finding the watts given off by convection plus those given off by radiation, it is usually desired to express the result in terms of amperes carried by the bus bar instead of watts. For direct current this involves merely the conductivity of the metal, which is easily measured and is usually accurately known. But with alternating current the resistance ratio R_{ac}/R_{dc} is required. The loss with alternating current is $I^2 R_{ac}$.

Values of the resistance ratio may be obtained from the curves of Chap. 25, where R_{ac} is denoted by R'. The resistance ratio R'/R_{dc} is the product of the skin-effect resistance ratio and the proximity effect resistance ratio. For the latter, see Figs. 6 and 7 of Chap. 25, except for the case of flat straps in closely adjacent parallel planes, as described in the third last paragraph of Chap. 25.

Equation (3) shows that the energy lost by natural convection is reduced when the air pressure is low. This is of importance for electrical installations at high altitudes. Values of average air pressure at different elevations are listed in Table IV.

TABLE IV, CHAP. 9

Altitude, Ft	Pressure in Atmospheres at 25°C and Normal Conditions
0	1.00
1,000	0.97
2,000	.93
4,000	.87
6,000	.81
8,000	.76
10,000	.71
12,000	.66
14,000	.61

If heat is carried from a hot body to a cool one by conduction, the watts are directly proportional to the temperature difference of the two bodies. In the case of convection, the watts are shown by formula (3) to be proportional to the 1.25 power of the temperature difference. This is not very different from the case of conduction, and indeed in the process of natural convection there is a considerable amount of conduction of heat through a layer of slowly moving air which clings rather closely to the surface of the warm body.

The conductivity of thin layers of confined air, up to about 1 cm thick, is a constant at a given temperature and is given by equation (1). Assuming that convection can be represented approximately by conduction through a motionless layer of air adjacent to the warm body and midway in temperature between the warm body and the room, the thickness of this equivalent motionless layer can be computed and is found to be about $\frac{1}{2}$ cm.

This may be useful in estimating heat flow in some irregular cases. If heat crosses a confined air space several centimeters thick, as in the space over the oil under the tank cover of a transformer, the entire resistance to conduction of heat across the air space may be taken as equivalent to that of two motionless layers of air, one on the oil surface and one next the tank cover, each about $\frac{1}{2}$ cm thick. The temperature of these layers may be taken as intermediate between the temperatures of the oil and the cover. It should be remembered that radiation takes place across air in addition to convection or conduction.

Example 1. Find the current-carrying capacity of a built-up bus bar, of three $\frac{1}{4}$- by 4-in. copper straps separated by $\frac{1}{4}$-in. air spaces. Conductivity of copper, 98%. Surface, oxidized. Frequency of current, 60 cycles. Allowable temperature rise, 30°C above 40°C air.

$$\text{Watts/In. of Bus}$$

Radiation from envelope surface $= 0.047 \times 10.5 = 0.49$
Convection from outer surfaces $\; = 0.109 \times \;\; 9.5 = 1.04$
Convection from inner surfaces $\; = 0.084 \times 16 \quad = \underline{1.35}$
$$2.88$$

$$R_{dc} \text{ per 1,000 ft} = 0.00331 \text{ ohm}$$
$$\sqrt{f/R_{dc}} = 135$$
$$R_{ac}/R_{dc} = 1.58 \qquad \text{from Fig. 1, Chap. 25}$$

Resistance for alternating current at 70°C $= 0.436 \times 10^{-6}$ ohm/in.

$$I^2 = \frac{2.88}{0.436 \times 10^{-6}} = 6,610,000$$
$$I = 2,570 \text{ amp}$$

Example 2. Find the temperature rise at 1,300 amp, 60 cps of an isolated rectangular copper conductor, $\frac{1}{4}$ by 4 in. with flat faces vertical, the longitudinal axis being horizontal. Oxidized surface, conductivity 100%, air temperature 25°C.

Example 3. Find the current-carrying capacity of a standard pipe-size 4-in. round copper tube, outside diameter 4.5 in., thickness of wall 0.25 in., oxidized surface, conductivity 98%, frequency 60 cps, air temperature 40°C, temperature rise 30°C.

Example 4.   Find the current-carrying capacity at 35°C rise of a square tubular copper bus bar.   Distance between outside faces 5 in., wall thickness 0.25 in., bright surface from recent manufacture, room temperature 25°C.

Example 5.   Find the current-carrying capacity at 30°C rise of a double-channel square copper bus, 5-in. side, thickness 0.26 in., oxidized surface, conductivity 98%, room temperature 40°C.

CHAPTER 10

RESISTANCE TO GROUND

Since practically all generating stations and substations have connections to ground, it is usually desirable to obtain the lowest number of ohms to ground which is possible without involving an unreasonable cost. To compare two or more arrangements of conductors for the same location requires formulas for resistance to ground.

The formulas involve the value of the conductivity of the earth in ohms per centimeter cube. As this is subject to large variations, the value for a given location should be found. If, as sometimes occurs, the bedrock is of quite different conductivity from the soil near the surface, the accuracy of the formulas may be seriously impaired, even for comparison of alternative arrangements of conductors for use at a given substation. The calculations given here are based on the assumption that the conductivity of the earth is constant in all directions including vertically downward for a considerable distance.

The calculations in this chapter are for direct current. They are usually suitable for 60 cycles where distances of not more than a few hundred feet are involved.

The problem of the resistance to ground of a conductor, or the resistance between two conductors which are in the ground, is essentially the same as the problem of finding the capacitance of the same conductor or conductors, because the flow of current corresponds exactly to the flow of dielectric flux. It is more convenient in many capacitance problems to compute the repulsion between charges than to solve the flow problem directly, and it is often convenient to solve a resistance problem by first solving the corresponding capacitance problem.

The method of changing a formula for capacitance into one for resistance to ground, or through the ground, may be found by considering the simple case of two parallel plates whose distance apart is small and the effect of whose edges may be neglected. Centimeter-gram-second units are used, except where noted.

If the two plates each have an area of B sq cm and if the charge density on one is q per square centimeter and that on the other $-q$ per square centimeter, the number of lines of dielectric flux through air from one plate to the other is $4\pi qB$. The statvolts per centimeter in the space between the plates is equal to $4\pi q$, the density of the lines, and the potential difference V between the plates is $4\pi qs$ where the separation of the plates is s cm. Then

$$\frac{1}{C} = \frac{V}{qB} = \frac{4\pi s}{B} \qquad (1)$$

For the flow of electricity between the same plates when they are embedded in earth of resistivity ρ abohms per cm cube, the resistance between the plates is

$$R = \frac{\rho s}{B} \qquad \text{abohms} \quad (2)$$

Thus in this case,

$$R = \frac{\rho}{4\pi C} \qquad \text{abohms} \quad (3)$$

where C is in statfarads. If ρ is in ohms per centimeter cube, R will be in ohms. Equation (3) shows merely the relation between the units and has nothing to do with the geometry of the flow of dielectric flux and current which in (1) and (2) is represented by the letters s/B. Equation (3) applies to any conductor or combination of conductors. See Ground Connections for Electrical Systems, *Bur. Standards Tech Paper* 108, Appendix III, p. 219.

Expressions are available for the capacitance of very few shapes of finite bodies. The capacitance of an isolated sphere in statfarads is equal to the number of centimeters in its radius. The capacitance of two spheres far apart is readily computed and will be taken up in the following pages. The capacitance of two spheres near together is used in electrical engineering in connection with the sphere gap. It is obtained by a rather complicated process. See "Theory of Alternating Currents," by Alexander Russell, ed. of 1914, Chap. VIII.

A formula is available for the capacitance of an isolated ellipsoid of revolution. A special case of this is the capacitance of a thin round plate, which is

$$C = \frac{2a}{\pi} \tag{4}$$

where a is the radius.   See "The Newtonian Potential Function," by B. O. Peirce, ed. of 1902, p. 161.

The capacitance of a very long, isolated cylinder is given by

$$\frac{1}{C} = \frac{1}{L} \left(\lambda - 0.306852 - \frac{0.17753}{\lambda} - \frac{0.5519}{\lambda^2} \cdots \right) \tag{5}$$

where $\lambda = \log n \ (2L/a)$, L being the half length. This was derived from the series for C given in the paper Lösung zweier Potentialprobleme der Elektrostatik, by E. Hallén, *Arkiv för Matematik, Astronomi och Fysik*, Vol. 21A, No. 22, Stockholm, 1929.

An approximate method of calculation which is used for a great many shapes of conductors is the average potential method of Dr. G. W. O. Howe. This consists in assuming uniform charge density over the surface of the conductor and calculating the average potential. Then the approximate capacitance is taken as equal to the total charge divided by the average potential. This method is correct within 2 or 3 parts in 1,000 for a long straight antenna wire, and within less than 1 per cent for a cylinder of the proportions of a ground rod. However, an estimate of its accuracy should be made for each shape or combination of conductors with which it is used, because in some cases it gives an error of several per cent. For example, it gives a value of $1/C$ for a thin round plate which is 8 per cent too high.

Capacitance is the ratio of electric charge to potential. The mathematical basis of calculations of potential is that the force in dynes on a unit charge at a distance x from a concentrated charge Q is Q/x^2. The potential at the distance x from Q is equal to the work that can be done by a unit charge in moving from distance x to an infinite distance. This is numerically equal to

$$\int_x^\infty \frac{Q \, dx}{x^2} = \frac{Q}{x} \qquad \text{statvolts} \tag{6}$$

To find the potential near a ring of radius a of extremely fine wire on which electric charge is uniformly distributed, one finds first an expression for the potential of a point on the axis of the ring at a distance y from the center of the ring. All parts of the electric charge on the circumference of the ring are at the same distance $\sqrt{y^2 + a^2}$ from the given point.

$$\text{Potential} = \frac{Q}{\sqrt{y^2 + a^2}} = \frac{Q}{y}\left(1 + \frac{a^2}{y^2}\right)^{-\frac{1}{2}}$$
$$= \frac{Q}{a}\left[\frac{a}{y} - \frac{1}{2}\frac{a^3}{y^3} + \frac{1 \times 3}{2 \times 4}\frac{a^5}{y^5} - \cdots\right] \tag{7}$$

The general expression for the potential at any point (r,θ) must satisfy Laplace's differential equation. As shown in Arts. 1, 9, and 78 of "Fourier's Series and Spherical, Cylindrical and Ellipsoidal Harmonics," by W. E. Byerly, the expression for potential at points not near the ring, when the center of the ring is the origin and

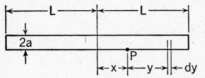

Fig. 1.—Cylindrical conductor.

$\theta = 0$ is along the axis of the ring, is obtained by putting $y = r$ in (7) and inserting zonal harmonics $P_{2m}(\cos\theta)$ as coefficients. This gives

$$V = \frac{Q}{a}\left[\frac{a}{r}P_0(\cos\theta) - \frac{1}{2}\frac{a^3}{r^3}P_2(\cos\theta) + \cdots\right] \tag{8}$$

Since $P_n(1) = 1$, this reduces to (7) when $\theta = 0$.

If a long circular cylinder (Fig. 1) has a charge q per cm on its curved surface, then in finding the potential of a point P on the surface due to the element of charge $q\,dy$ which is in the form of a ring, we have

$$r = \sqrt{a^2 + y^2}$$

measured from the center of the ring to P,

$$\theta = \frac{y}{r}$$
$$P_0(\cos\theta) = 1$$
$$P_2(\cos\theta) = \tfrac{1}{2}(3\cos^2\theta - 1)$$

from Art. 77 of the book mentioned, or see equation (55), Chap. 32. Then, for the point P,

$$V = \frac{q\,dy}{a}\left[\frac{a}{r} - \frac{1}{2^2}\frac{a^3}{r^3}\left(\frac{3y^2}{r^2} - 1\right) + \cdots\right] \tag{9}$$

For the average potential method, which is an approximate calculation of capacitance, expression (9) is integrated from $y = 0$ to $L - x$, and also from 0 to $L + x$, obtaining the potential at P resulting from the parts of the cylinder to the right and left of P. Then, to obtain the average of this potential, multiply by dx/L and integrate from $x = 0$ to L. Thus, the average potential of the cylinder resulting from uniform charge density on its curved surface is

$$\frac{V_{av}}{2q} = \operatorname{logn} \frac{4L}{a} - 1 + \frac{a}{L}\left(\frac{1}{2} + \frac{1}{8} + \frac{1}{128} + \cdots\right)$$
$$- \frac{a^2}{L^2}\left(\frac{3}{16} - \frac{1}{32} \cdots\right) + \frac{a^4}{L^4}\left(\frac{1}{64} - \frac{1}{1{,}024} \cdots\right)$$

$$\frac{1}{C} = \frac{V_{av}}{2qL} = \frac{1}{L}\left(\operatorname{logn} \frac{4L}{a} - 1 + 0.63 \frac{a}{L} - 0.16 \frac{a^2}{L^2}\right.$$
$$\left. + 0.015 \frac{a^4}{L^4} \cdots\right) \quad (10)$$

If, as is often done, only the first term of (9) is used, the result is

$$\frac{1}{C} = \frac{1}{L}\left[\operatorname{logn} \frac{2L + \sqrt{a^2 + 4L^2}}{a} + \frac{a}{2L} - \sqrt{1 + \frac{a^2}{4L^2}}\right] \quad (11)$$

Note that the length of the cylinder is $2L$, as shown in Fig. 1. Equation (11) can be expanded into a power series, as follows:

$$\frac{1}{C} = \frac{1}{L}\left[\operatorname{logn} \frac{4L}{a} - 1 + \frac{a}{2L} - \frac{a^2}{16L^2} + \cdots\right] \quad (12)$$

However, in the derivation just given, terms in powers of a in (9) were omitted, and so the coefficients of the powers of a/L in (12) are not the same as in (10) and are not the correct ones, even for the average potential method. Accordingly, the only part of (12) that should be used is the following:

$$\frac{1}{C} = \frac{1}{L}\left(\operatorname{logn} \frac{4L}{a} - 1\right) \quad (13)$$

This gives an error of less than 1 per cent in practical cases of resistance to ground. The error is due to the approximation inherent in the average potential method. If a more accurate formula is desired, equation (5) should be used. The small error in (13) cannot be avoided by including terms in a/L or by using more complicated expressions in logarithms or inverse hyperbolic functions such as (11) or its equivalent forms.

The formula

$$\frac{1}{C} = \frac{1}{L} \operatorname{logn} \frac{2L}{a}$$

which is based on the capacitance of an ellipsoid of revolution of the same diameter and length as the cylinder, has a larger error than (13) and should not be used.

Logarithms to base 10 may be used, by noting that

$$\operatorname{logn} p = 2.303 \log_{10} p$$

The resistance of a buried straight wire of length $2L$ cm, no part of which is near the surface of the ground, is given by (3) and (13) and is

$$R = \frac{\rho}{4\pi L} \left(\operatorname{logn} \frac{4L}{a} - 1 \right) \tag{14}$$

A vertical ground rod which penetrates to a depth of L cm must be considered along with its image in the ground surface. The voltage and the shape of current flow are the same as for a completely buried cylinder of length $2L$ cm, but the total current is one-half as much, making the resistance twice as great. Therefore, the resistance to ground of a vertical ground rod of depth L cm is

$$R = \frac{\rho}{2\pi L} \left(\operatorname{logn} \frac{4L}{a} - 1 \right) \tag{15}$$

In general, if C includes the capacitance of the images of a conductor or conductors in the earth, the resistance to ground is

$$R = \frac{\rho}{2\pi C} \tag{16}$$

Vertical ground rods are used a great deal, sometimes in large groups, because they can be driven in place with little or no excavation and because they are likely to reach permanent moisture and earth of good conductivity.

Two Ground Rods in Parallel. Let two ground rods of radius a cm be shown in Fig. 2, and let them be electrically in parallel. Find the air capacitance C of the two rods and their images, that is, of two cylinders each of length $2L$. Let the cylinders have uniform charge of q per cm and let the axial spacing between the cylinders be s, which is considered large compared with a. The potential at a point on one cylinder at a distance x from its center, due to $q\,dy$ on the other cylinder, is

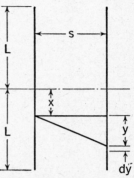

FIG. 2.—Two rods connected in parallel.

$$\frac{q\,dy}{\sqrt{s^2 + y^2}}$$

The potential at x due to the other cylinder is obtained by integrating this expression from $y = 0$ to $L - x$ and from $y = 0$ to $L + x$. The average potential on one cylinder due to uniform charge on the other is then obtained by multiplying by dx/L and integrating from $x = 0$ to L, and is

$$q\left[2\operatorname{logn}\frac{2L + \sqrt{s^2 + 4L^2}}{s} + \frac{s}{L} - \frac{\sqrt{s^2 + 4L^2}}{L} \right] \qquad (17)$$

For large values of s/L, this becomes

$$\frac{2qL}{s}\left[1 - \frac{L^2}{3s^2} + \frac{2}{5}\frac{L^4}{s^4} \cdots \right] \qquad (18)$$

For small values of s/L, it is

$$2q\left[\operatorname{logn}\frac{4L}{s} - 1 + \frac{s}{2L} - \frac{s^2}{16L^2} + \frac{s^4}{512L^4} \cdots \right] \qquad (19)$$

Add the average potential of the cylinder due to its own charge,

$$\frac{2qL}{C} = 2q\left(\operatorname{logn}\frac{4L}{a} - 1 \right) \qquad (20)$$

Divide by $4qL$, the total charge on the two cylinders, thus obtaining the value of $1/C$ for the pair of ground rods and their images. Then, by (16), the resistance to ground of the pair of rods is

$$R = \frac{\rho}{4\pi L}\left[\operatorname{logn}\frac{4L}{a} - 1 + \operatorname{logn}\frac{2L + \sqrt{s^2 + 4L^2}}{s} \right.$$
$$\left. + \frac{s}{2L} - \frac{\sqrt{s^2 + 4L^2}}{2L} \right] \qquad (21)$$

That is, for large values of s/L,

$$R = \frac{\rho}{4\pi L}\left[\operatorname{logn}\frac{4L}{a} - 1\right] + \frac{\rho}{4\pi s}\left[1 - \frac{L^2}{3s^2} + \frac{2}{5}\frac{L^4}{s^4}\cdots\right] \quad (22)$$

or, for small values of s/L,

$$R = \frac{\rho}{4\pi L}\left[\operatorname{logn}\frac{4L}{a} + \operatorname{logn}\frac{4L}{s} - 2 + \frac{s}{2L} - \frac{s^2}{16L^2} \right.$$
$$\left. + \frac{s^4}{512L^4}\cdots\right] \quad (23)$$

A short alternative calculation for (22), which is found by trial to be good for spacings of 20 ft or more, is to replace each ground rod by a half-buried sphere which is equivalent in resistance to one isolated ground rod. This procedure can be illustrated by a numerical example.

The resistance to earth of a ground rod of $\frac{3}{4}$ in. in diameter and 10 ft in depth, by (15), is

$$R = \frac{\rho}{2\pi L}\left(\operatorname{logn}\frac{4L}{a} - 1\right) = \frac{\rho}{2\pi L} \times 6.155$$

The hemisphere, which is buried, and its image above the ground surface make a complete sphere whose air capacitance as an isolated conductor is, by a well-known proposition, equal to its radius, A, in centimeters. By (16), the resistance to ground of the hemisphere is

$$R = \frac{\rho}{2\pi A} \quad (24)$$

Then the radius of the hemisphere which is equivalent to the isolated ground rod is

$$A = \frac{L}{\operatorname{logn}\dfrac{4L}{a} - 1} = \frac{L}{6.155}$$

Here, A and L may be both in centimeters or both in feet and so $A = 10/6.155 = 1.625$ ft.

The capacitance of two equal spheres at a distance s, center to center, connected in parallel, is readily calculated when s is not small and the charges can be assumed uniformly distributed

around the spheres.   By symmetry, the spheres will carry equal
charges.   Let each charge be q.

The potential of the surface of each sphere is

$$q \left(\frac{1}{A} + \frac{1}{s} \right)$$

and

$$\frac{1}{C} = \frac{1}{2} \left(\frac{1}{A} + \frac{1}{s} \right)$$

where the dimensions are in centimeters.   Then

$$R = \frac{\rho}{4\pi} \left(\frac{1}{A} + \frac{1}{s} \right) \tag{25}$$

This is the same as (22), omitting the terms in L^2 and L^4.

From numerical examples, it is found that the results of (21)
and (25) differ by about 0.5 per cent for 20-ft spacing between
two ground rods, and by a few per cent for 10-ft spacing.

Groups of Ground Rods.   The potential of a rod due to its
own charge and the charges of several other rods can be found by
using (18) or (19) several times, assuming equal charges on all
the rods.   Similarly, the potential of the surface of a sphere due
to its own charge and the charges of a number of other spheres is

$$\frac{q_1}{A} + \frac{q_2}{s_2} + \frac{q_3}{s_3} + \cdots \tag{26}$$

where for an approximate calculation q_1, q_2, q_3, etc., may be
assumed equal.

For somewhat better accuracy, the values of q for the rods near
the center of the group may be taken a little lower than for the
rods near the outer parts of the group, by an amount sufficient to
make the potential of each rod the same.   Thus the values for
the outer parts may be taken equal to q, and others to $0.95q$, $0.9q$,
etc., according to judgment and to the test of equal potentials.

In order to design groups of ground rods for transmission line
towers, station and substation grounds, etc., and to decide on the
best number and spacing of rods, it is desirable to be able to
compare various groups of rods, assuming uniform conductivity
of the soil.   Accordingly, sets of curves are given in Figs. 3 to 5.
From them it is possible to estimate how many rods and how
much area will be required for a certain number of ohms to

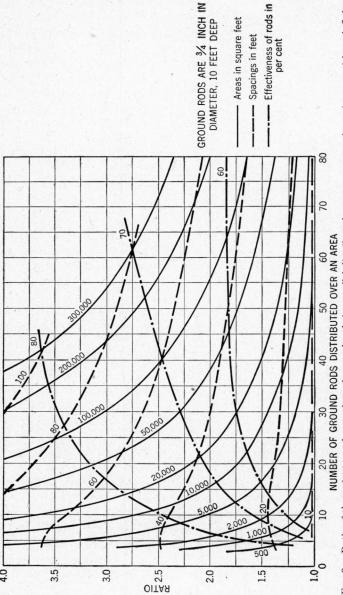

GROUND RODS ARE ¾ INCH IN DIAMETER, 10 FEET DEEP

— Areas in square feet
—·— Spacings in feet
—··— Effectiveness of rods in per cent

NUMBER OF GROUND RODS DISTRIBUTED OVER AN AREA

RATIO

FIG. 3.—Ratio of the resistance of a number of ground rods in parallel distributed over an area to the resistance with an infinite number of rods.

ground in a given locality, from measurements on a few temporary test ground rods.

The basis of comparison is the resistance of one isolated ground rod of ¾ in. diameter and 10 ft depth.   In Fig. 4 the conductivity of 2, 3, and 4 rods is given in terms of the conductivity of isolated rods, and in Fig. 5 results are shown for larger numbers of rods.

In Fig. 3 the information is presented in different form, and the lowest resistance that can be obtained from a given area is shown.

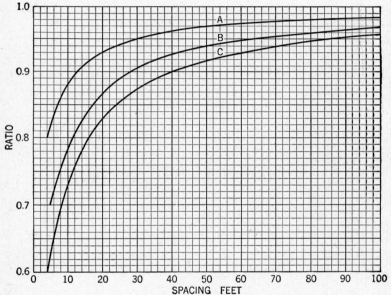

Fig. 4.—Ratio of conductivity of ground rods in parallel to that of isolated rods.   Ground rods are ¾ in. in diameter, 10 ft deep; three rods on equilateral triangle, four rods on square.   Curves: *A*, two rods; *B*, three rods; *C*, four rods.

This information is often of value as it may be the means of preventing the wasteful attempt of putting additional ground rods in an area that could not give the desired low resistance even if an infinite number of rods were used.   For instance, if 36 ground rods are distributed over a square area of 10,000 sq ft, that is, 100 by 100 ft, the spacing will be 20 ft.   Figure 3 shows that the resistance is 1.3 times the resistance of an infinite number of rods in the same area.   Therefore, no matter what the resistance in ohms may be nor what the uniform conductivity of the ground may be, if it is desired to have less than 75 per cent of the resistance with 36 rods there is no use in putting more rods in the area of 10,000 sq ft, but it will be necessary to make use of a larger area.

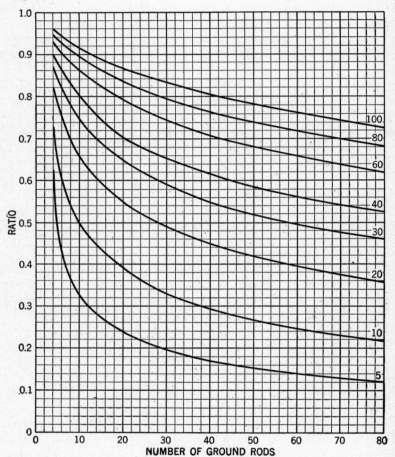

Fig. 5.—Ratio of conductivity of ground rods in parallel on an area to that of isolated rods.   Numbers on curves are spacings in feet.

Figure 3 shows also that if there are more than 10 rods, 10 ft deep, there is no use in having closer than 10-ft spacing.

It is generally desirable not only to utilize the ground area effectively but to make effective use of the rods, since they represent a considerable cost of metal. If one wishes the rods to be at least 60 per cent as effective as they would be if isolated, that is, to have at least 60 per cent of the conductivity of isolated rods, it is seen from both Figs. 3 and 5 that it is necessary to use over 20-ft spacing for 16 rods in a square area, about 30-ft spacing for 25 rods, and over 40 ft for 49 rods.

The curves of Figs. 3 and 5 are based on uniform distribution of ground rods in square areas, the boundary of the area running through the outer rods. Although the curves are computed for square areas, they give an estimate for rectangular areas. The curves cannot be used for a part of a group of rods nor for a group that is near other groups, but a reading from the curves is to apply to an area which contains all the ground rods in the vicinity.

In the calculation of cases involving more than four rods or the spheres that are substantially equivalent to them, equal charges were assumed for the spheres. The potential of a corner sphere was calculated and that of an innermost sphere and the average taken, thus approximating the Howe average potential method. For a small number of spheres, this was checked and good agreement obtained, by computing the actual charges by simultaneous equations. For a large number of ground rods, the results shown in Figs. 3 and 5 are approximate.

The effect of the buried wires used to connect the ground rods together was not included in the computations for the figures that have been described. If the conductivity of each ground rod is assumed to be increased by the same percentage by the connecting wires, the latter will have little effect on the comparison of different groups of rods made by means of the curves.

Buried Horizontal Wire. In some cases, connection to the earth is made by means of a buried, horizontal wire. The image of this wire in the ground surface requires the use of formula (21) or (23), where, in this case, the length of the buried wire is $2L$ cm and the axial distance from the wire to its image is s cm, which is twice the distance from the axis of the wire to the ground surface. If the image were not taken into account, a serious change in the result would often ensue.

Example 1.   Length of No. 4/0 wire, 200 ft; depth, 10 ft; ρ, 200,000 ohms per cm cube. $R = 57.6$ ohms.

Two Parallel Buried Wires. The resistance to ground of two parallel buried wires, including the effect of their images in the ground surface, is calculated by the same method as for four ground rods at the corners of a rectangle. The average potential of one of the wires due to its own charge, equation (20), is to be added to the average potential due to each of the other wires. Thus, one item is to be computed by (20) and three items by (17) or (19), using three values of s. The sum, divided by the total charge of the four wires, $8qL$, is $1/C$ and then equation (16) can be applied.

Example 2. Find the resistance to ground of two wires, 100 ft long, 0.46 in. in diameter, 7 ft apart, and 10 ft below the surface of the ground, the resistivity of the ground being 200,000 ohms per cm cube. The wires are connected in parallel, electrically.

Potential of a wire due to its own charge, by (20).... $16.51q$
Potential by (17) or (19) for $s = 7$................. $4.84q$
Potential by (17) or (19) for $s_1 = 20$.............. $2.99q$
Potential by (17) or (19) for $s_2 = 21.19$........... $2.89q$

  Potential..................................... $27.23q$

Total charge = $4 \times 1,200 \times 2.540 \times q = 12,190q$

$$\frac{1}{C} = \frac{27.23}{12,190}$$

$$R = \frac{\rho}{2\pi C} = \frac{200,000 \times 27.23}{2\pi \times 12,190} = 71.1 \qquad \text{ohms}$$

The average potential on a straight wire due to an assumed uniform charge density on another straight wire at an angle to the first, is given in Appendix 2, p. 569, of Methods, Formulas and Tables for the Calculation of Antenna Capacity, by F. W. Grover, *Bur. Standards Sci. Paper* 568, Washington, D.C., 1928. These results can be used to obtain expressions (27) to (31) given in Table I for the resistance to ground of a buried right angle of wire and of buried stars of wire.

For use in deriving these expressions, the average potential of one wire caused by a uniformly distributed charge q per cm on another equal wire which meets it at one end at angle θ is

$$V_{av} = 2q \, \text{logn} \left(1 + \text{cosec} \, \frac{\theta}{2}\right) \qquad (32)$$

If θ should be extremely small, the radius of the wire would need to be brought into the computation, and equation (32) would be inapplicable.

The expressions for stars of wire, being series that need to be computed only until the terms become negligible, often require less work than if the results were expressed by more complicated mathematical functions.

If L is in centimeters and ρ in ohms per centimeter cube, R is in ohms. Also, if L is in inches and ρ in ohms per inch cube, R is in ohms. Inside the brackets, only ratios of dimensions occur. The numerator of each fraction should be in the same units as the denominator of that fraction. Note that s is the distance from the wire to the image and is twice the distance from the wire to the ground surface.

In order to estimate relative accuracy, the potential of the wire at various distances from the center of a four-point star was plotted and compared with the potential distribution of a round plate. Approximately the same amount of deviation from the average potential was found in the two cases. Accordingly, it can be concluded that the resistance of stars of wire obtained by (28) to (31) is an approximation within several per cent.

For numerical examples for these formulas, let each arm be 100 ft of No. 4/0 wire, buried 10 ft deep in earth having $\rho = 200,000$ ohms per cm cube. The results are as follows:

Resistance to Ground, Ohms

Right angle of wire	59	by (27)
Three-point star	44	by (28)
Four-point star	37	by (29)
Six-point star	31	by (30)
Eight-point star	28	by (31)

Buried Ring of Wire. The capacitance of an isolated ring of round wire is given by

$$\frac{1}{C} = \frac{2}{\pi D} \operatorname{logn} \frac{4D}{a}$$

where the diameter of the ring, D cm, is much larger than the diameter of the wire, $2a$ cm.

The capacitance of a ring and its image at distance s is given by

$$\frac{1}{C} = \frac{1}{\pi D} \left(\operatorname{logn} \frac{4D}{a} + \operatorname{logn} \frac{4D}{s} \right)$$

where s is considerably larger than a and also considerably smaller than D. See the paper by R. Rüdenberg, *Eleck. Zeit.*, Vol. 46, p. 1342, Sept. 3, 1925.

TABLE I, CHAP. 10.—APPROXIMATE FORMULAS FOR RESISTANCE TO GROUND INCLUDING EFFECT OF IMAGES

Description	Formula	Eq.
Hemisphere, radius a	$R = \dfrac{\rho}{2\pi a}$	(24)
One ground rod, length L, radius a	$R = \dfrac{\rho}{2\pi L}\left(\log n\,\dfrac{4L}{a} - 1\right)$	(13)
Two ground rods, s > L, spacing s	$R = \dfrac{\rho}{4\pi L}\left(\log n\,\dfrac{4L}{a} - 1\right) + \dfrac{\rho}{4\pi s}\left(1 - \dfrac{L^2}{3s^2} + \dfrac{2}{5}\dfrac{L^4}{s^4}\cdots\right)$	(22)
Two ground rods, s < L, spacing s	$R = \dfrac{\rho}{4\pi L}\left(\log n\,\dfrac{4L}{a} + \log n\,\dfrac{4L}{s} - 2 + \dfrac{s}{2L} - \dfrac{s^2}{16L^2} + \dfrac{s^4}{512L^4}\cdots\right)$	(23)
Buried horizontal wire, length 2L, depth s/2	$R = \dfrac{\rho}{4\pi L}\left(\log n\,\dfrac{4L}{a} + \log n\,\dfrac{4L}{s} - 2 + \dfrac{s}{2L} - \dfrac{s^2}{16L^2} + \dfrac{s^4}{512L^4}\cdots\right)$	(23)
Right-angle turn of wire, length of arm L, depth s/2	$R = \dfrac{\rho}{4\pi L}\left(\log n\,\dfrac{2L}{a} + \log n\,\dfrac{2L}{s} - 0.2373 + 0.2146\dfrac{s}{L} + 0.1035\dfrac{s^2}{L^2} - 0.0424\dfrac{s^4}{L^4}\cdots\right)$	(27)
Three-point star, length of arm L, depth s/2	$R = \dfrac{\rho}{6\pi L}\left(\log n\,\dfrac{2L}{a} + \log n\,\dfrac{2L}{s} + 1.071 - 0.209\dfrac{s}{L} + 0.238\dfrac{s^2}{L^2} - 0.054\dfrac{s^4}{L^4}\cdots\right)$	(28)
Four-point star, length of arm L, depth s/2	$R = \dfrac{\rho}{8\pi L}\left(\log n\,\dfrac{2L}{a} + \log n\,\dfrac{2L}{s} + 2.912 - 1.071\dfrac{s}{L} + 0.645\dfrac{s^2}{L^2} - 0.145\dfrac{s^4}{L^4}\cdots\right)$	(29)

	Description	Formula	
	Six-point star, length of arm L, depth $s/2$	$R = \dfrac{\rho}{12\pi L}\left(\log n \dfrac{2L}{a} + \log n \dfrac{2L}{s} + 6.851 - 3.128\dfrac{s}{L} + 1.758\dfrac{s^2}{L^2} - 0.490\dfrac{s^4}{L^4}\cdots\right)$	(30)
	Eight-point star, length of arm L, depth $s/2$	$R = \dfrac{\rho}{16\pi L}\left(\log n \dfrac{2L}{a} + \log n \dfrac{2L}{s} + 10.98 - 5.51\dfrac{s}{L} + 3.26\dfrac{s^2}{L^2} - 1.17\dfrac{s^4}{L^4}\cdots\right)$	(31)
	Horizontal ring of wire, diam. of ring D, depth $s/2$	$R = \dfrac{\rho}{2\pi^2 D}\left(\log n \dfrac{4D}{a} + \log n \dfrac{4D}{s}\right)$	(33)
	Buried horizontal strip, length $2L$, section a by b, $b < a/8$, depth $s/2$	$R = \dfrac{\rho}{4\pi L}\left(\log n \dfrac{4L}{a} + \log n \dfrac{4L}{s} + \dfrac{a^2 - \pi ab}{2(a+b)^2} - 1 + \dfrac{s}{2L} - \dfrac{s^2}{16L^2} + \dfrac{s^4}{512L^4}\cdots\right)$	(34)
	Buried horizontal round plate, radius a, depth $s/2$	$R = \dfrac{\rho}{8a} + \dfrac{\rho}{4\pi s}\left(1 - \dfrac{7}{12}\dfrac{a^2}{s^2} + \dfrac{33}{40}\dfrac{a^4}{s^4}\cdots\right)$	(35), (38)
	Buried vertical round plate, radius a, depth $s/2$	$R = \dfrac{\rho}{8a} + \dfrac{\rho}{4\pi s}\left(1 + \dfrac{7}{24}\dfrac{a^2}{s^2} + \dfrac{99}{320}\dfrac{a^4}{s^4}\cdots\right)$	(35), (40)

The resistance to ground of a buried horizontal ring, taking the effect of the ground surface into account, is

$$R = \frac{\rho}{2\pi C} = \frac{\rho}{2\pi^2 D}\left(\log n\,\frac{4D}{a} + \log n\,\frac{4D}{s}\right) \tag{33}$$

Buried Strip Conductor. The resistance to ground of a buried horizontal strip conductor is given by equation (34), Table I. For a description of the derivation, see the author's paper in *Jour. Math. Phys.*, Vol. 10, p. 50, 1931, which, together with the paper Calculation of Resistances to Ground, *Trans. A.I.E.E.*, 1936, p. 1319, will form the references for this chapter.

Round Plate. The capacitance of a single, isolated, thin, round plate as given by the precise mathematical solution[1] is

$$\frac{1}{C} = \frac{\pi}{2a} = \frac{1.5708}{a} \tag{35}$$

where a = radius of the plate, cm.

It is of interest to show that the average potential method, if used in this case, produces an error of 8 per cent, giving a value of $1/C$ which is 8 per cent too large. Expressions for the potential due to a ring carrying uniform charge density are given on p. 11 and 153 of Reference 1 (footnote 1) of this chapter. From these is obtained the average potential of a thin, round plate of radius a cm, due to uniform charge density q per square centimeter, in the form of three series whose sum is

$$V_{av} = \frac{2\pi q a}{3}\left[2 + \frac{1}{4} + \frac{3^2}{4^2 \cdot 6} + \frac{3^2 \cdot 5^2}{4^2 \cdot 6^2 \cdot 8} + \cdots\right] \tag{36}$$

The sum of this slowly converging series can be found by comparing it with the series

$$\frac{\pi^2}{8} = 1 + \frac{1}{3^2} + \frac{1}{5^2} + \frac{1}{7^2} + \cdots \tag{37}$$

Multiply the bracket of (36) by 0.401723 to make the 11th terms of (36) and (37) alike. It is found that $1/C$ or $V_{av}/(\pi a^2 q)$ is slightly greater than $1.69721/a$. Multiply the bracket of (36) by 0.329595 to make its 10th term equal to the 11th term of (37)

---

[1] "Fourier's Series and Spherical, Cylindrical and Ellipsoidal Harmonics," by W. E. Byerly, p. 154, putting $r = 0$.

and all its succeeding terms distinctly less than the corresponding terms of (37). It is found that $1/C$ is less than $1.70169a$. The difference between the two limiting values is 0.27 per cent and an inspection of the series shows that the value of $1/C$ by the average potential method is much nearer the smaller limit than the larger, and so is nearly equal to

$$\frac{1.6972}{a}$$

The true value of $1/C$ is, however, by equation (35),

$$\frac{\pi}{2a} = \frac{1.5708}{a}$$

The average potential method, therefore, gives a value of $1/C$ for a thin round plate which is 8 per cent too high.

This result has been confirmed by Dr. F. W. Grover by a method using mechanical integration, which gave

$$\frac{V_{av}}{\pi a^2 q} = \frac{1.6966}{a}$$

There is a connection between the error due to the average potential method and the amount of the variation in potential over the conductor caused by uniform charge distribution. If the potential in every part is very close to the average value, the error from using the average value throughout would be expected to be small. The potential of the center of the plate due to uniform charge distribution is $2\pi aq$, using the formulas of Reference 1. But the average value is

$$\frac{1.697}{a} \times \pi a^2 q = 1.697\pi aq$$

Thus, the potential of the center is seen to be 18 per cent higher than the average potential. This comparatively large percentage may account in some degree for the 8 per cent error in the case of a round plate, owing to the use of the average potential method. In the case of a typical long cylinder, the potential of the middle point was 4.7 per cent higher than the average potential and in that case the average potential method was shown to give a very correct value of $1/C$.

Two Round Plates in Parallel Planes. The potential caused by a charged round plate, at points not near the plate, is given by the last series on p. 154 of Reference 1 of this chapter. Integrating that series over the surface of a second disk having the same axis and the same length of radius as the first, the average potential on the second disk due to the charge on the first is

$$V_{av} = \frac{Q}{s}\left(1 - \frac{7}{12}\frac{a^2}{s^2} + \frac{33}{40}\frac{a^4}{s^4} \cdot \cdot \cdot \right) \tag{38}$$

where Q is the total charge in statfarads on the first disk, a is the radius in centimeters of both plates, and s is the distance in centimeters between the two plates.

This power series should not be used unless the last term is quite small and so the largest value of a/s for which it is useful is about $\frac{1}{2}$. Since (38) gives the average potential, it is not a precise calculation for capacitance or resistance. However, the order of its precision can be estimated by finding the potential at the center of the second disk, which is $\frac{Q}{s} \tan^{-1} \frac{a}{s}$. See the series on p. 154 of Reference 1.

When $s = 2a$ the potential at the center is 4 per cent greater than the average potential and, for larger values of the separation s, the discrepancy is smaller. It will be remembered that for one isolated round plate the potential of the center was 18 per cent more than the average potential, and the error in the value of capacitance was 8 per cent. In the case of the calculation for one isolated ground rod of average proportions the potential at the middle of the cylinder is 4.7 per cent greater than the average potential, and the error in the capacitance is less than 1 per cent. It may be concluded that the use of average potential gives the same order of accuracy in the case of (38) as in the case of a long cylinder.

Values of aV/Q calculated by (38) are plotted in curve B of Fig. 6. This curve has been extended to apply to small values of s by using the two series on p. 154 of Reference 1, to compute the potential at the rim and at the center of the second disk caused by the charge on the first disk, and by taking the average for plotting in Fig. 6. This process is shown to give good results by comparing it with (38) for s/a between 2 and 4. The potential at the rim is equal to the potential at the center when $s = 0$.

More accurate values for the curve of Fig. 6 could be computed by dividing the circular area into bands, computing the potential for each band, and averaging, this being a process of mechanical integration.   However, no matter how carefully this is done, the result would be subject to the error inherent in the average potential method.

It is seen from (38) that when the separation is large, the potential on one plate due to the other is closely given by

$$V = \frac{Q}{s} \qquad (39)$$

which is the same as assuming that the charge is on the surface of a sphere, or concentrated at a point.   For example, when

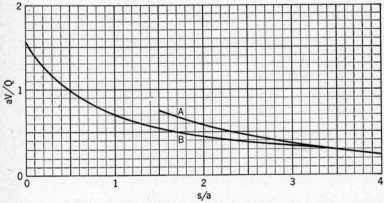

Fig. 6.—Average potential on a round plate caused by an equal plate.   A, same plane; B, parallel planes; a, radius of plates in cm; s, distance between centers in cm.

$s/a = 5$, the result of (39) is 2 per cent larger than that of (38) and the value of Q/s itself is only 13 per cent of the potential of an isolated plate to which it is to be added.   Accordingly, (39) can usually be used for the images of the buried plates, which are at distances s_1 and s_2, center to center.

When the two round plates are connected in parallel, then in the capacitance problem the plates and their images all carry charges equal to Q.   By symmetry, the potential is the same for them all and is made up of the following four items which are added together: (1) the potential, $\pi Q/(2a)$, given by (35), due to the plate's own charge; (2) the potential, given by (38), due to the other coaxial buried plate which lies in a vertical plane parallel to that of the first plate; (3) the potential, Q/s_1, due to the plate's image, where s_1 is the distance in centimeters from the center of the plate to the center of the image, that is, s_1 is twice the distance to the surface of the ground; (4) the potential, Q/s_2, due to the other image.

The sum of these four items is equal to V and the capacitance of the four plates is given by $1/C = V/(4Q)$. Then the resistance to ground of the two buried plates connected in parallel is $R = \rho/(2\pi C)$ by (16).

When the two round plates are connected in series, in the resistance problem current flows from one to the other through the ground, and in the capacitance problem one plate carries a charge Q and the other $-Q$. The images carry charges Q and $-Q$, each being of the same sign as the charge directly beneath it.

Equations (3) and (16) are still used to change from the capacitance problem to the resistance problem.

Two Round Plates in the Same Plane. When the two plates of radius a cm are in the same plane, the distance between the centers being s cm, the average potential on one due to the charge on the other is

$$V_{av} = \frac{Q}{s}\left(1 + \frac{7}{24}\frac{a^2}{s^2} + \frac{99}{320}\frac{a^4}{s^4} + \cdots\right) \tag{40}$$

In this case, there is more error due to the use of average potential than in (38), for when $s/a = 2$, the potential at the center differs from the average potential by 15 per cent. As in other cases, if the term in a^2/s^2 is negligibly small compared to 1, the simple expression Q/s may be used and the error due to the use of average potential is negligible. Values of aV/Q are plotted in curve A of Fig. 6.

Rectangular Plates. The capacitance of an isolated, thin, rectangular plate, a by b cm, according to the average potential method, is given by

$$\frac{1}{C} = 2\left[\frac{1}{a}\operatorname{logn}\frac{a + \sqrt{a^2 + b^2}}{b} + \frac{1}{b}\operatorname{logn}\frac{b + \sqrt{a^2 + b^2}}{a}\right.$$
$$\left. + \frac{a}{3b^2} + \frac{b}{3a^2} - \frac{(a^2 + b^2)\sqrt{a^2 + b^2}}{3a^2b^2}\right] \tag{41}$$

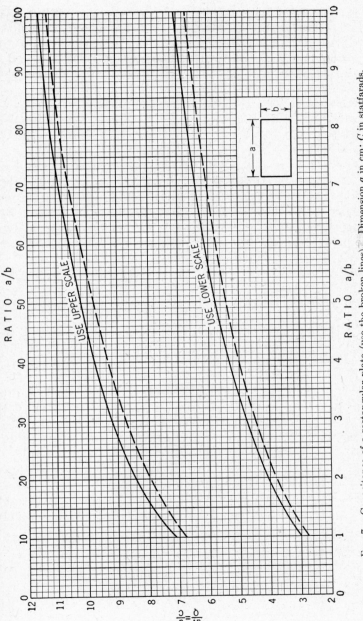

Fig. 7.—Capacitance of a rectangular plate (use the broken lines). Dimension a in cm; C in statfarads.

The potential of the center of a square plate is 18 per cent greater than the average potential, and this difference is reduced to 15 per cent for a rectangle whose length is 5 times its width. Accordingly, the correction for the average potential method found for a circular plate will apply, and approximately 8 per cent should be subtracted from the value of $1/C$ given by (41) for a square or nearly square plate, and almost as much should be subtracted for a rectangular plate of length about 5 times the width (see Fig. 7).

A formula for the average potential of a rectangular plate due to the charge on a similar plate in the same plane can be given, but it is not short and it is subject to the errors inherent in the average potential method. It seems better to replace the rectangular plates by circular plates of the same area and on the same centers and to use (35), (38), (39), or (40) for the effect of one plate on another.

CHAPTER 11

INVERSE FUNCTIONS OF COMPLEX QUANTITIES

Formulas for inverse functions of complex quantities, such as $\sin^{-1}(x + i\,y)$, are of use in several branches of electrical engineering. Calculations for transmission circuits require them, particularly in connection with communication circuits. Integration of expressions involving complex quantities can involve inverse functions. They are encountered also in conformal transformations.

In writing these formulas, it is necessary to specify angles with sufficient detail to avoid ambiguity and the liability of incorrect results. Also, all the appropriate multiple values should be included. It is not always obvious by inspection that two different complex values are only values of different branches of the same function and are both correct.

In all cases, numerical examples are given as illustrations.[1]

Inverse Sine. $\sin^{-1}(x \pm i\,y)$. Let

$$\sin^{-1}(x + i\,y) = u + i\,v$$

where x, y, u, and v are real quantities and $i = \sqrt{-1}$.

$$\sin(u + i\,v) = (x + i\,y)$$
$$\sin u \cosh v = x \tag{1}$$
$$\cos u \sinh v = y \tag{2}$$

Squaring (1) and (2) and putting

$$\sin^2 u = 1 - \cos^2 u$$

and
$$\cosh^2 v = 1 + \sinh^2 v$$

there is obtained, by eliminating $\sinh^2 v$ $\left(\text{put} \sinh^2 v = \dfrac{y^2}{\cos^2 u}\right)$,

$$\cos^4 u - (1 - x^2 - y^2)\cos^2 u - y^2 = 0 \tag{3}$$

from which $\cos^2 u = \frac{1}{2}[1 - x^2 - y^2 \pm \sqrt{(1 - x^2 - y^2)^2 + 4y^2}] \tag{4}$

[1] Inverse Functions of Complex Quantities, by H. B. Dwight, *Trans. A.I.E.E.*, 1942, p. 850.

Since u is real and $\cos^2 u$ is positive, the positive value of the root is taken.

The quantity under the radical sign may be factored and is

$$\{(1 + x)^2 + y^2\}\{(1 - x)^2 + y^2\} \tag{5}$$

From (4) and (5),

$$\sin^2 u = \tfrac{1}{2}[1 + x^2 + y^2 - \sqrt{\{(1 + x)^2 + y^2\}\{(1 - x)^2 + y^2\}}]$$
$$= \tfrac{1}{4}[\sqrt{(1 + x)^2 + y^2} - \sqrt{(1 - x)^2 + y^2}]^2$$

$$\sin u = \pm \left(\frac{p - q}{2}\right) = \frac{\pm 2x}{p + q} \tag{6}$$

where $p = \sqrt{(1 + x)^2 + y^2}$ \qquad (positive value) \quad (7)

$q = \sqrt{(1 - x)^2 + y^2}$ \qquad (positive value) \quad (8)

The second solution in (6) is obtained by rationalizing the numerator. It involves the sum of two quantities instead of the difference and so allows more convenient precise computation.

Since v is real, $\cosh v$ is positive, as may be seen from the series expansion. Therefore, by (1), $\sin u$ is the same sign as x. This allows $\pm$ in (6) to be changed to $+$.

Then $$u = \sin^{-1} \frac{2x}{p + q} \tag{9}$$

Take the principal value of u, that is, the value between $-\pi/2$ and $\pi/2$. Since u lies in this range, $\cos u$ is positive.

The following expression corresponding to (3) can be obtained by eliminating $\cos^2 u$:

$$\sinh^4 v + (1 - x^2 - y^2) \sinh^2 v - y^2 = 0$$
$$\sinh^2 v = \tfrac{1}{2}[x^2 + y^2 - 1 \pm \sqrt{(1 - x^2 - y^2)^2 + 4y^2}]$$

The quantity under the radical sign is the same as (5) so that

$$\cosh v = \pm \tfrac{1}{2}(p + q)$$

Since v is real, the positive value is to be taken.

$$v = \cosh^{-1} \frac{p + q}{2} \tag{10}$$

Since $\cos v$ is positive, then by (2) $\sinh v$ and v are the same sign as y. This may be secured by writing

$$\sin^{-1}(x \pm iy) = \sin^{-1} \frac{2x}{p + q} \pm i \cosh^{-1} \frac{p + q}{2}$$

where y is positive and the positive value of $\cosh^{-1}$ is taken. See p. 58 of the reference in footnote 2 and p. 264 of that in footnote 3.

For any angle θ, there are angles $2k\pi + \theta$ which are the same as θ in all respects and there are angles $(2k + 1)\pi - \theta$ which have the same sine, where k is a positive or negative integer or 0. These can be combined by stating that angles having the same sine as θ are

$$n\pi + (-1)^n\theta \qquad (11)$$

where n is an integer or zero.   Therefore,

$$\sin^{-1}(x \pm iy) = n\pi + (-1)^n \sin^{-1}\frac{2x}{p+q}$$
$$\pm i(-1)^n \cosh^{-1}\frac{p+q}{2} \qquad (12)$$

taking the principal value of $\sin^{-1}$ and the positive values of $\cosh^{-1}$ and of the radicals p and q. The quantity x may be positive or negative but the quantity y is positive.

Note that if $y = 0$ and $x > 1$, $q = x - 1$ and $p + q = 2x$. If $y = 0$ and $x < 1$, $q = 1 - x$ and $p + q = 2$.

An alternative computation may be made by means of the well-known formula

$$\sinh^{-1} m = \operatorname{logn}\left(m + \sqrt{m^2 + 1}\right) \qquad (13)$$

where logn denotes natural logarithm.

Let
$$\sin^{-1} A = u$$

where A and u are complex quantities.

$$\sin u = A$$
$$iA = \sinh iu$$
$$iu = \sinh^{-1} iA$$
$$\sin^{-1} A = -i \sinh^{-1} iA + 2k\pi$$
$$= -i \operatorname{logn}\left(\pm \sqrt{1 - A^2} + iA\right) + 2k\pi \qquad (14a)$$
or $$\qquad = i \operatorname{logn}\left(\pm \sqrt{1 - A^2} - iA\right) + 2k\pi \qquad (14b)$$

[2] "Application of Hyperbolic Functions to Electrical Engineering Problems," by A. E. Kennelly, McGraw-Hill Book Company, Inc., New York, ed. of 1925.

[3] "Transmission Circuits for Telephonic Communication," by K. S. Johnson, D. Van Nostrand Company, Inc., New York, ed. of 1939.

The two solutions of (14a) indicated by $\pm$ correspond to the two angles θ and $\pi - \theta$ which have the same sine. The second or alternative form (14b) is identical with (14a). The expression involving $+$ in (14b) is obtained from that involving $+$ in (14a) by rationalizing the numerator in (14a). In practice, the form should be used which involves the numerical sum of quantities instead of the difference, thus giving more convenient precise computation.

Square Root. $\sqrt{x \pm i\,y}$. In the computation just described, the square root of a complex quantity is required. It may be expressed as follows:

$$\sqrt{x + iy} = \pm \left[\sqrt{\frac{m + x}{2}} + i\sqrt{\frac{m - x}{2}} \right] \tag{15}$$

$$\sqrt{x - iy} = \pm \left[\sqrt{\frac{m + x}{2}} - i\sqrt{\frac{m - x}{2}} \right] \tag{16}$$

where x may be positive or negative, y is positive, and

$$m = + \sqrt{x^2 + y^2}. \tag{17}$$

The positive square roots of $(m + x)/2$ and $(m - x)/2$ are used. See p. 260 of the reference in footnote 3.

An alternative method is to express the complex quantity in the polar form

$$r\underline{/\theta} = re^{i\theta} = r(\cos \theta + i \sin \theta) \tag{18}$$

where, if the complex quantity is $x + iy$,

$$r = + \sqrt{x^2 + y^2}, \quad \cos \theta = \frac{x}{r} \quad \text{and} \quad \sin \theta = \frac{y}{r} \tag{19}$$

Then, $\quad \sqrt{x + iy} = \pm \sqrt{r}\ \underline{/\tfrac{1}{2}\theta} = \pm \sqrt{r}\left(\cos \dfrac{\theta}{2} + i \sin \dfrac{\theta}{2} \right) \tag{20}$

The angle θ may be in any one of the four quadrants, depending on whether x and y are positive or negative quantities. The angle is not specified according to the principal values of $\tan^{-1}$ and $\cos^{-1}$, etc., though the numerical value of θ may be conveniently found by using a table of tan or $\tan^{-1}$ and then determining the quadrant for θ by (19).

Logarithm. $\log_n (x + i\,y)$. In using equation (14), the logarithm of a complex quantity is required. This is computed as an inverse function of e^z.

Let
$$\text{logn } (x + i\,y) = u + i\,v$$
$$e^{u+iv} = e^u \,(\cos v + i \sin v)$$
$$= x + i\,y$$
$$e^u \cos v = x \qquad\qquad (21)$$
$$e^u \sin v = y \qquad\qquad (22)$$

Squaring and adding, $e^{2u} = x^2 + y^2$

Let $r = \sqrt{x^2 + y^2}$

The positive value of the root is to be taken since u is real and e^u is positive.

The angle v is to be specified with sufficient completeness so that the numerical values of $\cos v$ and $\sin v$ will have the correct signs.

$$\text{logn } (x + i\,y) = \tfrac{1}{2} \text{logn } (x^2 + y^2) + i(\theta + 2\pi k) \qquad (23)$$

where $\cos \theta = x/r$, $\sin \theta = y/r$, $r = \sqrt{x^2 + y^2}$ and k is an integer or 0, the positive value of r being taken.   See p. 3 of the reference in footnote 4.   The quantities x and y may be positive or negative.

The angle θ, according to this specification, is not always a principal value of $\cos^{-1}$, $\sin^{-1}$, or $\tan^{-1}$.   If both x and y are negative, $\tan \theta$ is positive and the angle θ is in the third quadrant.

Another case where
$$\theta = \tan^{-1} \frac{m}{n}$$

is not a sufficient specification is in the equation
$$m \cos A + n \sin A = r \sin (A + \theta) \qquad (24)$$

where $r = \sqrt{m^2 + n^2}$, $\sin \theta = m/r$ and $\cos \theta = n/r$.   See No. 401.2 of the reference in footnote 5.

Example 1. $\sin^{-1} (2 + i\,3)$

$$p = \sqrt{9 + 9} = 4.243$$
$$q = \sqrt{1 + 9} = 3.162$$
$$p + q \qquad = \overline{7.405}$$
$$\sin^{-1} \frac{4}{7.405} = \sin^{-1} 0.540 = 0.570 \qquad\qquad \text{radian}$$
$$\cosh^{-1} \frac{7.405}{2} = 1.983$$

---

[4] "A Short Table of Integrals," by B. O. Peirce, Ginn and Company, Boston, ed. of   929.

[5] "Tables of Integrals and Other Mathematical Data," by H. B. Dwight, The Macmillan Company, New York, 1934.

Putting $n = 0$ in (12),

$$\sin^{-1}(2 + i\,3) = 0.570 + i\,1.983$$

Putting $n = 1$,

$$\sin^{-1}(2 + i\,3) = 3.142 - 0.570 - i\,1.983$$
$$= 2.572 - i\,1.983$$

In this computation, tables of $\sin^{-1} x$, $\cosh^{-1} x$, etc., for real values of x, as in the reference in footnote 6, may be used.

To check, $\sin(0.570 + i\,1.983) = 0.540 \times 3.702 + i\,0.842 \times 3.563$
$$= 2.00 + i\,3.00$$
and $\sin(2.572 - i\,1.983) = 0.540 \times 3.702 - i\,(-0.842 \times 3.563)$
$$= 2.00 + i\,3.00$$

If the only purpose of the real part of the value of $\sin^{-1}(2 + i\,3)$ is to take the sin, cos, or tan, or to add it to other angles which are given in degrees, then a trigonometric table in degrees might be used, but care would be needed in choosing an appropriate notation.

In using equation (14) to obtain $\sin^{-1}(2 + i\,3) = \sin^{-1} A$,

$$1 - A^2 = 6 - i\,12$$
$$= x - i\,y \qquad \text{as in (16)}$$
$$m = \sqrt{36 + 144} = 13.42 \qquad \text{by (17)}$$
$$m + x = 19.42, \qquad m - x = 7.42$$

$$\sqrt{1 - A^2} = \sqrt{\frac{19.42}{2}} - i\,\sqrt{\frac{7.42}{2}} \qquad \text{by (16), using the + sign}$$
$$= 3.116 - i\,1.926$$
$$-i\,A = 3 \qquad - i\,2$$
$$\sqrt{1 - A^2} - i\,A = 6.116 - i\,3.926$$

Equation (14b) is used instead of (14a) so as to avoid the small difference of nearly equal quantities.

Let

$$6.116 - i\,3.926 = x + i\,y \qquad \text{as in (23)}$$
$$6.116^2 = 37.4$$
$$3.926^2 = 15.4$$
$$\overline{52.8}$$

$$\frac{1}{2}\log_n 52.8 = \frac{1}{2}(1.664 + 2.303) = 1.983$$

The angle θ of (23) is in the fourth quadrant.

$$\tan(-\theta) = \frac{3.926}{6.116} = 0.642$$
$$\theta = -0.571 \qquad \text{radian}$$
$$\log_n(x + i\,y) = 1.983 - i\,0.571 \qquad \text{by (23)}$$
$$\sin^{-1}(2 + i\,3) = 0.571 + i\,1.983 \qquad \text{by (14b)}$$

6 "Mathematical Tables," by H. B. Dwight, McGraw-Hill Book Company, Inc., New York, 1941.

The second solution is given by the minus sign in (14a) or (14b), the former being preferable.

$$- \sqrt{1 - A^2} + i\,A = -6.116 + i\,3.926$$

The angle θ of (23) is in the second quadrant.

$$\sin^{-1}(2 + i\,3) = 2.571 - i\,1.983$$

The quantity $2k\pi$ may be added to either of these solutions.

Inverse Cosine. $\cos^{-1}(x \pm iy)$. Let

$$\cos^{-1}(x + i\,y) = u + i\,v$$
$$\cos(u + i\,v) = x + i\,y$$
$$\cos u \cosh v = x \tag{25}$$
$$\sin u \sinh v = -y \tag{26}$$

Squaring and eliminating $\sinh^2 v$,

$$\sin^4 u - (1 - x^2 - y^2)\sin^2 u - y^2 = 0$$
$$\sin^2 u = \tfrac{1}{2}\left[1 - x^2 - y^2 \pm \sqrt{(1 - x^2 - y^2)^2 + 4y^2}\right]$$

Since u is real and $\sin^2 u$ is positive, use the positive value of the root.

$$\cos^2 u = \tfrac{1}{2}(1 + x^2 + y^2 - pq)$$
$$\cos u = \pm \tfrac{1}{2}(p - q)$$

Since v is real, $\cosh v$ is positive and $\cos u$ is the same sign as x, by (25). Then,

$$\cos u = \frac{1}{2}(p - q) = \frac{2x}{p + q}$$
$$u = \cos^{-1}\frac{2x}{p + q}$$

Take the principal value, that is, the value between 0 and π. Then $\sin u$ is positive.

Similarly, $\sinh^4 v + (1 - x^2 - y^2)\sinh^2 v - y^2 = 0$

$$\sinh^2 v = \tfrac{1}{2}\left[x^2 + y^2 - 1 + \sqrt{(1 - x^2 - y^2)^2 + 4y^2}\right]$$

taking the positive value of the root since $\sinh^2 v$ is positive.

$$\cosh^2 v = \tfrac{1}{4}(p + q)^2$$
$$\cosh v = \tfrac{1}{2}(p + q)$$

taking the positive value since v is real.

$$v = \cosh^{-1} \frac{p + q}{2}$$

Since $\sin u$ is positive, $\sinh v$ and v are the same sign as $-y$, from (26).

$$\cos^{-1}(x + i y) = \pm \left[\cos^{-1} \frac{2x}{p + q} + 2k\pi - i \cosh^{-1} \frac{p + q}{2} \right] \quad (27)$$

where y is positive, taking the principal value of $\cos^{-1}$ and the positive values of $\cosh^{-1}$ and of p and q. Also,

$$\cos^{-1}(x - i y) = \pm \left[\cos^{-1} \frac{2x}{p + q} + 2k\pi + i \cosh^{-1} \frac{p + q}{2} \right] \quad (28)$$

taking the same values of $\sin^{-1}$ and $\cosh^{-1}$ as with (27).
For p and q see equations (7) and (8).

The quantity x may be positive or negative. The quantity y is positive.

An alternative method is by use of the equation

$$\cosh^{-1} p = \pm \operatorname{logn}(x + \sqrt{x^2 - 1})$$

Let $\cos^{-1} A = u$, a complex quantity.

$$A = \cos u = \cosh i u$$
$$i u = \cosh^{-1} A$$
$$\cos^{-1} A = -i \cosh^{-1} A = \mp i \operatorname{logn}(A + \sqrt{A^2 - 1}) + 2k\pi \quad (29a)$$

or
$$= \pm i \operatorname{logn}(A - \sqrt{A^2 - 1}) + 2k\pi \quad (29b)$$

The second equation is obtained by rationalizing the numerator of the first and is to be used when it avoids the numerical difference of quantities.

Example 2. $\cos^{-1}(-2 - i 4)$
By (28), putting $k = 0$,

$$\cos^{-1}(-2 - i 4) = \pm [\cos^{-1}(-0.4385) + i \cosh^{-1} 4.56]$$
$$= \pm [2.025 + i 2.198]$$

To check, $\cos(2.025 + i 2.198) = -0.4385 \times 4.56 - i \, 0.899 \times 4.45$
$$= -2.00 - i 4.00$$

By the alternative method, let $A = -2 - i\,4$

$$A^2 - 1 = -13 + i\,16$$
$$\sqrt{A^2 - 1} = 1.952 + i\,4.10$$
$$A = -2 - i\,4$$

Using (29b) to avoid the numerical difference of quantities,

$$A - \sqrt{A^2 - 1} = -3.952 - i\,8.10$$

In finding the logarithm of this, logn $r = 2.20$ and the angle θ is in the third quadrant and is 4.258 radians.

$$\cos^{-1}(-2 - i\,4) = \pm(-4.258 + i\,2.20) + 2k\pi$$
$$= \pm(2.025 + i\,2.20)$$
putting $\qquad\qquad k = 1.$

Inverse Tangent. $\tan^{-1}(x + i\,y)$.   Let

$$\tan^{-1}(x + i\,y) = u + i\,v$$
$$\tan(u + i\,v) = x + i\,y = i\,\tanh\frac{u + i\,v}{i}$$

since $\qquad\qquad\qquad \tan z = i\,\tanh\dfrac{z}{i}$

$$\tanh\frac{u + i\,v}{i} = \frac{x + i\,y}{i}$$

$$v - i\,u = \tanh^{-1}(y - i\,x) = \frac{1}{2}\,\text{logn}\,\frac{1 + y - i\,x}{1 - y + i\,x} \qquad (30)$$

where logn denotes natural logarithm.

$$e^{2v}(\cos 2u - i\,\sin 2u) = \frac{1 + y - i\,x}{1 - y + i\,x}$$

Rationalizing the denominator,

$$e^{2v}\cos 2u = \frac{1 - x^2 - y^2}{(1 - y)^2 + x^2} \qquad (31)$$

$$e^{2v}\sin 2u = \frac{2x}{(1 - y)^2 + x^2} \qquad (32)$$

Squaring, adding, and factoring the numerator,

$$e^{4v} = \frac{(1 + y)^2 + x^2}{(1 - y)^2 + x^2} \qquad \text{by} \quad (5)$$

$$v = \frac{1}{4}\,\text{logn}\,\frac{(1 + y)^2 + x^2}{(1 - y)^2 + x^2} \qquad (33)$$

Dividing (32) by (31), $\tan 2u = \dfrac{2x}{1 - x^2 - y^2}$ (34)

Let $2u = \pi - \tan^{-1}\dfrac{1 + y}{x} - \tan^{-1}\dfrac{1 - y}{x}$ (35)

$$= \pi - \alpha - \beta$$

where the principal values of $\tan^{-1}$ are taken, that is, α and β are between $-\pi/2$ and $\pi/2$.

$$\begin{aligned} \sin (\pi - \alpha - \beta) &= \sin (\alpha + \beta) \\ &= (\tan \alpha + \tan \beta) \cos \alpha \cos \beta \\ &= \frac{2}{x} \cos \alpha \cos \beta \end{aligned}$$

which is the same sign as x, as it should be, from (32).   Cos α and cos β are positive.

$$\begin{aligned} \cos (\pi - \alpha - \beta) &= - \cos (\alpha + \beta) \\ &= (-1 + \tan \alpha \tan \beta) \cos \alpha \cos \beta \\ &= (1 - x^2 - y^2) \frac{\cos \alpha \cos \beta}{x^2} \end{aligned}$$

which is the same sign as $1 - x^2 - y^2$ and proportional to it. See (31).

The quantity $2k\pi$, where k is an integer, may be added to (35).

Therefore,

$$\tan^{-1} (x + i\,y) = \frac{1}{2} \left\{ (2k + 1)\pi - \tan^{-1}\frac{1 + y}{x} - \tan^{-1}\frac{1 - y}{x} \right\}$$
$$+ \frac{i}{4} \operatorname{logn} \frac{(1 + y)^2 + x^2}{(1 - y)^2 + x^2} \quad (36)$$

where the principal values of $\tan^{-1}$ are taken and where x and y may be positive or negative.

An alternative method of computation is by means of equation (30):

$$\tan^{-1} (x + i\,y) = \frac{i}{2} \operatorname{logn} \frac{1 + y - i\,x}{1 - y + i\,x} + 2k\pi \quad (37)$$

Example 3. $\tan^{-1} (-2 - i\,4) = 1.675 - i\,0.2006$
When computing this by (37), $k = -1$.   Other values, given by adding $2k\pi$, are equally appropriate.

Inverse Hyperbolic Sine. $\sinh^{-1}(\pm x + i y)$.   Let

$$\sinh^{-1}(x + i y) = u + i v$$
$$x + i y = \sinh(u + i v)$$
$$= i \sin \frac{u + i v}{i}$$
$$y - i x = \sin \frac{u + i v}{i}$$
$$u + i v = i \sin^{-1}(y - i x) \tag{38}$$

By (12), $\sinh^{-1}(\pm x + i y) = \pm(-1)^n \cosh^{-1}\dfrac{s + t}{2}$

$$+ i(-1)^n \sin^{-1}\frac{2y}{s + t} + i\,n\pi \tag{39}$$

where n is an integer or 0,

    x is positive,

    y is positive or negative,

$$s = \sqrt{(1 + y)^2 + x^2} \qquad \text{(positive value)} \tag{40}$$
$$t = \sqrt{(1 - y)^2 + x^2} \quad \text{(positive value)} \tag{41}$$

The principal value of $\sin^{-1}$ (between $-\pi/2$ and $\pi/2$) and the positive value of $\cosh^{-1}$ are taken.

Note that if $x = 0$ and $y > 1$, $s + t = 2y$ and if $y < 1$, $s + t = 2$.

An alternative solution is

$$\sinh^{-1} A = \operatorname{logn}(\pm \sqrt{1 + A^2} + A) + i\,2k\pi \tag{42a}$$
or $$= -\operatorname{logn}(\pm \sqrt{1 + A^2} - A) + i\,2k\pi \tag{42b}$$

The two solutions of (42a) indicated by $\pm$ correspond to the two angles θ and $\pi - \theta$ which have the same sine. Logn $(A - \sqrt{A^2 + 1})$ is a value of $\sinh^{-1} A$ which differs from logn $(A + \sqrt{A^2 + 1})$ by logn (-1) or $i\,(2k + 1)\pi$. Evidently one at least of the two values is complex, for any given value of A, whether A is real or complex.

The second or alternative form (42b) gives the same results as (42a). It should be used when it enables one to avoid computing the numerical difference of two quantities.

Example 4. $\sinh^{-1}(-2 - i\,4) = -2.184 - i\,1.097$

putting $n = 0$ in (39) or using the $+$ sign in (42b).

Also, $\sinh^{-1}(-2 - i\,4) = 2.184 + i\,4.239$

putting $n = 1$ in (39) or using the $-$ sign in (42a).

The quantity $i\,2k\pi$ may be added to both these solutions.

The results may be checked by computing sinh, which gives $-2 - i\,4$.

Inverse Hyperbolic Cosine. $\cosh^{-1}(x + i\,y)$.

Let

$$\cosh^{-1}(x + i\,y) = u + i\,v$$

$$x + i\,y = \cosh(u + i\,v) = \cos\frac{u + i\,v}{i}$$

$$u + i\,v = i\cos^{-1}(x + i\,y)$$

If y is positive, by (28),

$$\cosh^{-1}(x + i\,y) = \pm\left[\cosh^{-1}\frac{p + q}{2} + i\cos^{-1}\frac{2x}{p + q} + i\,2k\pi\right] \tag{43}$$

Also, if y in the following equation is positive, by (29),

$$\cosh^{-1}(x - i\,y) = \pm\left[\cosh^{-1}\frac{p + q}{2} - i\cos^{-1}\frac{2x}{p + q} + i\,2k\pi\right] \tag{44}$$

The quantities p and q are positive and are given by (7) and (8). The quantity x is positive or negative. The positive value of $\cosh^{-1}$ and the principal value of $\cos^{-1}$ are taken.

An alternative solution is

$$\cosh^{-1} A = \pm\log_n\left(A + \sqrt{A^2 - 1}\right) + i\,2k\pi \tag{45a}$$

or

$$= \pm\log_n\left(A - \sqrt{A^2 - 1}\right) + i\,2k\pi \tag{45b}$$

Equations (45a) and (45b) give the same results, and the one that involves the numerical sum of two quantities should be used in any given case.

Example 5. $\cosh^{-1}(2 - i\,3) = \pm(1.983 - i\,1.000)$ by (44) or (45a).

Inverse Hyperbolic Tangent. $\tanh^{-1}(x + i\,y)$.   Let

$$\tanh^{-1}(x + i\,y) = u + i\,v$$

$$= \frac{1}{2}\log_n\frac{1 + x + i\,y}{1 - x - i\,y} \tag{46}$$

$$e^{2u}\cos 2v = \frac{1 - x^2 - y^2}{(1 - x)^2 + y^2} \tag{47}$$

$$e^{2u}\sin 2v = \frac{2y}{(1 - x)^2 + y^2} \tag{48}$$

Squaring, adding, and factoring the numerator,

$$e^{4u} = \frac{(1 + x)^2 + y^2}{(1 - x)^2 + y^2}$$

$$u = \frac{1}{4} \operatorname{logn} \frac{(1 + x)^2 + y^2}{(1 - x)^2 + y^2} \tag{49}$$

Dividing (33) by (32),

$$\tan 2v = \frac{2y}{1 - x^2 - y^2} \tag{50}$$

Let

$$2v = \pi - \tan^{-1} \frac{(1 + x)}{y} - \tan^{-1} \frac{(1 - x)}{y} \tag{51}$$

$$= \pi - \alpha - \beta$$

where the principal values of $\tan^{-1}$ are taken, that is, α and β are between $-\pi/2$ and $\pi/2$.

$$\begin{aligned}
\sin (\pi - \alpha - \beta) &= \sin (\alpha + \beta) \\
&= (\tan \alpha + \tan \beta) \cos \alpha \cos \beta \\
&= \frac{2}{y} \cos \alpha \cos \beta
\end{aligned}$$

which is the same sign as y, as it should be, from (48).   Cos α and cos β are positive.

$$\begin{aligned}
\cos (\pi - \alpha - \beta) &= - \cos (\alpha + \beta) \\
&= (-1 + \tan \alpha \tan \beta) \cos \alpha \cos \beta \\
&= (1 - x^2 - y^2) \frac{\cos \alpha \cos \beta}{y^2}
\end{aligned}$$

which is the same sign as $1 - x^2 - y^2$ and proportional to it. See (47).   The quantity $2k\pi$, where k is an integer, may be added to (51).

Therefore, $\tanh^{-1} (x + i y) = \frac{1}{4} \operatorname{logn} \frac{(1 + x)^2 + y^2}{(1 - x)^2 + y^2}$

$$+ \frac{i}{2} \left\{ (2k + 1)\pi - \tan^{-1} \frac{1 + x}{y} - \tan^{-1} \frac{1 - x}{y} \right\} \tag{52}$$

where the principal values of $\tan^{-1}$ are taken and where x and y may be positive or negative. See p. 115 of the reference in footnote 7, and No. 715 of that in footnote 5.

[7] "Principles of Electric Power Transmission," by L. F. Woodruff, John Wiley & Sons, Inc., New York, ed. of 1938.

An alternative method of computation is to use equation (46) directly. Multiple values will be obtained since expression (23) for logn has a term $i\,2k\pi$.

Example 6.　$\tanh^{-1}(-2+i\,3) = -0.1469 + i\,1.339$
putting $k = 0$ in (52),

or　　　　　　　　　　　　$= -0.1469 + i\,4.4806$

putting $k = 1$.

The choice of the alternative formulas involving logarithms of complex quantities, which have been given in each case in this chapter, depends to some extent on the practice and preference of each individual. Although the algebraic logarithmic formulas are shorter to write than the others, the solution of the numerical problems in this paper is longer by the logarithmic formulas. The use of logarithmic formulas for obtaining results involving inverse functions is given in equations (125), p. 71, and (428), p. 179, Vol. 2, of the reference in footnote 8.

[8] "Communication Networks," by E. A. Guillemin, John Wiley & Sons, Inc., New York, 1935.

CHAPTER 12

EXERCISE IN GRAPHICAL FLUX PLOTTING
WITH A COMPUTED TEST FOR ACCURACY

A very useful way of solving many magnetic, electric, and other problems is found in the method of graphical flux plotting. The flux plots are families of flow and equipotential lines, the one group crossing the other at right angles. The lines are drawn freehand according to two main rules, for two-dimensional problems: (1) that the lines shall cross exactly at right angles and (2) that the figures formed by them shall be what have been called "curvilinear squares." These, besides having right-angle corners, each have equal diameters as commonly measured for such a purpose with a pair of dividers between the middle points of the opposite sides.

If the correct, computed solution of an exercise in graphical flux plotting consists of circles, they can be easily drawn alongside the freehand solution. The computed circles show where the freehand lines ought to be, and a comparison of the two solutions gives practice in estimating the correctness of right angles and of curvilinear squares. The beginnings of errors in the freehand plot can be located.

Such a problem is the two-dimensional one of drawing the curvilinear squares of the flux plot between two boundary circles, as described in the article An Accuracy Test for Flux Plotting Methods, by R. B. Wright and N. F. Tsang, *Gen. Elec. Rev.*, March, 1929, p. 149. This was written in connection with work in classes of the author, at Massachusetts Institute of Technology.

From this general problem a considerable variety of graphical exercises may be obtained. Two boundary circles that are nearly concentric give a comparatively easy freehand graphical problem, while the flow between two unequal circles that are external to each other is more difficult to draw by the freehand method.

The centers and radii of the circles of the computed solution may be obtained, if desired, by the method of *conformal mapping*. Straight lines having the equations $u = $ constant and $v = $ constant are drawn in a location called the W plane. In this problem the constants are so chosen that the straight lines are equidistant, forming squares.

In order to obtain orthogonal curves, some function $w = f(z)$ is taken, in which

$$w = u + j\,v$$
and
$$z = x + j\,y$$

When u is put equal to a constant, u is a function of x and y, and so x and y can be plotted to give a curve on another piece of section paper called the Z plane. Similarly when v is put equal to a constant, orthogonal lines to the others are obtained on the Z plane. The sets of lines on the Z plane are as though the straight lines on the W plane had been warped out of shape, but in general they cross exactly at right angles. It has been proved that, at any point in the Z plane, the magnification of the lines at right angles is the same, and consequently the diameters of a curvilinear square are practically equal if the square is small.

For the electrostatic field of two parallel wires of opposite polarity, which is a well-known problem, the field lines have been found to be given by the following logarithmic expression. Let

$$w = u + j\,v = f(z) = f(x + j\,y)$$
$$= \frac{1}{2\pi} \operatorname{logn} \frac{z - d}{z + d}$$
$$= \frac{1}{2\pi} \operatorname{logn} \frac{x - d + j\,y}{x + d + j\,y}$$

where logn denotes natural logarithm.

To change from rectangular to polar coordinates,

$$m + j\,n = r(\cos\theta + j\sin\theta) = re^{j\theta}$$

where $\quad \dfrac{m}{r} = \cos\theta, \qquad \dfrac{n}{r} = \sin\theta, \qquad r = \sqrt{m^2 + n^2}.$

$$\operatorname{logn}(m + j\,n) = \operatorname{logn} r + j\,\theta.$$

Let
$$u = \frac{V}{4\pi q}$$

thus representing potential and let $v = n/p =$ fraction of the total lines of force

$$\frac{V}{4\pi q} + j\,\frac{n}{p} = \frac{1}{4\pi}\,\text{logn}\,\frac{(x-d)^2 + y^2}{(x+d)^2 + y^2}$$

$$+ \frac{j}{2\pi}\left(\tan^{-1}\frac{y}{x-d} - \tan^{-1}\frac{y}{x+d}\right) \quad (1)$$

using values of $\tan^{-1}$ on the same branch.

Equating the real parts, an equipotential line is obtained.

$$e^{V/q} = \frac{(x-d)^2 + y^2}{(x+d)^2 + y^2}$$

$$(x^2 + 2xd + d^2)e^{V/q} + y^2 e^{V/q} = x^2 - 2xd + d^2 + y^2$$

$$x^2(1 - e^{V/q}) - 2xd(1 + e^{V/q}) + d^2(1 - e^{V/q}) + y^2(1 - e^{V/q}) = 0$$

$$x^2(1 - e^{V/q})^2 - 2xd(1 - e^{2V/q}) + d^2(1 - e^{V/q})^2 + y^2(1 - e^{V/q})^2$$
$$= 0$$

$$[x(1 - e^{V/q}) - d(1 + e^{V/q})]^2 + y^2(1 - e^{V/q})^2$$
$$= d^2(1 + 2e^{V/q} + e^{2V/q} - 1 + 2e^{V/q} - e^{2V/q})$$

$$= d^2 4e^{V/q} = d^2(2e^{\frac{V}{2q}})^2$$

$$\left(x - d\,\frac{1 + e^{V/q}}{1 - e^{V/q}}\right)^2 + y^2 = d^2\left(\frac{2e^{\frac{V}{2q}}}{1 - e^{V/q}}\right)^2 \quad (2)$$

This is a circle, whose radius and the location of whose center can be recognized.

Equating the imaginary parts, a flow line is obtained, since it is a line up to which the fraction of the total lines of force is a constant.

$$\frac{2\pi n}{p} = \tan^{-1}\frac{y}{x-d} - \tan^{-1}\frac{y}{x+d}$$

$$\tan(A - B) = \frac{\tan A - \tan B}{1 + \tan A \tan B}$$

$$\frac{2\pi n}{p} = \tan^{-1}\left[\frac{\dfrac{y}{x-d} - \dfrac{y}{x+d}}{1 + \dfrac{y^2}{x^2 - d^2}}\right]$$

$$\tan\frac{2\pi n}{p} = \frac{y(x+d) - y(x-d)}{x^2 + y^2 - d^2} = \frac{2dy}{x^2 + y^2 - d^2}$$

$$x^2 + y^2 - d^2 = \frac{2dy}{\tan \dfrac{2\pi n}{p}} = 2dy \cot \frac{2\pi n}{p}$$

$$x^2 + \left(y - d \cot \frac{2\pi n}{p} \right)^2 = d^2 \left(\cot^2 \frac{2\pi n}{p} + 1 \right)$$

$$= \frac{d^2}{\sin^2 \left(\dfrac{2\pi n}{p} \right)} \tag{3}$$

This gives a flow-line circle.

In order to find the equations for circles making a flux plot of curvilinear squares, consider two parallel plates 1 cm wide, of area A, and l cm apart. If the charge on one plate is Q and on the other, $-Q$, and if V is the potential between them, then the capacitance is Q/V. The number of electrostatic lines crossing from one plate to the other is $4\pi Q$. If the plates are close together, the lines outside them can e neglected and the density of lines between them, which gives the change of potential per centimeter, is $\pi Q/A$. The potential is $4\pi Q l/A$, and the capacitance is $A/(4\pi l)$. If this flux plot is drawn in squares, A is proportional to p, the number of squares counted along an equipotential line, and l is proportional to f, the number of squares along a flow line. Then the capacitance is

$$\frac{1}{4\pi} \frac{p}{f} \tag{4}$$

This is true if part or all of the flux plot is curved, for the potential between two equipotential lines is constant and the electrostatic flux between two flow lines is constant.

To find an expression for the capacitance of two parallel cylinders in terms of a, b, and c, where a and b are the radii and c is the distance between centers, we have from (2) the radius of the circle whose potential is V_1 equal to

$$a = \frac{2de^{\frac{V_1}{2q}}}{e^{V_1/q} - 1} \tag{5}$$

when V_1 is positive. The distance from the origin to the center, from the equation of the circle, equation (2), is

$$d \frac{1 + e^{V_1/q}}{1 - e^{V_1/q}} \tag{6}$$

which is a negative quantity when V_1 is positive. The value of

this is

$$\sqrt{d^2 + a^2} \tag{7}$$

since

$$d^2 + a^2 = d^2 \frac{1 - 2e^{V_1/q} + e^{2V_1/q} + 4e^{V_1/q}}{(1 - e^{V_1/q})^2}$$

$$= d^2 \frac{(1 + e^{V_1/q})^2}{(1 - e^{V_1/q})^2}$$

Similarly, the distance from the origin to the center of the circle of potential V_2, which is the surface of the cylinder of radius b, is

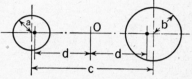

$$d \frac{1 + e^{V_2/q}}{1 - e^{V_2/q}} = \sqrt{d^2 + b^2}$$

This is a positive quantity when V_2 is negative.

Fig. 1.—Case of one circle not enclosing the other.

When one circle does not enclose the other, as in Fig. 1, the distance between their centers is

$$c = \sqrt{d^2 + a^2} + \sqrt{d^2 + b^2} \tag{8}$$

$$c^2 = 2d^2 + a^2 + b^2 + 2\sqrt{d^4 + a^2d^2 + b^2d^2 + a^2b^2}$$

$$4(d^4 + a^2d^2 + b^2d^2 + a^2b^2) = 4d^4 + 4d^2(a^2 + b^2 - c^2)$$

$$+ a^4 + b^4 + c^4 + 2a^2b^2 - 2b^2c^2 - 2c^2a^2$$

$$4c^2d^2 = a^4 + b^4 + c^4 - 2a^2b^2 - 2b^2c^2 - 2c^2a^2$$

$$= (c^2 - a^2 - b^2)^2 - 4a^2b^2 \tag{9}$$

$$= (c^2 + a^2 - b^2)^2 - 4a^2c^2$$

$$= (c^2 - a^2 + b^2)^2 - 4b^2c^2$$

$$\sqrt{d^2 + a^2} = \frac{c^2 + a^2 - b^2}{2c} \tag{10}$$

$$\sqrt{d^2 + b^2} = \frac{c^2 - a^2 + b^2}{2c} \tag{11}$$

These are positive quantities.

From (6),

$$\frac{e^{V_1/q} + 1}{e^{V_1/q} - 1} = \frac{\sqrt{d^2 + a^2}}{d}$$

$$e^{V_1/q} = \frac{\sqrt{d^2 + a^2} + d}{\sqrt{d^2 + a^2} - d}$$

Similarly,

$$e^{V_2/q} = \frac{\sqrt{d^2 + b^2} - d}{\sqrt{d^2 + b^2} + d}$$

If the capacitance $= C$,

$$\frac{1}{C} = \frac{V_1}{q} - \frac{V_2}{q} = \operatorname{logn} \frac{\sqrt{d^2 + a^2} + d}{\sqrt{d^2 + a^2} - d} - \operatorname{logn} \frac{\sqrt{d^2 + b^2} - d}{\sqrt{d^2 + b^2} + d} \quad (12)$$

$$\frac{1}{C} = \operatorname{logn} \frac{(\sqrt{d^2 + a^2} + d)(c + d - \sqrt{d^2 + a^2})}{(\sqrt{d^2 + a^2} - d)(c - d - \sqrt{d^2 + a^2})}$$

$$= \operatorname{logn} \frac{c\sqrt{d^2 + a^2} + cd - a^2}{c\sqrt{d^2 + a^2} - cd - a^2}$$

$$= \operatorname{logn} \frac{c^2 + a^2 - b^2 + 2cd - 2a^2}{c^2 + a^2 - b^2 - 2cd - 2a^2} \quad \text{from} \quad (10)$$

$$= \operatorname{logn} \frac{c^2 - a^2 - b^2 + 2cd}{c^2 - a^2 - b^2 - 2cd}$$

$$= \operatorname{logn} \frac{(c^2 - a^2 - b^2 + 2cd)^2}{4a^2b^2} \quad \text{from} \quad (9)$$

$$C = \frac{1}{2 \operatorname{logn} \dfrac{c^2 - a^2 - b^2 + 2cd}{2ab}} \quad (13)$$

To draw the flux plot with circles forming curvilinear squares, where one of the boundary circles does not enclose or cut the other, find d from (9). Choose a value of f to give a suitable size of squares and equate (4) to (13), thus determining p. Divide the quantity

$$\frac{1}{C} = \frac{V_1}{q} - \frac{V_2}{q}$$

[equations (12) and (13)] into f parts and let V/q be any one of the dividing values so obtained. The radius of the equipotential circle of potential V is

$$r = \frac{\pm 2de^{\frac{V}{2q}}}{1 - e^{V/q}} \quad (14)$$

the positive value of r being taken. Note that $e^{\frac{V}{2q}}$ is the square root of $e^{V/q}$.

A table of e^x or a logarithm table may be used for (14). If desired, common logarithms instead of natural can be used with (13), giving $0.434/C$ instead of $1/C$ and giving correspondingly small dividing values. Then the common antilogarithm of one of the intermediate values will be

$$10^{0.434V/q} = e^{V/q}$$

which is required in (14).

In order to locate the centers of the equipotential circles, note that the circle of radius r has its center on the x axis, at a horizontal distance from the center of the circle of radius a equal to

$$\sqrt{d^2 + r^2} + \sqrt{d^2 + a^2}$$

when V and V_1 are of unlike signs, one positive and one negative, and at a distance equal to

$$\sqrt{d^2 + r^2} - \sqrt{d^2 + a^2}$$

when V and V_1 are of the same sign. Use equation (10). This distance is to be taken in such a direction that the centers of the computed equipotential circles will be outside, and not between, the centers of the two given circles of radii a and b, and such that a circle of radius r will enclose the one of the given circles which has the same polarity.

The flow lines are given by equation (3). They are circles whose centers are on the axis of y, which is perpendicular to the line joining the centers of the two given circles and which passes through the point of zero potential, O, on that line. This point of zero potential is the origin for the original equations. It is at a distance $\sqrt{d^2 + a^2}$ from the center of the circle of radius a, and at a distance $\sqrt{d^2 + b^2}$ from the center of the circle of radius b. The center of the nth circle of flow is at a vertical distance from the x axis equal to

$$d \cot \frac{2\pi n}{p} \tag{15}$$

and the radius is

$$\frac{d}{\sin \dfrac{2\pi n}{p}} \tag{16}$$

as may be seen from equation (3).

From equation (12), q and $-q$ are the amounts of charge per centimeter on the two cylinders of radii a and b. Taking d and q to be constant, the circle for any given potential V, [equation (2)], and the flow-line circle for any given value of n/p, [equation (3)], are not dependent on the sizes of a and b. Thus the intermediate circles would be the same if a and b became smaller and smaller, so that the charges q and $-q$ became concentrated at two points in Fig. 1. Since the distance from the origin to the center of a circle of radius a is $\sqrt{d^2 + a^2}$ by equation (7), the distance to the concentrated charge is d, putting $a = 0$. The locations of the equivalent concentrated charges which would give the same flux plot as the given circles are shown by round dots in Figs. 1 and 2.

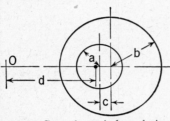

FIG. 2.—Case of one circle enclosing the other.

The flow circles all pass through the locations of the concentrated charges. The tangents to any two flow circles, at these points, meet at an angle which is proportional to the amount of electrostatic flux between those two flow lines.

When one circle encloses the other, as in Fig. 2, a very similar calculation is made. In this case, V_1 and V_2 are of the same sign and the distance between the centers of the boundary circles is

$$c = \sqrt{d^2 + b^2} - \sqrt{d^2 + a^2} \qquad (17)$$

where b is greater than a (see Fig. 2). This results in equation (9). From this, for the enclosing case,

$$\sqrt{d^2 + a^2} = \frac{b^2 - c^2 - a^2}{2c} \qquad (18)$$

This is a positive quantity. It is seen from Fig. 2 that b is greater than $a + c$ in order for the larger circle to enclose the other and not cut it.

$$\sqrt{d^2 + b^2} = \frac{c^2 - a^2 + b^2}{2c} \qquad (19)$$

This also is a positive quantity since b is greater than a.

Since V_1 is negative,

$$\frac{1 + e^{V_1/q}}{1 - e^{V_1/q}} = \frac{\sqrt{d^2 + a^2}}{d}$$

$$e^{V_1/q} = \frac{\sqrt{d^2 + a^2} - d}{\sqrt{d^2 + a^2} + d}$$

Similarly, $$e^{V_2/q} = \frac{\sqrt{d^2 + b^2} - d}{\sqrt{d^2 + b^2} + d}$$

where V_2 is negative.

The capacitance, C, may be found from

$$\frac{1}{C} = \frac{V_2}{q} - \frac{V_1}{q}$$

$$= \operatorname{logn} \frac{\sqrt{d^2 + b^2} - d}{\sqrt{d^2 + b^2} + d} - \operatorname{logn} \frac{\sqrt{d^2 + a^2} - d}{\sqrt{d^2 + a^2} + d}$$

$$= \operatorname{logn} \frac{(\sqrt{d^2 + a^2} + c - d)(\sqrt{d^2 + a^2} + d)}{(\sqrt{d^2 + a^2} + c + d)(\sqrt{d^2 + a^2} - d)}$$

$$\text{by} \quad (17)$$

$$= \operatorname{logn} \frac{c\sqrt{d^2 + a^2} + a^2 + cd}{c\sqrt{d^2 + a^2} + a^2 - cd}$$

Substituting (18) and simplifying,

$$C = \frac{1}{2\operatorname{logn} \dfrac{a^2 + b^2 - c^2 + 2cd}{2ab}} \qquad (20)$$

for the enclosing case.   The quantity d is given by (9).

The value of C is equated to (4), after choosing f, thus finding the value of p.   The quantity $1/C$ is divided into f parts, and values of r are found by (14).   Since the flux plot is entirely inside the circle of radius b, the potentials are all negative.   The distance from the center of the equipotential circle of radius r to the center of the circle of radius a, along the axis of x, is

$$\sqrt{d^2 + r^2} - \sqrt{d^2 + a^2} \qquad \text{(See Fig. 2)}$$

The flow circles are computed in the manner described for the nonenclosing case.

A more difficult graphical problem is to plot the magnetic field of a coil or a magnet that has symmetry about an axis.[1] Although the flow lines must cross the equipotential lines exactly at right angles, the figures in general are curvilinear rectangles instead of squares, and each one involves a slide-rule computation.   Columns are made, headed: Rectangle No., Mean Radius, Thickness, Sectional Area, Length, Gilberts, Density, Flux per Path, Total Flux.   A path for the flow of a certain amount of flux is taken, usually at the axis, and portions of mmf are

---

[1] The Shape of Core for Laboratory Electromagnets, by H. B. Dwight and C. F. Abt, *Rev. Sci. Instruments*, Vol. 7, p. 144, March, 1936.

taken along it, which remain constant throughout the computation until the lines enter the cross section of the current-carrying coil. The flow lines finally become infinitesimal circles about a kernel or kernels located somewhere in the coil section or sections. The bands that cross the flow lines at right angles must enclose an amount of current proportional to their mmf along a flow line. The map can be continued into the iron section by using a saturation curve of the iron.

If a computed test for accuracy is desired for this type of flux plot, the iron core may be taken to be a single ellipsoid of revolution of zero reluctance, without any magnetic return, and the mmf provided by a fine wire around its surface.

A computed solution is also obtainable for circular coils without iron, as given in Chap. 32.

CHAPTER 13

SAG CALCULATIONS FOR TRANSMISSION-LINE CONDUCTORS

Sag calculations for transmission lines are frequently made by means of formulas based on the assumption that the curve of a cable in a span is a parabola. Formulas for the calculations are also published, which use the equation for the catenary, a curve so named because it has the shape of a suspended chain. This equation involves hyperbolic cosines.

In this chapter a group of convergent series is given, which will be found convenient and accurate for making sag calculations.[1] They give the results of the hyperbolic catenary formula as accurately as desired, provided enough terms are computed. Usually, two or three terms are all that are required. Since the series are convergent series derived from the expansions of hyperbolic functions, they can be said to be themselves hyperbolic formulas. The first term of the series is in many cases the same as the well-known parabolic formulas, the majority of which consist of only one term. The series herewith presented should therefore be easily understood and applied by those accustomed to the parabolic formulas.

The series moreover give directly and automatically the percentage error involved by using the parabolic formulas. Even where the latter have good accuracy, it is always worth while estimating the amount of their error in a given case. Often the worst feature of an approximate formula consists in the fact that the amount of its error is not indicated and remains unknown, so that in some more or less unusual case the error may be unexpectedly large. An approximate formula in the form of a convergent series is much safer to employ, since when the terms do not become smaller and smaller, the last one being negligibly small, it is obvious that the formula is not applicable to the case considered.

[1] Sag Calculations for Transmission Lines, by H. B. Dwight, *Trans. A.I.E.E.*, 1926, p. 796.

If, therefore, a formula is really the first term of a convergent series, it is practically always advisable to publish two or three terms of the series, so that the appropriateness of the formula for a given case may be quickly estimated.

The series are given in the form in which they can be most conveniently used for practical sag calculations. A few examples of their use are given, followed by the derivation of some of the series. The derivation of the others can be obtained by following the method of the examples given.

The description of the engineering problem is often as follows: A certain maximum tension T is specified for a cable and it is desired to know what will be the sag corresponding to this tension under given conditions of temperature, wind, and ice loading. Further, it is desired to know what changes in temperature and tension correspond to given changes in sag or loading. These results are required when the two ends of the span are supported at the same height or at unequal heights.

SAG FORMULAS

It is particularly to be remembered that in the formulas in this chapter, l represents a half span only.

Supports at Equal Heights.

$$\text{Sag or deflection} = d = l\left[\frac{1}{2}\frac{wl}{T} + \frac{7}{24}\left(\frac{wl}{T}\right)^3 + \frac{241}{720}\left(\frac{wl}{T}\right)^5 \cdots\right] \quad \text{ft} \quad (1)$$

where $l = \frac{1}{2}$ span $= \frac{1}{2}$ horizontal distance between supports, ft.

T = tension, lb, in cable at supports, where the tension is greatest.

w = resultant loading, lb/ft of cable.

Note that $w^2 = v^2 + h^2$ where v is the vertical force per foot acting on the cable due to gravity on the cable itself and on the ice covering, if any, and where h is the horizontal pressure in pounds per foot due to wind. The deflection d is not vertically downward. The distance vertically downward by which the lowest point of the cable is lower than the supports is vd/w ft.

When the deflection, d, is given,

$$T = wl\left[\frac{1}{2}\frac{l}{d} + \frac{7}{6}\frac{d}{l} - \frac{4}{45}\frac{d^3}{l^3} \cdots\right] \quad \text{lb} \quad (2)$$

The unstressed length of cable in the span is

$$L_u = 2l \left(1 + \frac{2}{3}\frac{d^2}{l^2} - \frac{14}{45}\frac{d^4}{l^4} + \frac{278}{945}\frac{d^6}{l^6} \cdots \right)$$
$$- \frac{wl^2}{AE}\left(\frac{l}{d} + \frac{5}{3}\frac{d}{l} + \frac{4}{9}\frac{d^3}{l^3} \cdots \right) \quad \text{ft} \quad (3)$$

where A = area of cross section of cable, sq. in.

E = modulus of elasticity, lb/sq. in.

The first part of equation (3) gives the actual perimeter of the catenary, and the second part gives the stretch in the conductor.

To find the changes in temperature t, corresponding to changes in deflection d, and loading w, find values of L_u corresponding to certain values of d and w. The changes in L_u are due to temperature, if the cable is assumed fastened to rigid supports, and

$$t = \frac{L_u - L_{uo}}{aL_{uo}} \quad \text{deg} \quad (4)$$

where t = change in temperature.

L_{uo} = value of L_u at the lower temperature.

L_u = value of L_u at the higher temperature.

a = temperature coefficient of expansion per degree. If a is specified per deg ee Fahrenheit, then t is in degrees Fahrenheit. Note that

$$L_u = L_{uo}(1 + at) \quad \text{ft} \quad (5)$$

When a is defined as the increase per degree above a certain temperature, then L_{uo} should be at that temperature, in using equation (4) or (5).

Curves can be plotted of d against t. Different curves for different values of w can be plotted.

To find changes in load w, corresponding to changes in d at a given temperature, insert values of d in equation (3). The value of w that will give the value of L_u for the given temperature, is obtained directly. L_u is given by equation (5).

Changes in temperature corresponding to changes in tension T are given by the following equation and by equation (4):

$$L_u = 2l\left[1 + \frac{1}{6}\left(\frac{wl}{T}\right)^2 + \frac{7}{40}\left(\frac{wl}{T}\right)^4 + \frac{241}{1,008}\left(\frac{wl}{T}\right)^6 \cdots \right]$$
$$- \frac{2wl^2}{AE}\left[\frac{T}{wl} - \frac{1}{6}\frac{wl}{T} - \frac{7}{120}\left(\frac{wl}{T}\right)^3 \cdots \right] \quad \text{ft} \quad (6)$$

Curves of tension T, against temperature t, can be plotted.

Supports at Unequal Heights. It is usually desirable to find first a solution of the catenary for a given maximum tension T at the higher support where the tension is the greatest, as was done in the case when the supports were at equal heights. Then, changes in temperature, loading, and tension can be calculated, corresponding to changes in deflection.

Let v and h be the vertical and horizontal forces per foot acting on the cable, as previously defined. Then, $w^2 = v^2 + h^2$. Let

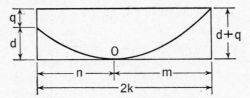

Fig. 1.—Span with supports at unequal heights.

p be the vertical height by which one support is higher than the other and let $2l$ be the horizontal distance between the supports.

$$q = \frac{pw}{v} \qquad\qquad \text{ft} \quad (7)$$

$$2k = \sqrt{4l^2 - q^2 + p^2}$$
$$= 2l - \frac{(q^2 - p^2)}{4l} - \frac{(q^2 - p^2)^2}{64l^3} \cdots \qquad \text{ft} \quad (8)$$

These dimensions are shown in Fig. 1, which is drawn in the plane of the cable and not in a vertical plane. If h, the wind pressure, is zero, then $q = p$ and $k = l$.

Equation (8) is based on the fact that the square o the distance between the supports is equal to $4l^2 + p^2$ and to $4k^2 + q^2$.

Let
$$b = \frac{q}{2k} \qquad\qquad (9)$$

$$m = k\left(1 - b^2 + \frac{2}{3}b^4 - \frac{8}{15}b^6 \cdots\right) + \frac{T}{w}\left(b - \frac{2}{3}b^3 + \frac{8}{15}b^5\right.$$
$$\left. - \frac{16}{35}b^7 \cdots\right) - k\left(\frac{wk}{T}\right)\left(\frac{2}{3}b + 0 + \frac{2}{45}b^5 \cdots\right)$$
$$- k\left(\frac{wk}{T}\right)^2\left(\frac{2}{3}b^2 + 0 \cdots\right) - k\left(\frac{wk}{T}\right)^3\left(\frac{16}{45}b + \frac{8}{9}b^3 \cdots\right)$$
$$\text{ft} \quad (10)$$

The deflection, $d + q$, is found from equation (1), putting $l = m$.

The distance vertically downward from the upper support to the lowest point of the cable is $\dfrac{v(d + q)}{w}$ ft.

For finding the effect of changes of temperature and loading, it would be possible to assume different values of T and find values of m and d as above. However, it will be a little shorter to assume values of H the horizontal tension and find m from the following:

$$m = k + \frac{H}{w}\left(b - \frac{1}{6}b^3 + \frac{3}{40}b^5 - \frac{5}{112}b^7 \cdots \right)$$
$$- \frac{k}{6}\left(\frac{wk}{H}\right)\left(b - \frac{1}{2}b^3 + \frac{3}{8}b^5 \cdots \right)$$
$$+ \frac{k}{30}\left(\frac{wk}{H}\right)^3\left(\frac{7}{12}b - \frac{17}{24}b^3 \cdots \right) \quad \text{ft} \quad (11)$$

The deflection in this case is found from

$$d = n\left[\frac{1}{2}\frac{wn}{H} + \frac{1}{24}\left(\frac{wn}{H}\right)^3 + \frac{1}{720}\left(\frac{wn}{H}\right)^5 \cdots \right] \quad \text{feet} \quad (12)$$

where $\qquad\qquad\qquad n = 2k - m \qquad\qquad\qquad\qquad$ ft $\quad (13)$

After m, n, and d are found, using either (10) or (11) for m, the unstressed length of cable is found by applying equation (3) to each part of the span separately, as follows:

$$L_u = m\left[1 + \frac{2}{3}\left(\frac{d + q}{m}\right)^2 - \frac{14}{45}\left(\frac{d + q}{m}\right)^4 + \frac{278}{945}\left(\frac{d + q}{m}\right)^6 \cdots \right]$$
$$- \frac{wm^2}{AE}\left[\frac{1}{2}\left(\frac{m}{d + q}\right) + \frac{5}{6}\left(\frac{d + q}{m}\right) + \frac{2}{9}\left(\frac{d + q}{m}\right)^3 \cdots \right]$$
$$+ n\left[1 + \frac{2}{3}\left(\frac{d}{n}\right)^2 - \frac{14}{45}\left(\frac{d}{n}\right)^4 + \frac{278}{945}\left(\frac{d}{n}\right)^6 \cdots \right]$$
$$- \frac{wn^2}{AE}\left[\frac{1}{2}\frac{n}{d} + \frac{5}{6}\frac{d}{n} + \frac{2}{9}\left(\frac{d}{n}\right)^3 \cdots \right] \quad \text{ft} \quad (14)$$

Curves for sag, temperature, loading, and tension can now be drawn, as described for the case of supports at equal heights. If a value of H has been assumed, the tension at each support can be found by applying equation (2) or (21) to each part of the span. The tension at a support is somewhat greater than H and is greater at the higher support.

If there is no horizontal part of the curve between the two supports, then m is greater than $2k$ and n is a negative quantity [see equation (13)].

Where a value of H is assumed, a table of hyperbolic sines (not too condensed a table) can be used with equation (18) to find m. However, this would not give a direct calculation for m in terms of T, such as is given by equation (10). If the difference in elevation of the supports is unusually great compared with the length of the span, the series may not converge rapidly enough, and a table of hyperbolic sines and cosines may be required. In such a case, trial-and-error methods may be necessary in order to obtain the results desired.

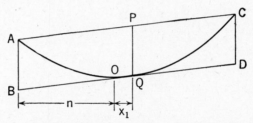

Fig. 2.—Deflection of cable from line of supports.

An illustration of this type of calculation is given in Example 5. Since it is a trial-and-error method, different values of H must be assumed until a satisfactory value of T is obtained.

When the supports are at equal heights, values of H may be assumed and a table of hyperbolic sines and cosines used in a somewhat similar manner to Example 5. This usually requires more work than to use the series. This is a trial-and-error method if one is working to a specified value of T. It may be necessary to do this if the series do not converge rapidly enough, as with an unusually large ratio of sag to span, but this is not likely to occur with practical transmission line spans having supports at equal heights.

Deflection from Line of Supports. After the location of the lowest point O (Figs. 1 and 2), and therefore the complete equation of the catenary for one set of conditions, have been found, it is possible to find by calculation the vertical distance PQ from the line of the supports A and C to a tangent BD which is parallel to AC. In Fig. 2, $PQ = AB = CD$, and the two latter distances may be measured on the towers and the line BD be used for sighting to determine the correct amount of sag to give the cable when stringing it. For this purpose, assume that there is no wind or ice load, and so the cable hangs vertically. The calculation would be practically the same if wind load were included.

Let the equation of a line parallel to the line of the supports be $y = gx + f$, where g is known but where f is unknown. For this line, $dy/dx = g = p/(2l)$. The height of any point on the catenary above O is given by

$$y = \frac{H}{w}\left(\cosh\frac{wx}{H} - 1\right)$$

$$\frac{dy}{dx} = \sinh\frac{wx}{H}$$

If the line BD is tangent to the catenary at Q, which is the point (x_1, y_1),

$$\sinh\frac{wx_1}{H} = g$$

Then

$$\cosh\frac{wx_1}{H} = \sqrt{1 + g^2}$$

$$y_1 = \frac{H}{w}\left(\sqrt{1 + g^2} - 1\right) \tag{15}$$

$$x_1 = \frac{H}{w}\sinh^{-1} g = \frac{H}{w}\left(g - \frac{1}{2\times 3}g^3 + \frac{1\times 3}{2\times 4\times 5}g^5\right.$$
$$\left. - \frac{1\times 3\times 5}{2\times 4\times 6\times 7}g^7 + \cdots\right) \tag{16}$$

Thus, numerical values of x_1 and y_1 can be obtained.

The height of P above O is $d + \dfrac{p(n + x_1)}{2l}$

and therefore, $PQ = AB = CD = d + \dfrac{p(n + x_1)}{2l} - y_1 \tag{17}$

all parts of which are known.

Example 1. Find the difference in temperature for the following two sets of data for the same span:

$$2l = 800 \text{ ft}$$

$$\frac{wl}{T} = 0.131\ 28$$

$$\frac{w}{AE} = 0.000\ 000\ 757\ 2$$

For the higher temperature, without wind or ice load,

$$\text{Sag} = 23.1760 \text{ ft.}$$

$$\frac{w}{AE} = 0.000\ 000\ 297\ 6$$

Temperature coefficient $= 0.000\ 009\ 6$

By equation (6),

$$L_{uo} = 800(1 + 0.002\ 872\ 4 + 0.000\ 051\ 9 + 0.000\ 001\ 2 \cdots)$$
$$- 800(0.002\ 307\ 0 - 0.000\ 006\ 6 + 0.000\ 000\ 04 \cdots)$$
$$= 800 \times 1.000\ 625\ 2$$

By equation (3),

$$L_u = 800(1 + 0.002\ 238\ 1 - 0.000\ 003\ 5 + 0.000\ 000\ 01 \cdots$$
$$- 0.001\ 027\ 3 - 0.000\ 005\ 7 - 0.000\ 000\ 01 \cdots)$$
$$= 800 \times 1.001\ 201\ 6$$

By equation (4),

$$t = \frac{0.000\ 576\ 4}{0.000\ 009\ 6 \times 1.000\ 625\ 2} = 60.1°\text{F}$$

This checks the result given in Problem 4 of J. S. Martin's paper, *Proc. Eng. Soc. West. Penna.*, 1922, p. 309.

Example 2. Find the deflection for the following span, the supports being at equal heights:

$$2l = 2,000 \text{ ft}$$
$$T = 70,000 \text{ lb}$$
$$w = 4.700 \text{ lb/ft}$$

(Problem 2, page 11, Transmission Line Design, by F. K. Kirsten, *Univ. Washington*, Bull. 17, Seattle, 1923.)

$$\frac{wl}{T} = \frac{4.700 \times 1,000}{70,000} = 0.067\ 143$$

$$\frac{l}{2}\left(\frac{wl}{T}\right) = 33.571$$

By equation (1), $d = 33.57 + 0.088 + 0.0005 = 33.66 \text{ ft}$

This agrees with the value of 33.6 ft given in the above reference. It is seen that the series gives quickly and directly a precise solution of this problem, and the degree of precision of the calculation is indicated by the convergence of the series. The first term is the well-known parabolic formula.

Example 3.   Find the horizontal point for the following catenary:

$$2\,l = 2,700 \text{ ft}$$

Supports at unequal heights, $p = 179$ ft

$$T = 60,587 \text{ lb at the higher support}$$
$$h = 1.321 \text{ lb/ft}$$
$$v = 2.870 \text{ lb/ft}$$
$$w = 3.158 \text{ lb/ft}$$

(Problem with cable loaded, Table VII, Transmission Line Design, by G. S. Smith, *Jour. A.I.E.E.*, December, 1925, p. 1352.   See complete paper.)

$$q = \frac{pw}{v} = 197.0$$
$$2k = 2,698.75$$
$$b = \frac{q}{2k} = 0.0730$$

By equation (10),

$$m = 1,342.2 + 1,395.6 - 4.6 - 0.02 - 0.01 = 2,733.2 \text{ ft}$$
$$n = 2,698.7 - 2,733.2 = -34.5 \text{ ft}$$

Example 4.   Find the deflection for the following span:

$$2\,l = 4,279 \text{ ft}$$

Supports at unequal heights, $p = 185.5$ ft

$$T = 33,000 \text{ lb at the higher support}$$
$$h = 2.036 \text{ lb/ft}$$
$$v = 2.623 \text{ lb/ft}$$
$$w = 3.322 \text{ lb/ft}$$

(Mississippi River Crossing, by H. W. Eales and E. Ettlinger, *Jour. A.I.-E.E.*, October, 1925, first problem in the appendix.   See complete paper.)

$$q = \frac{pw}{v} = 235.0 \text{ ft}$$
$$2k = 4,276.57 \text{ ft}$$
$$b = \frac{q}{2k} = 0.054\ 95$$

By equation (10), $m = 2,132 + 545 - 17.0 - 0.2 - 0.4 \cdots$
$$= 2,659 \text{ ft}$$
By equation (1), $d + q = 356 + 15 + 1$
$$= 372 \text{ ft}$$

Example 5.   To illustrate the use of a table of hyperbolic sines and cosines.

Let

$$H = 31,940 \text{ in Example 4.}$$

$$\frac{wk}{H} = \frac{3.322 \times 2,138.28}{31,940} = 0.222\ 40$$

$$\sinh 0.222\ 40 = 0.222\ 24$$

$$\sinh \frac{w(k-n)}{H} = \frac{qw}{2H \times 0.224\ 24}$$

$$= \frac{235.0 \times 3.322}{2 \times 31,940 \times 0.224\ 24}$$

$$= 0.054\ 50$$

$$\frac{w(k-n)}{H} = 0.054\ 47$$

$$n = 2,138.28 - \frac{0.054\ 47 \times 31,940}{3.322}$$

$$= 1,614.6 \text{ ft}$$

$$m = 4,276.57 - 1,614.6 = 2,662.0 \text{ ft}$$

The value of T can now be calculated, and it will be slightly different from 33,000 since a value of H was assumed as part of the trial-and-error method.

Derivation of Formulas.   I. Sag, or deflection, when supports are of equal height.

Let $l = \frac{1}{2}$ length of span, ft.

    w = force, lb/ft, acting on the cable, due to gravity and wind pressure.

    H = horizontal component of tension in cable.

    T = tension in cable at support, lb.

By the well-known catenary formulas,

$$d = \text{sag or deflection} = \frac{H}{w}\left(\cosh\frac{wl}{H} - 1\right)$$

and

$$T = H\cosh\frac{wl}{H}$$

(For the derivation of these, see "Principles of Electric Power Transmission," by L. F. Woodruff, or other texts.)

$$\frac{T}{wl} = \frac{H}{wl}\left[1 + \frac{1}{2}\left(\frac{wl}{H}\right)^2 + \frac{1}{24}\left(\frac{wl}{H}\right)^4 \cdots\right]$$

$$\frac{wl}{T} = \frac{wl}{H}\left[1 - \frac{1}{2}\left(\frac{wl}{H}\right)^2 + \frac{5}{24}\left(\frac{wl}{H}\right)^4 \cdots\right],$$

the last by long division or by multinomial expansion.

$$\left(\frac{wl}{T}\right)^5 = \left(\frac{wl}{H}\right)^5 \cdots$$

$$\left(\frac{wl}{T}\right)^3 = \left(\frac{wl}{H}\right)^3 \left[1 - \frac{3}{2}\left(\frac{wl}{H}\right)^2\right]$$

$$= \left(\frac{wl}{H}\right)^3 - \frac{3}{2}\left(\frac{wl}{T}\right)^5 \cdots$$

$$\frac{wl}{H} = \frac{wl}{T} + \frac{1}{2}\left(\frac{wl}{H}\right)^3 - \frac{5}{24}\left(\frac{wl}{H}\right)^5 \cdots$$

$$= \frac{wl}{T} + \frac{1}{2}\left(\frac{wl}{T}\right)^3 + \frac{3}{4}\left(\frac{wl}{T}\right)^5 - \frac{5}{24}\left(\frac{wl}{T}\right)^5 \cdots$$

$$= \frac{wl}{T} + \frac{1}{2}\left(\frac{wl}{T}\right)^3 + \frac{13}{24}\left(\frac{wl}{T}\right)^5 \cdots$$

If desired, the tabulated coefficients for inversion of series may be used for obtaining this result. For instance, see item 50, "Tables of Integrals and Other Mathematical Data," by H. B. Dwight.

$$d = l\frac{H}{wl}\left[\frac{1}{2}\left(\frac{wl}{H}\right)^2 + \frac{1}{24}\left(\frac{wl}{H}\right)^4 + \frac{1}{720}\left(\frac{wl}{H}\right)^6 \cdots\right]$$

$$= l\left[\frac{1}{2}\left(\frac{wl}{H}\right) + \frac{1}{24}\left(\frac{wl}{H}\right)^3 + \frac{1}{720}\left(\frac{wl}{H}\right)^5 \cdots\right]$$

$$= l\left[\frac{1}{2}\frac{wl}{T} + \frac{1}{4}\left(\frac{wl}{T}\right)^3 + \frac{13}{48}\left(\frac{wl}{T}\right)^5 + \frac{1}{24}\left(\frac{wl}{T}\right)^3 + \frac{3}{48}\left(\frac{wl}{T}\right)^5\right.$$

$$\left. + \frac{1}{720}\left(\frac{wl}{T}\right)^5 \cdots\right]$$

$$d = l\left[\frac{1}{2}\frac{wl}{T} + \frac{7}{24}\left(\frac{wl}{T}\right)^3 + \frac{241}{720}\left(\frac{wl}{T}\right)^5 \cdots\right]$$

This is equation (1).

II. Equation (1) can be transformed by a similar process to give a series for T in terms of d.

$$\frac{d^4}{l^4} = \frac{1}{16}\left(\frac{wl}{T}\right)^4 \cdots$$

$$\frac{d^2}{l^2} = \frac{1}{4}\left(\frac{wl}{T}\right)^2 + \frac{7}{24}\left(\frac{wl}{T}\right)^4 \cdots$$

$$= \frac{1}{4}\left(\frac{wl}{T}\right)^2 + \frac{14}{3}\frac{d^4}{l^4}$$

$$\left(\frac{wl}{T}\right)^2 = 4\frac{d^2}{l^2} - \frac{56}{3}\frac{d^4}{l^4}$$

$$\frac{d}{l} = \frac{1}{2}\frac{wl}{T}\left[1 + \frac{7}{3}\frac{d^2}{l^2} - \frac{98}{9}\frac{d^4}{l^4} + \frac{241}{360}\times16\frac{d^4}{l^4}\cdots\right]$$

$$\frac{T}{wl} = \frac{1}{2}\frac{l}{d} + \frac{7}{6}\frac{d}{l} - \frac{4}{45}\frac{d^3}{l^3}\cdots$$

This is equation (2).

III. Perimeter of catenary in terms of sag.

$$\text{Perimeter} = 2l\frac{H}{wl}\sinh\frac{wl}{H}$$

$$= 2l\left[1 + \frac{1}{6}\left(\frac{wl}{H}\right)^2 + \frac{1}{120}\left(\frac{wl}{H}\right)^4 + \frac{1}{5,040}\left(\frac{wl}{H}\right)^6 + \cdots\right]$$

As in I,
$$\frac{d}{l} = \frac{1}{2}\frac{wl}{H} + \frac{1}{24}\left(\frac{wl}{H}\right)^3 + \frac{1}{720}\left(\frac{wl}{H}\right)^5\cdots$$

$$\frac{d^6}{l^6} = \frac{1}{64}\left(\frac{wl}{H}\right)^6\cdots$$

$$\frac{d^4}{l^4} = \frac{1}{16}\left(\frac{wl}{H}\right)^4 + \frac{1}{48}\left(\frac{wl}{H}\right)^6\cdots$$

$$= \frac{1}{16}\left(\frac{wl}{H}\right)^4 + \frac{64}{48}\frac{d^6}{l^6}\cdots$$

$$\left(\frac{wl}{H}\right)^4 = 16\frac{d^4}{l^4} - \frac{64}{3}\frac{d^6}{l^6}\cdots$$

$$\frac{d^2}{l^2} = \frac{1}{4}\left(\frac{wl}{H}\right)^2 + \frac{1}{24}\left(\frac{wl}{H}\right)^4 + \frac{1}{720}\left(\frac{wl}{H}\right)^6 + \frac{1}{576}\left(\frac{wl}{H}\right)^6\cdots$$

$$= \frac{1}{4}\left(\frac{wl}{H}\right)^2 + \frac{2}{3}\frac{d^4}{l^4} - \frac{8}{9}\frac{d^6}{l^6} + \frac{4}{45}\frac{d^6}{l^6} + \frac{1}{9}\frac{d^6}{l^6}\cdots$$

$$\left(\frac{wl}{H}\right)^2 = 4\frac{d^2}{l^2} - \frac{8}{3}\frac{d^4}{l^4} + \frac{124}{45}\frac{d^6}{l^6}\cdots$$

$$\text{Perimeter} = 2l\left(1 + \frac{2}{3}\frac{d^2}{l^2} - \frac{4}{9}\frac{d^4}{l^4} + \frac{62}{135}\frac{d^6}{l^6} + \frac{2}{15}\frac{d^4}{l^4} - \frac{8}{45}\frac{d^6}{l^6}\right.$$
$$\left. + \frac{4}{315}\frac{d^6}{l^6}\cdots\right)$$

$$= 2l\left(1 + \frac{2}{3}\frac{d^2}{l^2} - \frac{14}{45}\frac{d^4}{l^4} + \frac{278}{945}\frac{d^6}{l^6}\cdots\right)$$

as in equation   (3)

IV. Stretch of cable. At any horizontal distance x from the lowest point of the span, the stress is

$$\frac{T}{A} = \frac{H}{A} \cosh \frac{wx}{H} \qquad \text{lb/sq in.}$$

where A = area of cross section.

Let u = perimeter of the catenary as far as the horizontal distance x. Increase in length of du is

$$\frac{T\,du}{EA} = \frac{H \cosh \dfrac{wx}{H}}{EA}\,du$$

Now

$$du^2 = \left[1 + \left(\frac{dy}{dx}\right)^2 \right] dx^2$$

$$= \left[1 + \sinh^2 \frac{wx}{H} \right] dx^2$$

$$du = \cosh \frac{wx}{H}\, dx$$

Increase in length of du is

$$\frac{H \cosh^2 \dfrac{wx}{H}}{EA}\, dx$$

Integrate from $x = -l$ to $x = l$ to obtain the increase in length of the cable. See "Tables of Integrals and Other Mathematical Data," by H. B. Dwight, Nos. 652.4 and 677.20.

Increase in length of cable is equal to

$$\frac{H^2}{2EAw} \left(\sinh \frac{2wl}{H} + \frac{2wl}{H} \right)$$

$$= \frac{H^2}{2EAw} \left[\frac{4wl}{H} + \frac{4}{3}\left(\frac{wl}{H}\right)^3 + \frac{4}{15}\left(\frac{wl}{H}\right)^5 \cdots \right]$$

$$= \frac{2wl^2}{EA} \left[\frac{H}{w} + \frac{1}{3}\frac{wl}{H} + \frac{1}{15}\left(\frac{wl}{H}\right)^3 \cdots \right]$$

Now from I, $\dfrac{d}{l} = \dfrac{1}{2}\dfrac{wl}{H}\left[1 + \dfrac{1}{12}\left(\dfrac{wl}{H}\right)^2 + \dfrac{1}{360}\left(\dfrac{wl}{H}\right)^4 \cdots \right]$

$$\frac{H}{wl} = \frac{1}{2}\frac{l}{d}\left[1 + \frac{1}{3}\frac{d^2}{l^2} - \frac{2}{9}\frac{d^4}{l^4} + \frac{2}{45}\frac{d^4}{l^4} \cdots \right]$$

$$= \frac{1}{2}\frac{l}{d}\left[1 + \frac{1}{3}\frac{d^2}{l^2} - \frac{8}{45}\frac{d^4}{l^4} \cdots \right]$$

$$\frac{wl}{H} = \frac{2d}{l}\left(1 - \frac{1}{3}\frac{d^2}{l^2}\right)\cdots$$

$$\left(\frac{wl}{H}\right)^3 = \frac{8d^3}{l^3}\cdots$$

Increase in length of cable due to tension

$$= \frac{2wl^2}{AE}\left(\frac{1}{2}\frac{l}{d} + \frac{1}{6}\frac{d}{l} - \frac{4}{45}\frac{d^3}{l^3} + \frac{2}{3}\frac{d}{l} - \frac{2}{9}\frac{d^3}{l^3} + \frac{8}{15}\frac{d^3}{l^3}\cdots\right)$$

$$= \frac{wl^2}{AE}\left(\frac{l}{d} + \frac{5}{3}\frac{d}{l} + \frac{4}{9}\frac{d^3}{l^3}\right) \qquad \text{as in equation (3)}$$

V. Supports at unequal heights. (See "Principles of Electric Power Transmission," by L. F. Woodruff.)

Referring to Fig. 1,

$$d = \frac{H}{w}\left[\cosh\frac{wn}{H} - 1\right]$$

$$d + q = \frac{H}{w}\left[\cosh\frac{w(2k - n)}{H} - 1\right]$$

$$q = \frac{H}{w}\left[\cosh\frac{wn}{H} - \cosh\frac{w(2k - n)}{H}\right]$$

$$\cosh a - \cosh b = 2\sinh\frac{a + b}{2}\sinh\frac{a - b}{2}$$

$$q = 2k\frac{H}{wk}\sinh\frac{wk}{H}\sinh\frac{w(k - n)}{H} \qquad \text{ft} \quad (18)$$

Let
$$b = \frac{q}{2k}$$

$$\sinh\frac{w(k - n)}{H} = b\left[1 + \frac{1}{6}\left(\frac{wk}{H}\right)^2 + \frac{1}{120}\left(\frac{wk}{H}\right)^4 + \cdots\right]^{-1}$$

$$= b\left[1 - \frac{1}{6}\left(\frac{wk}{H}\right)^2 + \frac{7}{360}\left(\frac{wk}{H}\right)^4 \cdots\right]$$

also
$$= \varphi + \frac{1}{6}\varphi^3 + \frac{1}{120}\varphi^5 + \frac{1}{5,040}\varphi^7 + \cdots$$

where
$$\varphi = \frac{w(k - n)}{H}$$

$$\varphi^7 = b^7 \cdots$$

$$\sinh^5\varphi = \varphi^5 + \frac{5}{6}\varphi^7 \cdots = b^5\left\{1 - \frac{5}{6}\left(\frac{wk}{H}\right)^2 \cdots\right\}$$

$$\varphi^5 = b^5\left\{1 - \frac{5}{6}\left(\frac{wk}{H}\right)^2 \cdots\right\} - \frac{5}{6}b^7$$

Similarly, it is found that

$$\varphi^3 = b^3 \left\{ 1 - \frac{1}{2}\left(\frac{wk}{H}\right)^2 + \frac{17}{120}\left(\frac{wk}{H}\right)^4 \cdots \right\}$$

$$- \frac{1}{2} b^5 \left\{ 1 - \frac{5}{6}\left(\frac{wk}{H}\right)^2 \cdots \right\} + \frac{37}{120} b^7 \cdots$$

$$\varphi = \frac{w(k-n)}{H} = \sinh \varphi - \frac{1}{6}\varphi^3 - \frac{1}{120}\varphi^5 - \frac{1}{5{,}040}\varphi^7 \cdots$$

Substituting the values given above and putting $n = 2k - m$, equation (11) is obtained.

VI. The following series may prove useful in certain cases:
Supports at equal heights:

$$H = wl\left[\frac{1}{2}\frac{l}{d} + \frac{1}{6}\frac{d}{l} - \frac{4}{45}\frac{d^3}{l^3} \cdots \right] \qquad \text{lb} \quad (19)$$

$$H = T\left[1 - \frac{1}{2}\left(\frac{wl}{T}\right)^2 - \frac{7}{24}\left(\frac{wl}{T}\right)^4 - \frac{241}{720}\left(\frac{wl}{T}\right)^6 \cdots \right] \quad \text{lb} \quad (20)$$

$$T = H\left[1 + \frac{1}{2}\left(\frac{wl}{H}\right)^2 + \frac{1}{24}\left(\frac{wl}{H}\right)^4 + \frac{1}{720}\left(\frac{wl}{H}\right)^6 \cdots \right] \quad \text{lb} \quad (21)$$

Supports at unequal heights:

$$\frac{d}{n} = \frac{n}{2k}\left[\left(\frac{q}{2z}\right)\left\{ 1 - \frac{1}{6}b^2 + \frac{3}{40}b^4 \cdots \right\} \right.$$

$$\left. - \frac{1}{6}\left(\frac{q}{2z}\right)^3\left\{ 1 - \frac{5}{6}b^2 \cdots \right\} + \frac{3}{40}\left(\frac{q}{2z}\right)^5 \cdots \right]$$

$$+ \frac{n^3}{24k^3}\left[\left(\frac{q}{2z}\right)^3\left\{ 1 - \frac{1}{2}b^2 \cdots \right\} - \frac{1}{2}\left(\frac{q}{2z}\right)^5 \cdots \right]$$

$$+ \frac{n^5}{720k^5}\left(\frac{q}{2z}\right)^5 \cdots \quad (22)$$

where $z = k - n$. Thus, a value of n can be assumed and d found directly. However, it seems somewhat preferable to assume a value of H and then find m, n, and d by (11) and (12).

Series (22) should be used only when the terms of higher orders which it contains, are all quite small.

VII. If a bare cable is suspended between two fixed supports, an increase in temperature will increase its length. However, the total weight of the cable remains the same, and so w, the weight per foot of cable, decreases by the same percentage that the actual perimeter of the catenary increases. This can be easily allowed for in connection with some of the formulas in this paper for finding differences of temperature.

The first part of equation (3) gives the actual perimeter of the catenary. In finding L_{uo} and L_u, corresponding to two values of d, the value of w used to obtain L_u may be decreased in inverse proportion to the actual perimeters in the two cases. A similar process can be used with equations (22) and (14) for supports at unequal heights.

The effect of change in w with change in perimeter of catenary has been included in the calculations in the paper by G. S. Smith to which reference has been made.

An investigation has been made to find the proportionate effect of this feature in a number of practical cases, including data very similar to those in the paper by G. S. Smith. The effect on the calculated value of tension was extremely small. The value of temperature, which is rather sensitive to the precision of the calculations, was changed by only a small fraction of one degree. Accordingly, w is shown as a constant in the formulas in the main part of this chapter.

CHAPTER 14

RESISTANCE LOSS AND CONDUCTOR SIZE

The design of electric power circuits and their conductors is made in several different ways, depending on the class to which the circuit belongs. For overhead lines of considerable length, the percentage of reactance drop is usually the deciding feature, the conductor diameter being sometimes determined by corona. Short lines, particularly underground cables or wiring, are most frequently designed according to the heating limit of the conductors.

The cost of the energy for resistance loss is also an important feature. In some cases where the heating limit might be expected to be used, the cost of resistance loss is such that it pays to rate the conductors at less than their heating limits. Although such cases probably represent a small percentage of all the circuits that occur, yet they are of considerable importance and include some types and sizes of single-conductor cables, bus bars, and insulated wires, of which examples will be described.[1]

With overhead lines, it is sometimes found that, because the length is short or because there is control of the voltage by synchronous condensers, the cost of resistance loss becomes the most important factor in deciding the size of conductor. Sometimes, after an overhead line is designed to have the required reactance, the resistance can be changed according to the cost of resistance losses without appreciably changing the reactance or impedance. This is especially true with hollow conductors.

Although this type of computation is not new, it seems worth while keeping it in mind in designing electric power circuits of almost all types.

Let the cross section of a bare overhead copper conductor be C circular mils.

---

[1] Resistance Loss and Conductor Size, by H. B. Dwight, *Gen. Elec. Rev.*, November, 1938, p. 484.

Weight $= 0.003\ 07C$ lb per 1,000 ft.

Cost of copper at 25 cents per pound, installed, including the portion of the supports which varies directly as the weight of copper $= 0.000\ 77C$ dollars per 1,000 ft.

Annual fixed charge at 12% $= 0.000\ 092\ C$ dollars per 1,000 ft.

Resistance $= \dfrac{10,900}{C}$ ohms per 1,000 ft.

Resistance loss $= \dfrac{10,900}{1,000}\dfrac{I^2}{C}$ kw per 1,000 ft for a current of I amp.

Let the energy for this loss be supplied from a steam station whose first cost is \$100 per kilowatt and whose fuel cost is 0.2 cent per kilowatt-hour. Let the station be enlarged enough to supply the resistance loss. The annual fixed charge for this part of the station including wages, etc., is, at 12 per cent,

$$0.12 \times 100 \times \frac{10,900}{1,000}\frac{I^2}{C} = 131\frac{I^2}{C} \quad \text{dollars} \quad (1)$$

Let the ratio of the average resistance loss to its peak value be 25 per cent. It will usually be considerably less than the load factor, since the resistance loss varies as I^2 and the load varies as I. The kilowatt-hours of resistance loss per year will then be

$$0.25 \times 8,760 \times \frac{10,900}{1,000}\frac{I^2}{C} = 23,900\frac{I^2}{C} \quad (2)$$

The annual fuel cost for resistance loss is

$$0.002 \times 23,900\frac{I^2}{C} = 48\frac{I^2}{C} \quad \text{dollars}$$

Total cost of energy for resistance loss is

$$(131 + 48)\frac{I^2}{C} = 179\frac{I^2}{C} \quad (3)$$

Total annual charge for the copper and its resistance loss is

$$0.000\ 092\ C + 179\frac{I^2}{C} \quad \text{dollars/1,000 ft of conductor} \quad (4)$$

Now let the conductor section be increased slightly to $C(1 + a)$. The saving in annual charge is

$$179 \frac{I^2}{C} \left(1 - \frac{1}{1 + a}\right) + 0.000\ 092\ C\ (1 - 1 - a) \qquad (5)$$

$$= 179 \frac{I^2}{C} a - 0.000\ 092\ Ca \qquad (6)$$

when a is small. So long as this is a positive quantity, it is economical to increase the conductor size, and therefore the most economical size is that for which

$$179 \frac{I^2}{C} = 0.000\ 092\ C \qquad (7)$$

It is to be noted that this is the same result as Kelvin's law, which states that the most economical size of copper is that for which the annual fixed charge for the copper and those parts which vary as the weight of the copper, is equal to the cost of the resistance loss. An extension of Kelvin's law is described in Example 4, to take care of the progressively lower price per pound of large conductors.

$$\frac{C^2}{I^2} = \frac{179}{0.000\ 092} = 1,950,000 \qquad \text{from} \quad (7)$$

$$\frac{C}{I} = 1,400 \qquad \text{circ mils/amp}$$

The current density is $\dfrac{4 \times 10^6}{1,400\ \pi} = 910$ amp/sq in.

This is a very general and important result, as is well known. For the costs specified, it is not economical to use a higher current density than 910 amp per sq in. (or a lower value of circular mils per ampere than 1,400) for a bare copper conductor, large or small, long or short, high or low voltage, round or rectangular, so long as 1 kw of resistance loss in the conductor adds 1 kw to the peak load. When the size of conductor is determined by the cost of resistance losses, the size is dependent only on the current density, and it does not matter whether the conductor is 20 ft long or 20 miles. For other amounts of cost, the current density will also be a constant, though of different value.

There are many circuits of short or moderate length with small voltage drop, where the heating capacity is higher than 910 amp per sq in. and it may therefore pay to run at less than the maximum allowable temperature rise, with the additional advantages of reduction in voltage drop, provision for increased loads, and reduction in risk from oxidizing of joints and connections as well as from annealing of hard-drawn copper.

Insulated conductors and underground cables have considerably higher cost per pound of copper than that of bare conductors but, even in those cases, particularly for smaller sizes and for single-conductor cables, it is sometimes economical to use a maximum current density lower than the heating limit. The advantages in reduced risk of breakdown, longer life, and reduced voltage drop are obvious, so that an investigation of the cost of energy losses is frequently worth making.

The results of the computation described are shown in Fig. 1. The upper curve shows 1,400 circular mils per ampere at $100 per kilowatt. If the cost per kilowatt of the station plus the

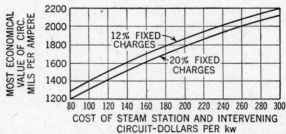

Fig. 1.—Relation of circular mils per amp to station cost. Fuel cost is 0.2 cent per kilowatt-hour; copper, 25 cents per pound installed.

cost per kilowatt of the intervening circuit is higher than $100 per kilowatt, larger conductors are indicated and there is a wider margin between the most economical conductor and the size given by the heating limit.

On the other hand, if the maximum current of the conductor in question does not occur at the time of the peak load of the station, the resistance loss cannot be considered as a direct increase of maximum load for the station. In designing such a conductor, an estimate should be made of its current at the time of the peak load of the station. Also, if there is doubt if the current of the conductor may reach the designed amount, an oversized conductor is not justified, and this is very often the case. However, although some conductors do not attain their estimated maximum current, others go beyond it, in spite of the usual allowances made for growth of load.

If the conductor in question is owned by the power company, the exact amount of the load factor of the resistance loss is a comparatively minor matter, as indicated in the calculations. If, however, the conductor is owned by a customer who pays for energy by the kilowatt-hour, the ratio of the yearly average resistance loss to the maximum should be carefully estimated and will often be very low, particularly on branch circuits.

In many systems, fixed charges are higher than 12 per cent. However, it is shown in Fig. 1 that if the fixed charges are 20 per cent the change in circular mils per ampere is a very few per cent. The first cost of the conductors is balanced largely against the first cost of the station.   If the percentage of fixed charges for the conductors is different from that for the station, that fact should be taken into account, as in Examples 5 and 6.

The equations and curves given in this article should be used as little as possible with the values of coefficients given.   In each case an equation similar to (7) should be derived, based on a study of the actual costs and load factors.   These will have a marked divergence in different cases.   See Examples 1 to 6.

If it is decided that the load of a completed station cannot reach the full station rating for many years, then the cost of resistance losses becomes extremely small and the computations in this paper should be almost entirely disregarded.   The smallest possible conductors should be used.   After the lapse of years other circuits may be added in parallel with them.   But when systems are considering making station extensions, it is appropriate to remember in designing conductors that a kilowatt of resistance loss saved at the time of the station peak load is as good as a kilowatt of station extension, or better.

To advocate using heavier conductors at maximum economy does not necessarily mean a larger investment by power companies that are contemplating extensions.   It is a question of choice in engineering design, whether a certain fraction of investment be made in copper or in station capacity.   The computation is definite, since it depends chiefly on the peak value rather than on the kilowatt-hours of resistance loss.   The percentage saving in annual charges of conductors made by using the most economical size instead of that based on the heating limit is considerable, in most of the examples described in this paper.

Example 1. In this example, the output of a generator whose maximum rating is 1,350 amp is carried away from the generator terminals by a circuit made up of ¼ by 4 in. copper bars. It appears evident that under these conditions each kilowatt of resistance loss in the copper straps at the time of maximum load on the generator reduces by 1 kw the rating of the generator and of the station to which it belongs.

The calculation carried out in the first part of this paper will apply. In this particular example, the cost data are those already used in this paper, and hence the most economical current density would be 910 amp per sq in. and it would pay to use a strap ⅜ by 4 in. This heavy strap would run cool, for 1,350 amp is the heating limit for ¼ by 4 in. strap, not adjacent to other straps. The heavy strap has also the advantage of reduced voltage drop. If the increase in resistance caused by skin effect is taken into account, there is a still greater incentive to use larger conductors.

Example 2. A 138-kv transmission line with 300,000-circ mil copper conductors is being designed and built at the same time as a 90,000-kva generating station. The line carries the output of the station to a city 38 miles away. The rated current in the line is 375 amp. The reactance drop is 15 %, and the resistance loss is 3.5 % at rated load. The voltage is regulated by synchronous condensers. The cost data are those used in the first part of this paper. This makes 1,400 circ mils per amp the most economical value. This would call for a much larger conductor than 300,000 circ mils, which has only 800 circ mils per amp.

The annual charge for the 300,000-circ mil conductor and its losses is 15 % greater than the minimum annual charge, using a larger conductor.

The capacity of the 300,000-circ mil conductor, by temperature rise, is 550 amp.

Example 3. A 65-mile, 70-kv transmission line with No. 0 aluminum conductors is designed and built at the same time as an 8,000-kva hydroelectric station whose entire output is to be transmitted over the line, there being no prospect of any appreciable local load. Here it may be assumed that the peak load for the line will be 8,000 kva, that is, 66 amp, for otherwise the station would not be designed and built for that rating. The cost of the hydro station, which has comparatively little water storage, is $175 per kilowatt.

The reactance drop is 8.5 % and the resistance loss, 9 %. A No. 2 copper conductor has the same resistance and, in this example, the same cost as the No. 0 aluminum conductor. In general, special coefficients should be computed for aluminum.

In equation (3), the number 131 is multiplied by $\frac{175}{100}$, becoming 230 and 48 becomes 0. Equation (7) becomes

$$230\,\frac{I^2}{C} = 0.000\ 092\ C$$

$$\frac{C}{I} = 1{,}580$$

This is the most economical value of circular mils per ampere for copper. The circular mils per ampere for the No. 2 copper conductor are 1,000.

It is economical to use a conductor 58 % larger than that given in the statement of this problem. The voltage regulation also would be improved. The size of aluminum conductor would be No. 000.

This is a case where it pays to use a larger conductor than that determined by either voltage drop or heating.

Example 4.   A 300,000-circ mil single-conductor cable with heat-resistant rubber insulation, used in wiring and located in free air, has burned out and is being replaced. The operating records show that the peak load current for this cable is 446 amp, with no probable increase beyond that. This is also its current capacity ("Standard Handbook for Electrical Engineers," ed. of 1941, p. 1402). So far as heating is concerned, 300,000 circ mils is large enough.

In this particular case, the cost of the 300,000-circ mil cable, installed, is 50¢ per pound of copper. It is found in this case, on plotting the price per 1,000 ft against the circular mils, that the cost in the neighborhood of the size considered increases only 80 % as fast as the circular mils. This is a matter that should be taken into account in practically all cases of insulated conductors. In equation (5), when the circular mils are multiplied by $(1 + a)$, the cost is multiplied by $(1 + 0.8a)$. In (6) and (7), the number 0.000 092 is multiplied by

$$\tfrac{50}{25} \times 0.8$$

Equation (7) then becomes

$$179 \frac{I^2}{C} = 0.000\ 147\ C$$

Most economical circular mils per ampere is 1,100.

This corresponds to a current of 270 amp, which is considerably below the capacity of 446 amp. If there is room for a larger conductor and if the generating equipment is likely to be increased, it would pay to put in a conductor larger than 300,000 circ mils, merely on account of the cost of resistance losses.

Example 5.   The turbine room of a steam station is lighted by groups of fixtures, each group taking 20 amp and being supplied by No. 12 wire, 6,530 circ mils. The lights are on full every night for 3 hr during half the year and 5 hr during the other half. The amount of lighting at other hours supplied by these particular circuits is negligible. The ratio of average resistance loss to the peak value is $\tfrac{4}{24} = 0.167$. In this example, the fixed charges for the wiring are 20 % owing to an estimated life of only a few years, on account of possible changes in lighting. The cost of the insulated wire, installed, is 80¢ per pound of copper and the cost per 1,000 ft increases 75 % as fast as the circular mils, in the neighborhood of No. 12 size.

In equation (7) the number 0.000 092 is multiplied by

$$\tfrac{80}{25} \times 0.75 \times \tfrac{20}{12}$$

and becomes 0.000 37.   In equation (3), 48 is multiplied by 16.7/25 and that equation becomes

$$(131 + 32) \frac{I^2}{C} = 163 \frac{I^2}{C}$$

Equation (7) becomes

$$163\frac{I^2}{C} = 0.000\ 37\ C$$

Most economical circular mils per ampere is 660. This corresponds to a current of 10 amp.

The capacity of No. 12 rubber-insulated wire according to the National Electrical Code is 20 amp. It would pay to use much heavier wire to carry 20 amp under the conditions described, if extensions of the generating equipment are probable.

Example 6. The groups of lighting fixtures of the main room of a large railway station are wired with No. 12 wire, and all data are the same as in Example 5 except that energy is purchased by the kilowatt-hour. In computing the saving from reduced resistance losses, the lowest step in the energy rate should be used, which in this case is 1¢ per kilowatt-hour.

As in Eq. (2), the kilowatt-hours of resistance loss per year are

$$0.167 \times 8,760 \times \frac{10,900}{1.000}\frac{I^2}{C} = 15,900\frac{I^2}{C}$$

Annual cost of energy for resistance loss is

$$159\frac{I^2}{C} \qquad\qquad \text{dollars/1,000 ft}$$

Fixed charges for the wire are

$$0.20 \times 0.80 \times 0.003\ 07\ C = 0.000\ 49\ C$$

Since the cost of the insulated wire increases 75 % as fast as the circular mils, in the neighborhood of size No. 12, the number 0.000 49 should be multiplied by 0.75, giving 0.000 37. As in equation (7),

$$159\frac{I^2}{C} = 0.000\ 37\ C$$

Most economical circular mils per ampere = 655. This corresponds to a current of 10 amp which is 50 % less than the heating limit of 20 amp for No. 12 wire, and so a size larger than No. 12 would be more economical for a 20-amp current.

At higher energy rates than 1¢ per kilowatt-hour, the economy from heavy wiring is still greater, for this case.

In this example, the total annual charges for No. 12 wire and its losses at 20 amp maximum, are 25 % greater than the minimum charges, with heavier wire.

CHAPTER 15

REACTANCE OF STRANDED CONDUCTORS[1]

A copper cable, or stranded conductor, is a bundle of round wires. The following formulas, which relate chiefly to overhead stranded conductors at wide spacing, were derived by computing the average logarithm of the distance between centers of the strands, that is, by the geometric-mean-distance, or GMD, method. The spiraling of the strands has negligible effect at commercial frequencies and so the strands are assumed to be straight and parallel, for the computation.

The GMD method is a very useful way of calculating the inductance and reactance of parallel conductors. It is based on the assumption of uniform current density in the conductors and gives the inductance at comparatively low frequency. When the current is distorted, owing to the effect of the frequency, the resulting decrease in inductance is usually much less than the increase in resistance. Accordingly, the change in inductance associated with skin effect is often neglected.

As stated before equation (8), Chap. 2, the logarithm of the geometric mean distance, or GMD, between two areas is defined as the average of the logarithms of all possible distances from points on one area to those on the other, and the logarithm of the self GMD is the average of the logarithms of all possible distances between two points on the area. See Maxwell, "Electricity and Magnetism," Par. 691.

If t is the distance between centers of any two wires of the cable, the voltage per centimeter induced in the second by 1 abamp in the first is

$$2\pi f \times 2 \operatorname{logn} \frac{s}{t} = 2\pi f M$$

where f is the frequency and s is the distance to the return cable or conductor. In a seven-strand cable there are $7 \times 6 = 42$

[1] Reactance of Stranded Conductors, by H. B. Dwight, *Elec. World*, Apr. 19, 1913, p. 828.

such voltages and there are in addition 7 self-inductive voltages, one in each strand, each equal to

$$2\pi f L_1 = 2\pi f \left(2 \operatorname{logn} \frac{s}{r} + \frac{1}{2} \right)$$

where r is the radius of a strand.

If the strands were connected all in series, the inductance would be

$$L' = 7L_1 + 12M_1 + 30M_2$$

where M_1 is the inductance for pairs consisting of the center wire and an outer wire, and M_2 is the average inductance for pairs consisting of two outer wires.

When the 7 strands are connected in parallel, the average voltage drop is $\frac{1}{7}$ as great and when, further, 1 abamp is assumed for the entire group, we have

$$L = \frac{L'}{49}$$

For M_1 the value of t is $2r$ and

$$M_1 = 2 \operatorname{logn} \frac{s}{2r}$$

The computation by the GMD method of the inductance of a group of wires spaced at regular intervals around the circumference of a circle was published by E. B. Rosa in 1908 in the *Bur. Standards Bull.*, Vol. 4, No. 2, p. 335, making use of Cotes's theorem. From this, if a circle of radius a is divided into m equal parts at A, B, C, D, etc., then

$$AB \cdot AC \cdot AD \cdot \cdot \cdot \text{ to } (m-1) \text{ factors } = ma^{m-1}$$

Thus, the mean value of $\operatorname{logn} t$ for the distances just described is

$$\operatorname{logn} am^{1/(m-1)}$$

In other words, the GMD of a wire in a ring, from the other wires whose cross sections are in the same ring, is

$$am^{1/(m-1)}$$

Putting $m = 6$ and $a = 2r$ for the outer wires of a 7-wire cable, the average value of M_2 is

$$M_2 = 2 \operatorname{logn} \frac{s}{2r \, 6^{1/5}}$$

For the complete 7-strand cable,

$$L = \frac{1}{49}\left(98 \operatorname{logn} \frac{s}{r} + \frac{7}{2} - 24 \operatorname{logn} 2 - 60 \operatorname{logn} 2 - 12 \operatorname{logn} 6\right) \tag{1}$$

Changing to practical units and referring to the maximum radius of the cable, $\rho = 3r$, we have

$$L = \left(103.3 + 741.1 \log_{10} \frac{s}{\rho}\right) 10^{-6} \text{ henries/mile of conductor} \tag{2}$$

Applying this method to an n-wire concentric cable composed of p layers around a center wire,

$$n = 1 + 6 + (6 \times 2) + (6 \times 3) + \cdots + (6 \times p)$$
$$= 3p^2 + 3p + 1$$

$$L = 2 \operatorname{logn} \frac{s}{\rho} + \frac{1}{2n} + 2 \operatorname{logn} (2p + 1) - \frac{2(n - 1)}{n^2} \operatorname{logn} 3$$

$$- \frac{24}{n^2} \{4 \operatorname{logn} 2 + 2 \times 13 \operatorname{logn} 4 + 3 \times 28 \operatorname{logn} 6 + \cdots$$

$$+ p(n - 3p) \operatorname{logn} (2p)\}$$

This gives formula (2) for $p = 1$ and $n = 7$ and it gives, for $p = 2$ and $n = 19$,

$$L = \left(89.3 + 741.1 \log_{10} \frac{s}{\rho}\right) 10^{-6} \quad \text{henries/mile} \tag{3}$$

and similar expressions for larger numbers of strands.

A 3-wire cable is a special case, since there is no central wire. The inductance is

$$L = 2 \operatorname{logn} \frac{s}{\rho} + \frac{1}{6} + 2 \operatorname{logn} \left(\frac{2 + \sqrt{3}}{\sqrt{3}}\right) - \frac{4}{3} \operatorname{logn} 2 \text{ abhenries/cm}$$

$$= \left(125.2 + 741.1 \log_{10} \frac{s}{\rho}\right) 10^{-6} \qquad \text{henries/mile} \tag{4}$$

where ρ is the radius of the circumscribing circle.

The reactance at 60 cycles and 18 in. spacing of No. 4/0 wire and cable, 211,600 circular mils, is

Solid wire......................	0.560	ohm/mile
7-wire cable...................	0.552	ohm/mile
19-wire cable..................	0.546	ohm/mile

The most commonly specified item pertaining to a stranded conductor is the number of circular mils, rather than the diameter. Accordingly, numerical formulas for reactance in terms of circular mils are found convenient and have been tabulated in recent years by L. F. Woodruff in "Principles of Electric Power Transmission,' Chap. 2 (see also "Standard Handbook for Electrical Engineers," ed. of 1941, p. 54).

Thus, if G is the self GMD of the stranded cable,

$$X = 2\pi f L = 2\pi f \, 2 \, \text{logn} \, \frac{s}{G} \quad \text{abohms/cm} \quad (5)$$

where s and G may both be in inches.

If the number of circular inches of a 7-strand cable is C, the cross section of one strand is

$$\frac{C}{7} = 4 r^2$$

and

$$\text{logn} \, r = \text{logn} \, \sqrt{C} - \text{logn} \, 2 - \tfrac{1}{2} \, \text{logn} \, 7$$

Substituting this in (1),

$$\text{logn} \, G = \text{logn} \, \sqrt{C} - 0.8883$$
$$G = 0.4114 \, \sqrt{C} \qquad \text{inches}$$

for 7-strand cable. The circular inches of a round wire are equal to the square of the diameter in inches.

A value of reactance X per unit length of a conductor is desired, which corresponds to the resistance R per unit length, so that the impedance Z is equal to $R + jX$. Changing (5) to practical units,

$$X = 2\pi f \times 140.4 \times 10^{-6} \log_{10} \frac{s}{G} \quad \text{ohms/1,000 ft} \quad (6)$$

or

$$X = 2\pi f \times 741 \times 10^{-6} \log_{10} \frac{s}{G} \quad \text{ohms/mile} \quad (7)$$

where s is the distance to the return conductor or the distance to which magnetic flux is counted. It is evident that the dimensions s and G should both be in the same units.

CHAPTER 16

REACTANCE OF ROUND TUBES

The logarithm of the self geometric mean distance, or GMD (see the third paragraph of Chap. 15) of a round tube of outside diameter d and inside diamter v was given by Maxwell[1] and is

$$\operatorname{logn} G = \operatorname{logn} \frac{d}{2} - \frac{v^4}{(d^2 - v^2)^2} \operatorname{logn} \frac{d}{v} + \frac{3v^2 - d^2}{4(d^2 - v^2)} \qquad (1)$$

For greater convenience with thin tubes, this may be put in the form of a convergent series:[2]

$$\operatorname{logn} G = \operatorname{logn} \frac{d}{2} - \frac{2}{3}\frac{t}{d} + \frac{4}{15}\frac{t^3}{d^3} + \frac{2}{5}\frac{t^5}{d^5} \cdots \qquad (2)$$

where $t = (d - v)/2$ = the tube thickness.

Values of G for tubes are given in Table I. The values of self GMD given in this table may be used for stranded tubular conductors or for round tubes of solid metal. The values for stranded tubular conductors may be computed also from the position and size of the strands. The effect of their spiraling on the reactance is practically negligible at power frequencies.

The concentric arrangement of round tubular conductors to carry heavy alternating currents gives compactness, low reactance drop, and reduced loss from skin effect or crowding of the current to the surface of the conductors. This arrangement is being used to a considerable extent.[3] Formulas are here given to enable the reactance of such conductors to be determined for three-phase and single-phase circuits.[4]

Reactive Drop.—In practical cases, the reactance of concentric tubular conductors is very little affected by the variable current

[1] "Electricity and Magnetism," by J. Clerk Maxwell, Vol. 2, Par. 692.
[2] Equation (14) of footnote 1, Chap. 18.
[3] See the article by L. R. Bogardus, *Elec. World*, Sept. 10, 1938, p. 702.
[4] Reactance and Skin Effect of Concentric Tubular Conductors, by H. B. Dwight, *Trans. A.I.E.E.*, 1942, p. 513.

density which causes skin effect.   When uniform current density is assumed, the GMD method of Clerk Maxwell may be used (see the third paragraph of Chap. 15).   Using values given in Par. 692 of his "Electricity and Magnetism," for GMD's of a

TABLE I, CHAP. 16.—SELF GMD OF ROUND TUBE SECTION

v/d[1]	G for tube	Difference
0	$0.389d$	
		0.002
0.1	$0.391d$	
		0.005
0.2	$0.396d$	
		0.008
0.3	$0.404d$	
		0.010
0.4	$0.414d$	
		0.012
0.5	$0.426d$	
		0.013
0.6	$0.439d$	
		0.014
0.7	$0.453d$	
		0.015
0.8	$0.468d$	
		0.016
0.9	$0.484d$	
		0.016
1.0	$0.500d$	

[1] v = inside diameter and d = outside diameter of tube.

tubular section from itself and from other sections (footnote 1), formulas for the reactance drop in each tube of a concentric, three-phase circuit are obtained.

The general formula for reactive drop in conductor 1 of a group of long, parallel conductors (see equation 55, p. 39 of footnote 5)[5] is

$$- j\omega 2 \times 10^{-9}[I_1 \operatorname{logn} D_{s1} + I_2 \operatorname{logn} D_{12} + I_3 \operatorname{logn} D_{13} + \cdots \,]$$
$$\text{volts/cm} \quad (3)$$

[5] "Principles of Electric Power Transmission," by L. F. Woodruff, ed. of 1938.

where $\omega = 2\pi \times$ frequency.

logn = natural logarithm.

D_{s1} = self GMD of conductor 1.

D_{12} = GMD of the cross section of conductor 1 to that of conductor 2, etc.

The currents are in amperes.   A conductor may have any shape of cross section.

Equation (3) is subject to the condition that

$$I_1 + I_2 + I_3 + I_4 + \cdots = 0$$

which is a relation usually obtained in any steady-state problem where a system consists of long, parallel conductors and all the conductors are taken into account.   In other words, there is as much return current as there is going current in such a system. A system of this kind may be made up of any number of phases and any number of conductors in parallel.

Let the inside and outside diameters of the tubes of a three-phase coaxial circuit, from the smallest to the largest, be d_1, d_2, d_3, d_4, d_5, and d_6.   Let there be no neutral current.

The reactive drop in the inner tube, which carries I_a amp, is, in volts per centimeter,

$$\frac{j\omega 2 I_a}{10^9} \left[\frac{d_1{}^4}{(d_2{}^2 - d_1{}^2)^2} \operatorname{logn} \frac{d_2}{d_1} - \frac{3d_1{}^2 - d_2{}^2}{4(d_2{}^2 - d_1{}^2)} \right]$$

$$+ \frac{j\omega 2 I_b}{10^9} \left[\frac{1}{2} + \frac{d_3{}^2}{d_4{}^2 - d_3{}^2} \operatorname{logn} \frac{d_3}{d_2} - \frac{d_4{}^2}{d_4{}^2 - d_3{}^2} \operatorname{logn} \frac{d_4}{d_2} \right]$$

$$+ \frac{j\omega 2 I_c}{10^9} \left[\frac{1}{2} + \frac{d_5{}^2}{d_6{}^2 - d_5{}^2} \operatorname{logn} \frac{d_5}{d_2} - \frac{d_6{}^2}{d_6{}^2 - d_5{}^2} \operatorname{logn} \frac{d_6}{d_2} \right] \quad (4)$$

The reactive drop in the intermediate tube, which carries I_b amp, is

$$\frac{j\omega 2 I_a}{10^9} \left[\frac{1}{2} - \frac{d_3{}^2}{d_4{}^2 - d_3{}^2} \operatorname{logn} \frac{d_4}{d_3} \right]$$

$$+ \frac{j\omega 2 I_b}{10^9} \left[\frac{d_3{}^4}{(d_4{}^2 - d_3{}^2)^2} \operatorname{logn} \frac{d_4}{d_3} - \frac{3d_3{}^2 - d_4{}^2}{4(d_4{}^2 - d_3{}^2)} \right]$$

$$+ \frac{j\omega 2 I_c}{10^9} \left[\frac{1}{2} + \frac{d_5{}^2}{d_6{}^2 - d_5{}^2} \operatorname{logn} \frac{d_5}{d_4} - \frac{d_6{}^2}{d_6{}^2 - d_5{}^2} \operatorname{logn} \frac{d_6}{d_4} \right]$$

$$\text{volts/cm} \quad (5)$$

Reactive drop in the outer tube, which carries I_c amp is

$$\frac{j\omega 2(I_a + I_b)}{10^9}\left[\frac{1}{2} - \frac{d_5^2}{d_6^2 - d_5^2}\operatorname{logn}\frac{d_6}{d_5}\right]$$

$$+ \frac{j\omega 2 I_c}{10^9}\left[\frac{d_5^4}{(d_6^2 - d_5^2)^2}\operatorname{logn}\frac{d_6}{d_5} - \frac{3d_5^2 - d_6^2}{4(d_6^2 - d_5^2)}\right]\quad\text{volts/cm}\quad(6)$$

The phase currents I_a, I_b, and I_c may be unbalanced. Therefore, by putting one of the currents equal to zero, the single-phase case is included.

For deriving the first expression, note that

$$I_a \operatorname{logn} d_2 = -I_b \operatorname{logn} d_2 - I_c \operatorname{logn} d_2$$

since there is no neutral current, and similarly for d_4 in the second expression and for d_6 in the third.

If the thickness of the foregoing tubes is considered negligible, regarding the effect on the reactive drop, and if, as before, there is no neutral current, the reactive drop in the inner tube is

$$-\frac{j\omega 2}{10^9}\left[I_b \operatorname{logn}\frac{d_4}{d_2} + I_c \operatorname{logn}\frac{d_6}{d_2}\right]\quad\text{volts/cm}\quad(7)$$

Reactive drop in the intermediate tube is

$$-\frac{j\omega 2}{10^9} I_c \operatorname{logn}\frac{d_6}{d_4}\quad\text{volts/cm}\quad(8)$$

Reactive drop in the outer tube $= 0$ (9)

It does not matter in what units the diameters are given, in equations (4) to (8), so long as they are all in the same units, since only ratios of diameters occur. For convenience in computation, it may be noted that there are

$$2.540 \times 12,000 = 3.05 \times 10^4\quad\text{cm in 1,000 ft}\quad(10)$$

Also, $$\operatorname{logn} u = 2.3026 \log_{10} u\quad(11)$$

The resistance drop in each tube is added vectorially to the reactance drop to give the impedance drop in that tube.

Example. Find the reactance drop in each tube of the following concentric, three-phase circuit. The inside and outside diameters of the inner tube are 1.2 and 3.0 in.; those of the intermediate tube are 4.0 and 4.5 in.; and those of the outer tube are 5.6 and 6.0 in. The current of the inner tube is 1 amp; that of the intermediate tube is

$$\cos 120° + j \sin 120° = -0.5 + j\,0.866$$

and that of the outer tube is

$$\cos 240° + j \sin 240° = -0.5 - j\,0.866$$

The reactive drop in the inner tube is

$$\frac{j\omega 2}{10^9}\,[0.188 - 0.349(-0.5 + j\,0.866) - 0.660(-0.5 - j\,0.866)]$$

$$= \frac{j\omega 2}{10^9}\,(0.692 + j\,0.270) \qquad\qquad \text{volts/cm}$$

to compare with $\frac{j\omega 2}{10^9}\,(0.55 + j\,0.25)$ by the approximate formula (7).

The reactive drop in the intermediate tube is

$$\frac{j\omega 2}{10^9}\,(0.164 + j\,0.253)$$

to compare with $\frac{j\omega 2}{10^9}\,(0.14 + j\,0.25)$ by the approximate formula (8).

The reactive drop in the outer tube is

$$\frac{j\omega 2}{10^9}\,(0.028 + j\,0.048)$$

to compare with 0 by the approximate formula (9).

CHAPTER 17

REACTANCE VALUES FOR RECTANGULAR CONDUCTORS

Rectangular or strap conductors are often used to carry heavy alternating currents, in bus bars on switchboards, in the supply circuits of electric furnaces, and elsewhere. The reactance drop in such circuits is most conveniently determined from a set of curves, since the formulas that would be required for calculating the result are long and complicated. Such a set of curves[1] is given in Fig. 1.

Very little explanation is required for using these curves. The curves apply to a single-phase circuit of solid strap conductors, but, as shown in the examples that follow, the curves may be used conveniently for three-phase circuits and for ventilated conductors, by making use of the fact that the reactance as plotted is proportional to the difference between the self-inductance and the mutual inductance (MI) of two straps. It is assumed that the rectangular conductors in a circuit are of the same size and are placed symmetrically opposite each other, as is nearly always the case in practice. Values of reactance are given both for the case when the straps are in parallel planes ($a < b$) and for the case when the straps lie edgewise to each other ($b < a$). The reactance values are plotted in microhms at 60 cycles, and the values at 25 cycles or any other frequency can be obtained by changing the plotted values in proportion to the frequency.

Example 1. Find the voltage drop due to reactance in a single-phase electric furnace circuit made up of two copper straps each 50 ft long, size ½ by 4 in., in parallel planes, the distance between centers of straps being 1 in. The current is 2,000 amp, 60 cycles.

$$\frac{a}{b} = \frac{1}{8} \quad \text{and} \quad \frac{s}{a+b} = \frac{1}{4.5} = 0.22$$

[1] Reactance Values for Rectangular Conductors, by H. B. Dwight, *Elec. Jour.*, June, 1919, p. 255.

Reactance, from curves, = 11.0 microhms/ft of strap.

$$\text{Reactive drop} = 11.0 \times 10^{-6} \times 50 \times 2 \times 2,000$$
$$= 2.2 \text{ volts}$$

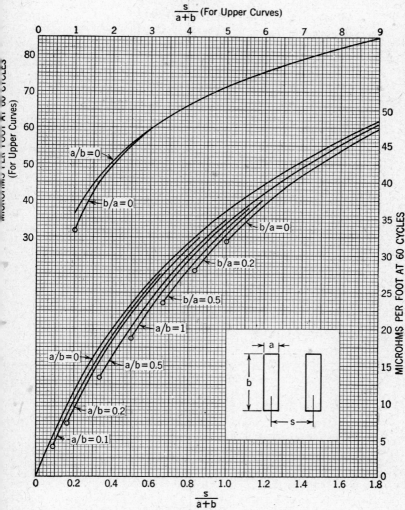

FIG. 1.—Reactance of rectangular conductors at 60 cycles.

Example 2. Find the reactive drop in a three-phase circuit made up of three copper straps each 100 ft long, size ¼ by 3 in., in parallel planes, the distance between centers of straps being 1½ in. The current is 750 amp per phase, 60 cycles.

Let the three straps, side by side, be called A, B, and C.

Let
$$I_A = 750 \quad \text{amp}$$
$$I_B = -375 + j\,375\sqrt{3} \quad \text{amp}$$
and
$$I_C = -375 - j\,375\sqrt{3} \quad \text{amp}$$

The reactive drop in A per foot is

$$2\pi \times 60[I_A L_A + I_B M_{AB} + I_C M_{AC}]$$

where L_A is the self-inductance of A per foot, and M_{AB} is the MI of A and B per foot, etc.

Since $I_A = -(I_B + I_C)$, the reactive drop in A per foot is

$$2\pi \times 60\,[I_B(M_{AB} - L_A) + I_C(M_{AC} - L_A)] = -I_B X_{AB} - I_C X_{AC}$$

where X_{AB} is the reactance per foot of conductor of the single-phase circuit composed of A and B. This can be obtained from the curves of Fig. 1.

Thus,
$$X_{AB} = 21.5 \quad \text{microhms per foot of strap}$$
since
$$\frac{a}{b} = \frac{1}{12} \quad \text{and} \quad \frac{s}{a+b} = \frac{1.5}{3.25} = 0.462$$
also,
$$X_{AC} = 34 \quad \text{microhms per foot of strap}$$
since
$$\frac{a}{b} = \frac{1}{12} \quad \text{and} \quad \frac{s}{a+b} = \frac{3}{3.25} = 0.924$$

The total reactive drop in conductor A is

$$(375 - j\,375\sqrt{3})21.5 \times 10^{-6} \times 100 + (375 + j\,375\sqrt{3})34 \times 10^{-6} \times 100$$
$$= 2.09 + j\,0.81 \quad \text{volts}$$
$$= 2.24 \quad \text{volts, numerical value}$$

The reactive drop in B is

$$-I_C X_{BC} - I_A X_{AB} = (375 + j\,375\sqrt{3})\,21.5 \times 10^{-6} \times 100$$
$$\qquad\qquad\qquad\qquad\qquad - 750 \times 21.5 \times 10^{-6} \times 100$$
$$= -0.81 + j\,1.40 \quad \text{volts}$$
$$= 1.62 \quad \text{volts, numerical value}$$

The reactive drop in conductor C has the same numerical value, 2.24 volts, as the reactive drop in A.

A circuit of this kind is usually not transposed, and the unbalance in voltage drop will cause an unbalance in current and phase. The average reactive drop in each strap is 2.03 volts, which should be expressed as a percentage of the line-to-neutral voltage.

Example 3. Find the reactive drop in a single-phase ventilated bus-bar circuit, each bus bar consisting of two straps at $\frac{1}{2}$-in. centers, size $\frac{1}{8}$ in. by 3 in. and 70 ft long. The distance between centers of bus bars is $2\frac{1}{2}$ in. (see Fig. 2). The current per bus bar is 900 amp, 60 cycles.

Neglecting circulating currents, each strap will carry 450 amp. The drop in conductor A per foot is

$2\pi \times 60(L_A + M_{AB} - M_{AC} - M_{AD}) \times 450 = 2\pi \times 60(L_A - M_{AC}$
$+ L_A - M_{AD} - L_A + M_{AB}) \times 450$
$$= 450(X_{AC} + X_{AD} - X_{AB})$$
$$= 450(31.5 + 35.0 - 9.0) \times 10^{-6} \quad \text{volts/ft, from Fig. 1}$$

The reactive drop in A is

$$450 \times 57.5 \times 10^{-6} \times 70 = 1.81 \qquad\qquad \text{volts}$$

In a similar way the drop in B is found to be

$$450(X_{BC} + X_{BD} - X_{AB}) \times 70 = 450(27.5 + 31.5 - 9.0) \times 10^{-6} \times 70$$
$$= 1.57 \quad \text{volts}$$

The difference in the voltage drop of A and B will be equalized by an unbalance of current, which is equivalent to a circulating current. The

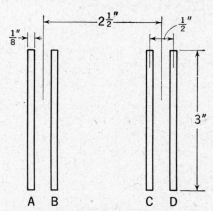

Fig. 2.—Ventilated bus-bar circuit.

average reactive drop in the complete bus bar is 1.69 volts. The drop in the single-phase circuit comprising both bus bars is 3.38 volts.

For an approximate calculation, each bus bar may be treated as a solid strap of the same outside dimensions as the ventilated bus bars, namely, 5/8 by 3 in.

Then, $\qquad \dfrac{a}{b} = 0.21 \qquad$ and $\qquad \dfrac{s}{a+b} = \dfrac{2.5}{3.625} = 0.69$

From Fig. 1, the reactive drop in the single-phase circuit is

$$28 \times 10^{-6} \times 900 \times 70 \times 2 = 3.53 \qquad\qquad \text{volts}$$

In a manner similar to Examples 2 and 3 the reactive drop in a three-phase ventilated bus-bar circuit could be determined.

The following formulas are given for reference.
Approximate formulas for widely spaced straps:[2]

$$L = 2 \operatorname{logn} \left(\frac{s}{a + b} \right) + 3 \quad \text{abhenries/cm of strap} \quad (1)$$

where logn denotes natural logarithm.   This becomes[3]

$$X = 52.9 \log_{10} \left(\frac{s}{a + b} \right) + 34.5$$
$$\text{microhms/ft of strap at 60 cycles} \quad (2)$$

The foregoing formulas give very accurate results for larger spacings than those indicated in Fig. 1, but the results are inaccurate with close spacings.
Formula for thin straps very close together:[4]

$$L = \frac{\pi}{b} \left(2s - 2a + \frac{4a}{3} \right) = \frac{\pi}{b} \left(2s - \frac{2a}{3} \right)$$
$$\text{abhenries/cm of strap} \quad (3)$$

where a is less than b.   This is a straight-line formula and, if the corresponding reactance values are plotted on Fig. 1, they are found to lie on straight lines parallel to the curves at their lowest points.   For this case the magnitude of the skin effect can be calculated.
Formula for two equal rectangular conductors (placed as in Fig. 1):

$$L = 2 \operatorname{logn} \frac{R_2}{R_1} \quad \text{abhenries/cm of strap} \quad (4)$$

where $\operatorname{logn} R_1 = \frac{1}{2} \operatorname{logn} (a^2 + b^2) - \frac{1}{12} \frac{a^2}{b^2} \operatorname{logn} \left(\frac{a^2 + b^2}{a^2} \right)$

$$- \frac{1}{12} \frac{b^2}{a^2} \operatorname{logn} \left(\frac{a^2 + b^2}{b^2} \right) + \frac{2}{3} \frac{a}{b} \tan^{-1} \frac{b}{a} + \frac{2}{3} \frac{b}{a} \tan^{-1} \frac{a}{b} - \frac{25}{12} \quad (5)^*$$

[2] Derived from equation (108) *Bur. Standards Bull.*, Vol. 8, No. 1, Washington.

[3] The Reactance of Strap Conductors, by H. B. Dwight, *Elec. Rev.*, June 30, 1917, p. 1098.

[4] Skin Effect of a Return Circuit of Two Adjacent Strap Conductors, by H. B. Dwight, *Elec. Jour.*, April, 1916, p. 157 (see Chap. 22).

* *Bur. Standards Bull.*, Vol. 8, No. 1, p. 167, equation (124) and Clerk Maxwell, "Electricity and Magnetism," Vol. 2, Par. 692.

and where
$$a^2b^2 \operatorname{logn} R_2 = \frac{1}{4}\left[(s+a)^2 \left\{ b^2 - \frac{(s+a)^2}{6} \right\} \right.$$
$$\left. - \frac{b^4}{6} \right] \operatorname{logn} \{(s+a)^2 + b^2\}$$
$$+ \frac{1}{4}\left[(s-a)^2 \left\{ b^2 - \frac{(s-a)^2}{6} \right\} - \frac{b^4}{6} \right] \operatorname{logn} \{(s-a)^2 + b^2\}$$
$$- \frac{1}{2}\left[s^2\left(b^2 - \frac{s^2}{6} \right) - \frac{b^4}{6} \right] \operatorname{logn} (s^2 + b^2)$$
$$+ \frac{1}{12}(s+a)^4 \operatorname{logn}(s+a) + \frac{1}{12}(s-a)^4 \operatorname{logn}(s-a)$$
$$- \frac{1}{6}s^4 \operatorname{logn} s + \frac{1}{3}\{b(s+a)^3 - b^3(s+a)\} \tan^{-1}\left(\frac{b}{s+a}\right)$$
$$+ \frac{1}{3}\{b(s-a)^3 - b^3(s-a)\} \tan^{-1}\left(\frac{b}{s-a}\right)$$
$$- \frac{2}{3}(bs^3 - b^3s) \tan^{-1}\frac{b}{s} - \frac{25}{12}a^2b^2 \qquad (6)$$

Equation (6) may be derived from the formula in *Bur. Standards Bull.*, Vol. 3, No. 1, p. 6.

Equations (1) to (6) all assume uniform current distribution over the section of the conductors, skin effect being neglected.

CHAPTER 18

REACTANCE OF SQUARE TUBULAR BUS BARS

Square tubular bus bars are coming into use to an increasing extent, as they are economical and convenient for joining to insulators and to branch circuits. The reactance of bus-bar circuits is frequently of importance, in order to compute the voltage drop under normal conditions and the current under short-circuit conditions. In this chapter are given formulas and curves by which the reactance of square tubular bus bars may be determined.[1]

In a few cases, the inductance of bus bars can be expressed by simple formulas. For instance, the inductance of round rods is

$$L = 2 \operatorname{logn} \frac{s}{r} + \frac{1}{2} \qquad \text{abhenries/cm}$$

as used in power-line computations. For round tubular bus bars, equation (1) or (2), Chap. 16, may be used. For copper straps, expressions are available [see equations (5) and (6) Chap. 17], but if the thickness is proportionately large or the spacing small, as frequently happens, the length of the mathematical expressions is almost prohibitive, and the only practical method of computation seems to be by means of curves, as given in Fig. 1, Chap. 17. Similarly, the curves given in this chapter in Figs. 1 to 3 for square tubular bus bars may often be more convenient than equations (8), (11), and (13).

Commercial square tubular bus bars have rounded corners with outside radius of curvature from about $\frac{3}{8}$ to $\frac{3}{4}$ in., and they have a wall thickness from about $\frac{1}{8}$ to $\frac{1}{2}$ in. However, the reactance is nearly the same as that of a very thin, hollow, square tube. The two features of rounded corners and thick walls are brought into the calculation by approximate methods in such a way that

---

[1] See Reactance of Square Tubular Bus Bars, by H. B. Dwight and T. K. Wang, *Trans. A.I.E.E.*, 1938, p. 762.

the error in the net reactance is estimated to be less than 1 per cent for practical cases in common use.

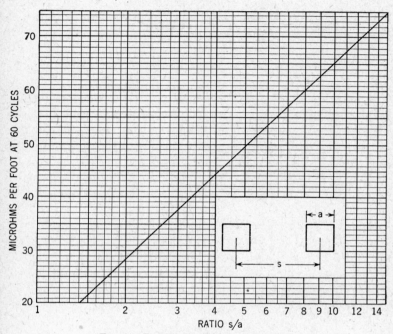

FIG. 1.—Reactance of thin square tubes.

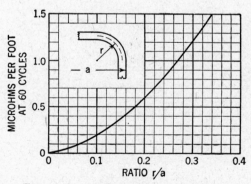

FIG. 2.—Increase caused by round corners.

In order to save time in determining reactances, curves are given in Figs. 1 to 3 which show, respectively, the reactance of

thin square tubes, assuming uniform distribution of current, and
the approximate corrections for rounded corners and thick walls.

Infinitely Thin Square Tubular Conductors.   The inductance L
of two duplicate, parallel conductors forming a return circuit,
assuming uniform current distribution, is

$$L = 2 \operatorname{logn} \frac{M}{T} \quad \text{abhenries/cm of conductor} \quad (1)$$

where logn denotes natural logarithm, M is the geometric mean
distance (GMD) between the two cross sections, and T is the
GMD of one of the cross-sectional areas from itself, that is, the

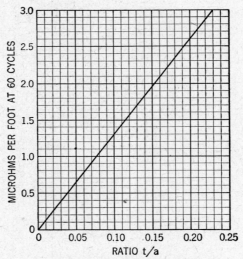

Fig. 3.—Increase caused by thickness of tubes.

self GMD of the section (see definition of GMD in the third
paragraph of Chap. 15).

The logarithm of the self GMD of a hollow square is given in
equation (20) and is

$$\operatorname{logn} T = \operatorname{logn} a + \frac{1}{4} \operatorname{logn} 2 + \frac{\pi}{4} - \frac{3}{2} \tag{2}$$

$$= \operatorname{logn} a - 0.5413 \tag{3}$$

$$= \operatorname{logn} 0.582a \tag{4}$$

where a is the length of a side of the square.

Also, as derived following equation (20),

$$\operatorname{logn} M = \operatorname{logn} s + \frac{1}{40} \left(\frac{a}{s}\right)^4 - \frac{17}{720} \left(\frac{a}{s}\right)^8 \cdots \tag{5}$$

where s is the distance between centers of two squares whose sides are parallel and perpendicular to s. If the sides are not perpendicular to s, as sometimes occurs with triangular spacing, the change in the reactance is in the terms in $(a/s)^4$ and higher powers. Their effect in usual cases is negligible, as shown in Example 1.

From the foregoing equations,

$$L = 2 \operatorname{logn} \frac{s}{a} + 1.083 + \frac{1}{20} \left(\frac{a}{s}\right)^4 - \frac{17}{360} \left(\frac{a}{s}\right)^8 \cdots$$
$$\text{abhenries/cm of conductor} \tag{6}$$

For square tubular conductors widely separated,

$$L = 2 \operatorname{logn} \frac{s}{a} + 1.083$$

or $$L = 2 \operatorname{logn} \frac{s}{0.582a} \qquad \text{abhenries/cm} \tag{7}$$

Changing to practical units, the reactance of thin, square, tubular conductors is

$$X_1 = 2\pi f \, 140.4 \times 10^{-6} \left[\log_{10} \frac{s}{a} + 0.235 + 0.0108 \left(\frac{a}{s}\right)^4 \right.$$
$$\left. - 0.0102 \left(\frac{a}{s}\right)^8 \cdots \right] \text{ohms/1,000 ft of conductor} \tag{8}$$

where f = frequency in cycles/sec. See the curve in Fig. 1.

Example 1. The reactance per 1,000 ft of a thin square tube of 2.5 in. diameter, that is, the distance between opposite sides, and 10 in. spacing, center to center, at 60 cycles is, by (8),

$$X_1 = 120 \, \pi \times 140.4 \times 10^{-6} \left(\log_{10} \frac{10}{2.5} + 0.235 + 0.00004 \cdots \right)$$
$$= 0.0443 \qquad\qquad\qquad \text{ohm/1,000 ft of conductor}$$

The terms in a^4/s^4, etc., are less than 0.01 % of the total, in this case. For comparison, the reactance of a thin round tube with the same diameter and spacing is

$$X = 120\pi \times 140.4 \times 10^{-6} \log_{10} \frac{10}{1.25}$$
$$= 0.0479$$

which is approximately 8 % greater than the other value. The reactance of a thin round tube large enough just to enclose the square tube described, is

$$X = 120\pi \times 140.4 \times 10^{-6} \log_{10} \frac{10}{1.25\ \sqrt{2}}$$

$$= 0.0398$$

that is, approximately 10 % less than the value for square tube.

It is seen from this example that the average of the reactances of an inscribed tube and a circumscribed tube is a fairly close approximation to the reactance of a square tube. This is equivalent to stating that the inductance of thin square tubes is approximately

$$L = 2 \operatorname{logn} \frac{s}{0.595a}$$

This approximation is not to be recommended for engineering

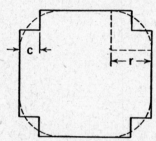

FIG. 4.—Approximation to thin tube with rounded corners.

calculations, since it is no more convenient in any way than the corresponding expression (7) for square tubes.

Effect of Rounded Corners. Let the thin square tube with rounded corners of radius r be replaced by a square tube with notches of side c at the corners, as shown in Fig. 4. The cross-shaped figure will lie along the mean position of the curves and will have nearly the same inductance, if the two figures have the same area. Then,

$$c^2 = r^2 - \frac{\pi r^2}{4} = 0.2146\ r^2$$

$$c = 0.463\ r \tag{9}$$

In practical cases, r is to be taken not as the outside radius but as the average of the outside and inside radii of the corners of a thick tube (see Fig. 2).

Putting the self GMD of the cross-shaped figure equal to T', there is obtained the correction

$$\operatorname{logn} T - \operatorname{logn} T' = \left(\frac{c}{a}\right)^2 \operatorname{logn} \frac{a}{c} + \left(\frac{3}{2} - \frac{\pi}{4}\right)\left(\frac{c}{a}\right)^2 + \frac{1}{2}\left(\frac{c}{a}\right)^3 \cdots \tag{10}$$

This gives such a small correction in practical cases (see Example 2 and Fig. 2) that the corresponding change in logn M caused by rounded corners is seen to be negligible.

Then the increase in reactance due to the rounded corners is, by (10),

$$\Delta_1 X = 2\pi f \, 140.4 \times 10^{-6} \left[\left(\frac{c}{a} \right)^2 \log_{10} \frac{a}{c} + 0.310 \left(\frac{c}{a} \right)^2 \right.$$
$$\left. + 0.217 \left(\frac{c}{a} \right)^3 \cdots \right] \text{ ohms/1,000 ft of conductor} \quad (11)$$

where $c = 0.463 \, r$, from (9).

Example 2. Let the corners of a 2.5-in. thin, square tube have a radius $r = 0.5$ in. and let the spacing s be 10 in., center to center.

$$\frac{c}{a} = 0.463 \times \frac{0.5}{2.5} = 0.0926 \qquad \frac{c^2}{a^2} = 0.0086$$

Reactance of tube with square corners

$$= 0.0443 \qquad\qquad\qquad \text{ohm/1,000 ft, by (8),} \quad \text{Example 1.}$$

Increase in reactance due to rounded corners is

$$120\pi \times 140.4 \times 10^{-6}(0.0089 + 0.0027 + 0.0002 \cdots)$$
$$= 0.0006 \qquad\qquad\qquad\qquad \text{ohm/1,000 ft by (11)}$$

The increase in reactance for this extreme case is 1.4 %.

Effect of Thickness. If a thin, square tube of side a has the same inductance as a thin, round tube of diameter d, the self GMD's will be equal; that is, from (4),

$$\frac{d}{2} = 0.582a \qquad \text{or} \qquad d = 1.164a \quad (12)$$

Corresponding thin tubes just inside these outer layers will have very nearly equal GMD's and therefore the increase in inductance, due to thickness, of a commercial, square tube will be approximately the same as for a round tube of the same thickness and with 1.164 times as large a diameter.

The logarithm of the self GMD of a round tube, expressed in a form involving the thickness t, is given in equation (2), Chap. 16.

Putting $d = 1.164a$, the increase in reactance, due to thickness, of a square tube of outside diameter a is

$$\Delta_2 X = 2\pi f \, 140.4 \times 10^{-6} \left[0.249 \frac{t}{a} - 0.073 \left(\frac{t}{a} \right)^3 \right.$$

$$\left. - 0.095 \left(\frac{t}{a} \right)^4 \cdots \right] \quad \text{ohms/1,000 ft of conductor} \quad (13)$$

Example 3. Let the outside diameter of a square tube be $a = 2.5$ in., the thickness $t = 0.5$ in., and the spacing $s = 10$ in., center to center.

$$\frac{t}{a} = 0.20$$

Increase in reactance due to thickness is

$$120\pi \times 140.4 \times 10^{-6}[0.0498 - 0.0006 - 0.0002 \cdots] = 0.0026$$
$$\text{ohm}/1000 \text{ ft by} \quad (15)$$

The increase is 6 % of 0.0443 (see Example 1).

Groups of Conductors. The reactive drop in each conductor of a three-phase circuit, or in each conductor of other groupings of parallel conductors, can be expressed in terms of single-phase reactances by first expressing them in terms of self-inductances and mutual inductances and then arranging them in pairs.

Thus, let the currents in conductors a, b, c, d, etc., in a given direction be I_a, I_b, I_c, I_d, etc. These may be polyphase currents or some of them may be the currents of branches in parallel. In any case, since a complete system of currents is specified, their sum is zero.

Voltage drop in conductor a, whose resistance is R, is

$$V_a = RI_a + j\omega[I_a L_a + I_b M_{ab} + I_c M_{ac} + I_d M_{ad} \cdots] \quad (14)$$

where the inductances are computed by taking into account flux up to a certain large distance u.

Put $\qquad\qquad I_a = -I_b - I_c - I_d - \cdots$
$$V_a = RI_a - j\omega \left[(L_a - M_{ab})I_b + (L_a - M_{ac}) I_c \right.$$
$$\left. + (L_a - M_{ad}) I_d + \cdots \right] \quad (15)$$

Each of the quantities in parentheses is the inductance of a single-phase circuit of conductors a and b, a and c, etc. The quantity u cancels out in each. Thus,

$$V_a = I_a R - j[I_b X_{ab} + I_c X_{ac} + I_d X_{ad} + \cdots] \quad (16)$$

where X_{ab} is the reactance of the return circuit made up of conductors a and b, etc.

In a similar way, V_b, V_c, etc., can be computed and so the formulas and curves given in this chapter are sufficient for computations for polyphase circuits and for conductors in parallel, where the conductors are alike.   This has been described already for the case of solid rectangular conductors, in Examples 2 and 3, Chap. 17.

Example 4.   A three-phase bus-bar circuit is composed of 8-in. square tubes arranged in a plane, at 24 in. spacing, center to center.   The wall thickness is $\frac{3}{8}$ in. and the outside radius of the corners is $\frac{3}{4}$ in.   Determine the drop in 200 ft for balanced three-phase current of 5,000 amp at 60 cycles.

Let the three conductors be a, b, and c.

$$\frac{r}{a} = \frac{0.75 + 0.375}{2 \times 8} = 0.0703$$

$$\frac{c}{a} = 0.0703 \times 0.463 = 0.0325$$

$$\frac{t}{a} = \frac{0.375}{8} = 0.0469$$

From (8), (11), and (13) or from Figs. 1 to 3,

$$X_{ab} = X_{bc} = 0.00754 + 0.00002 + 0.00012$$
$$= 0.00768 \qquad \text{ohm for 200 ft}$$
$$X_{ac} = 0.01073 + 0.00002 + 0.00012$$
$$= 0.01087 \qquad \text{ohm for 200 ft}$$
$$\text{Resistance} = R = 0.000138 \qquad \text{ohm for 200 ft}$$

Let
$$I_a = 5,000$$
$$I_b = 5,000(-0.5 + j\,0.866)$$
$$I_c = 5,000(-0.5 - j\,0.866)$$

From (16),
$$V_a = -13 + j\,46$$
Similarly
$$V_b = -34 - j\,19$$
$$V_c = 33 - j\,36$$
$$|V_a| = 48, \qquad |V_b| = 38, \qquad |V_c| = 49 \qquad \text{volts}$$

The drop in the voltage between conductors is obtained by subtracting vectorially V_b from V_a, etc.

Derivation of Series for Logn *M*.   The logarithm of the GMD of a straight line from itself is

$$\text{logn } a - \frac{3}{2} \tag{17}$$

where a is the length of the line (see footnote 1).   The logarithm of the GMD of one side of a square from the opposite side, where the side is a, is[2]

$$\text{logn } a + \frac{\pi}{2} - \frac{3}{2} \tag{18}$$

The logarithm of the GMD of one side from an adjacent side is

$$\frac{1}{2a^2} \int_0^a \int_0^a \text{logn } (x^2 + y^2) \, dx \, dy = \text{logn } a + \frac{1}{2} \text{logn } 2 + \frac{\pi}{4} - \frac{3}{2} \tag{19}$$

For the four sides of the square,

$$\text{logn GMD} = \frac{1}{4} [(17) + (18) + 2 \times (19)]$$

$$= \text{logn } a + \frac{1}{4} \text{logn } 2 + \frac{\pi}{4} - \frac{3}{2} \tag{20}$$

as in (2).

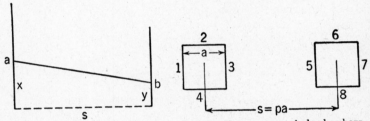

FIG. 5.—Two parallel lines.   FIG. 6.—Two square tubular bus bars.

The logarithm of the GMD of two lines (Fig. 5) of lengths a and b drawn perpendicular to a line of length s at its ends and on the same side of it, is

$$\frac{1}{ab} \int_0^b \int_0^a \frac{1}{2} \text{logn } \{s^2 + (x - y)^2\} \, dx \, dy$$

$$= \frac{1}{ab} \left[\frac{1}{4} \{s^2 - (a - b)^2\} \text{logn } \{s^2 + (a - b)^2\} \right.$$

$$+ \frac{1}{4} (a^2 - s^2) \text{logn } (a^2 + s^2)$$

$$+ \frac{1}{4} (b^2 - s^2) \text{logn } (b^2 + s^2) + \frac{1}{2} s^2 \text{logn } s$$

$$\left. - s(a - b) \tan^{-1} \frac{a - b}{s} + as \tan^{-1} \frac{a}{s} + bs \tan^{-1} \frac{b}{s} - \frac{3}{2} ab \right] \tag{21}$$

[2] *Bur. Standards Sci. Paper* 169, by E. B. Rosa and F. W. Grover, equation (133).

Putting $a = b$,

$$\operatorname{logn} G_{15} = \frac{s^2}{b^2} \operatorname{logn} s + \frac{1}{2}\left(1 - \frac{s^2}{b^2}\right) \operatorname{logn} (b^2 + s^2)$$
$$+ \frac{2s}{b} \tan^{-1} \frac{b}{s} - \frac{3}{2} \quad (22)$$

as in equation (132) of footnote 2. G_{15} is the GMD of sides 1 and 5 in Fig. 6.

Putting $s = b$, equation (18) is obtained.   See equation (133) of footnote 2.

$$\operatorname{logn} G_{27} \text{ (Fig. 6)} = \frac{1}{2a^2} \int_0^a \int_0^a \operatorname{logn} \{y^2 + (pa + x)^2\} \, dx \, dy$$

$$= \frac{p + 1}{2} \operatorname{logn} \{1 + (p + 1)^2\} - \frac{p}{2} \operatorname{logn} (p^2 + 1) + \operatorname{logn} a$$

$$+ \frac{1}{2} \{1 - (p + 1)^2\} \tan^{-1} (p + 1) + \frac{1}{2} (p^2 - 1) \tan^{-1} p$$

$$+ \frac{\pi}{2}\left(p + \frac{1}{2}\right) - \frac{3}{2} \quad (23)$$

Logn G_{25} is obtained by putting $p = p - 1$ in (23).

$$\operatorname{logn} G_{26} = \frac{(p + 1)^2}{2} \operatorname{logn} \{(p + 1)a\} - p^2 \operatorname{logn} (pa)$$

$$+ \frac{(p - 1)^2}{2} \operatorname{logn} \{(p - 1)a\} - \frac{3}{2} \quad (24)$$

See equation (130) in footnote 2.

$$\operatorname{logn} G_{28} = \tfrac{1}{4}\{(p + 1)^2 - 1\} \operatorname{logn} \{(p + 1)^2 + 1\}$$
$$- \tfrac{1}{2}(p^2 - 1) \operatorname{logn} (p^2 + 1)$$
$$+ \tfrac{1}{4}\{(p - 1)^2 - 1\} \operatorname{logn} \{(p - 1)^2 + 1\} + \operatorname{logn} a$$
$$+ (p + 1) \tan^{-1} (p + 1) - 2 p \tan^{-1} p$$
$$+ (p - 1) \tan^{-1} (p - 1) - \tfrac{3}{2} \quad (25)$$

In averaging these and corresponding expressions, similar terms can be combined.   The GMD of one hollow square from the other is given by

$\operatorname{logn} M$

$= \tfrac{1}{8} [(p + 1) \operatorname{logn} \{(p + 1)^2 + 1\} - (p^2 - 1) \operatorname{logn} (p^2 + 1)$
$- (p - 1) \operatorname{logn} \{(p - 1)^2 + 1\} + (p + 1)^2 \operatorname{logn} (p + 1)$
$+ (p - 1)^2 \operatorname{logn} (p - 1) + 8 \operatorname{logn} a - (p^2 + 2p) \tan^{-1} (p + 1)$
$+ (p^2 - 2p) \tan^{-1} (p - 1) - 4 p \tan^{-1} p + 4\pi p - 12] \quad (26)$

For putting this expression in the form of a power series, the following may be used:

$$\tan^{-1}(p+1) = \frac{\pi}{2} - \frac{1}{p} + \frac{1}{p^2} - \frac{2}{3p^3} + \frac{4}{5p^5} - \frac{4}{3p^6} + \frac{8}{7p^7} - \frac{16}{9p^9}$$
$$+ \frac{16}{5p^{10}} \cdots \quad (27)$$

$$\tan^{-1}(p-1) = \frac{\pi}{2} - \frac{1}{p} - \frac{1}{p^2} - \frac{2}{3p^3} + \frac{4}{5p^5} + \frac{4}{3p^6} + \frac{8}{7p^7} - \frac{16}{9p^9}$$
$$- \frac{16}{5p^{10}} \cdots \quad (28)$$

$$\text{logn } M = \text{logn } s + \frac{1}{40}\left(\frac{a}{s}\right)^4 - \frac{17}{720}\left(\frac{a}{s}\right)^8 \cdots \quad \text{as in} \quad (5)$$

CHAPTER 19

EDDY-CURRENT LOSS IN ROUND WIRE

The current distribution and resistance loss, with alternating current, in a round conductor are needed to be known in connection with current-carrying parts in reactors, electric furnaces, transformer connectors, high-frequency apparatus, etc., as well as in transmission and distribution.

It is desirable first to find the differential equation for current density in the round conductor.

Current inside radius r_2 is $\int_0^{r_2} 2\pi r_1 i \, dr_1$

where r_1 and r_2 are radii and i is the variable current density in abamperes per square centimeter.

Flux density at radius r_2 is $\dfrac{2}{r_2} \int_0^{r_2} 2\pi r_1 i \, dr_1$

Total flux in outer ring $= \int_r^a \dfrac{1}{r_2} \int_0^{r_2} 4\pi r_1 i \, dr_1 \, dr_2$

The voltage drop at every section is the same.

$$i\rho + j\,\omega \int_r^a \frac{1}{r_2} \int_0^{r_2} 4\pi r_1 i \, dr_1 \, dr_2 = \text{constant}$$

where ρ is the resistivity in abohms per centimeter cube, a is the conductor radius in centimeters and r is a radius less than a.

$$\rho \frac{di}{dr} - \frac{j\,\omega}{r} \int_0^r 4\pi r_1 i \, dr_1 = 0$$

$$\rho r \frac{di}{dr} - j\,\omega 4\pi \int_0^r r_1 i \, dr_1 = 0$$

$$\rho r \frac{d^2 i}{dr^2} + \rho \frac{di}{dr} - j\,\omega 4\pi r i = 0$$

$$\frac{d^2 i}{dr^2} + \frac{1}{r} \frac{di}{dr} - \frac{j\,\omega\,4\,\pi}{\rho} i = 0 \qquad (1)$$

Let this be written

$$\frac{d^2i}{dr^2} + \frac{1}{r}\frac{di}{dr} + p^2i = 0 \tag{2}$$

and let $pr = z$, then

$$\frac{d^2i}{dz^2} + \frac{1}{z}\frac{di}{dz} + i = 0 \tag{3}$$

This is the standard form of Bessel's differential equation of order zero. The solution is

$$i = AI_0(mr\sqrt{j}) + BK_0(mr\sqrt{j}) \tag{4}$$

where

$$m^2 = \frac{\omega 4\pi}{\rho} \tag{5}$$

and where I_0 and K_0 are modified Bessel functions of order zero and of the first and second kinds. A and B are unknown constants to be determined by the boundary conditions.

The function K_0 contains logn mr and so is infinite when r is zero. However, the current density cannot be zero at the center of a solid wire, and therefore the constant $B = 0$. Now by definition we have

$$I_0(mr\sqrt{j}) = J_0(mrj\sqrt{j}) = \text{ber } mr + j \text{ bei } mr \tag{6}$$

The differential equation can be solved by assuming for i a power series with undetermined coefficients and solving for the coefficients, thus obtaining series for the functions as follows:

$$\text{ber } mr = 1 - \frac{(\tfrac{1}{2}mr)^4}{(2!)^2} + \frac{(\tfrac{1}{2}mr)^8}{(4!)^2} - \cdots \tag{7}$$

$$\text{bei } mr = \frac{(\tfrac{1}{2}mr)^2}{(1!)^2} - \frac{(\tfrac{1}{2}mr)^6}{(3!)^2} + \frac{(\tfrac{1}{2}mr)^{10}}{(5!)^2} - \cdots \tag{8}$$

$$\text{ber' } mr = -\frac{(\tfrac{1}{2}mr)^3}{1!\,2!} + \frac{(\tfrac{1}{2}mr)^7}{3!\,4!} - \frac{(\tfrac{1}{2}mr)^{11}}{5!\,6!} + \cdots \tag{9}$$

$$\text{bei' } mr = \tfrac{1}{2}mr - \frac{(\tfrac{1}{2}mr)^5}{2!\,3!} + \frac{(\tfrac{1}{2}mr)^9}{4!\,5!} - \cdots \tag{10}$$

These "power series" are convergent for all values of mr, but if it is desired to use only three or four terms, mr should not be greater than about 2.

For large values of mr, asymptotic series have been derived from the differential equation, which give the following formulas:

$$\text{ber } mr = \frac{e^{mr/\sqrt{2}}}{\sqrt{2\pi mr}} \left[L_0(mr) \cos\left(\frac{mr}{\sqrt{2}} - \frac{\pi}{8}\right) \right.$$
$$\left. - M_0(mr) \sin\left(\frac{mr}{\sqrt{2}} - \frac{\pi}{8}\right) \right] - \frac{1}{\pi} \text{ kei } mr \quad (11)$$

$$\text{bei } mr = \frac{e^{mr/\sqrt{2}}}{\sqrt{2\pi mr}} \left[M_0(mr) \cos\left(\frac{mr}{\sqrt{2}} - \frac{\pi}{8}\right) \right.$$
$$\left. + L_0(mr) \sin\left(\frac{mr}{\sqrt{2}} - \frac{\pi}{8}\right) \right] + \frac{1}{\pi} \text{ ker } mr \quad (12)$$

where $L_0(mr) \approx 1 + \dfrac{1^2}{1! \, 8mr} \cos\dfrac{\pi}{4} + \dfrac{1^2 \cdot 3^2}{2! \, (8mr)^2} \cos\dfrac{2\pi}{4}$

$$+ \frac{1^2 \cdot 3^2 \cdot 5^2}{3! \, (8mr)^3} \cos\frac{3\pi}{4} + \cdots \quad (13)$$

$M_0(mr) \approx - \dfrac{1^2}{1! \, 8mr} \sin\dfrac{\pi}{4} - \dfrac{1^2 \cdot 3^2}{2! \, (8mr)^2} \sin\dfrac{2\pi}{4}$

$$- \frac{1^2 \cdot 3^2 \cdot 5^2}{3! \, (8mr)^3} \sin\frac{3\pi}{4} - \cdots \quad (14)$$

The symbol $\approx$ denotes approximate equality.   These asymptotic series are "semi-convergent."   When mr is large, a few terms give a precise numerical value of the function, the error being less than the multiplier of $\cos\dfrac{k\pi}{4}$ or $\sin\dfrac{k\pi}{4}$ in the last term used.   See "Advanced Calculus" by E. B. Wilson, p. 398.   This rule can be checked by computing precise values by the asymptotic series, for mr between 5 and 10, and comparing them with values computed by the power series, such as those usually tabulated in that range.

$$\text{ber}' \, mr = \frac{e^{mr/\sqrt{2}}}{\sqrt{2\pi mr}} \left[S_0(mr) \cos\left(\frac{mr}{\sqrt{2}} + \frac{\pi}{8}\right) \right.$$
$$\left. - T_0(mr) \sin\left(\frac{mr}{\sqrt{2}} + \frac{\pi}{8}\right) \right] - \frac{1}{\pi} \text{ kei}' \, mr \quad (15)$$

$$\text{bei}' \, mr = \frac{e^{mr/\sqrt{2}}}{\sqrt{2\pi mr}} \left[T_0(mr) \cos\left(\frac{mr}{\sqrt{2}} + \frac{\pi}{8}\right) \right.$$
$$\left. + S_0(mr) \sin\left(\frac{mr}{\sqrt{2}} + \frac{\pi}{8}\right) \right] + \frac{1}{\pi} \text{ ker}' \, mr \quad (16)$$

where $S_0(mr) \approx 1 - \dfrac{1 \cdot 3}{1! \, 8mr} \cos\dfrac{\pi}{4} - \dfrac{1^2 \cdot 3 \cdot 5}{2! \, (8mr)^2} \cos\dfrac{2\pi}{4}$

$$- \frac{1^2 \cdot 3^2 \cdot 5 \cdot 7}{3! \, (8mr)^3} \cos\frac{3\pi}{4} - \frac{1^2 \cdot 3^2 \cdot 5^2 \cdot 7 \cdot 9}{4! \, (8mr)^4} \cos\frac{4\pi}{4} - \cdots \quad (17)$$

$$T_0(mr) \approx \frac{1 \cdot 3}{1! \, 8mr} \sin \frac{\pi}{4} + \frac{1^2 \cdot 3 \cdot 5}{2! \, (8mr)^2} \sin \frac{2\pi}{4}$$

$$+ \frac{1^2 \cdot 3^2 \cdot 5 \cdot 7}{3! \, (8mr)^3} \sin \frac{3\pi}{4} + \frac{1^2 \cdot 3^2 \cdot 5^2 \cdot 7 \cdot 9}{4! \, (8mr)^4} \sin \frac{4\pi}{4} + \cdots \quad (18)$$

These asymptotic series were published in the author's paper Bessel Functions for A-C Calculations, *Trans. A.I.E.E.*, 1929, p. 812.

The terms $-\dfrac{1}{\pi}$ kei mr and $\dfrac{1}{\pi}$ ker mr were given by J. R. Airey in The "Converging Factor" in Asymptotic Series and the Calculation of Bessel, Laguerre and Other Functions, *Phil. Mag.*, Vol. 24, p. 546, 1937. They are usually small where asymptotic series are used, but they are needed in order to make use of the rule about the last term used, stated after equation (14).

Tables of the functions ber mr, bei mr, and their derivatives have been published,[1,2] which are complete for mr from 0 to 20.

From the series in powers of mr it is found that

$$\int mr \text{ ber } mr \, d \, mr = mr \text{ bei}' \, mr \quad (19)$$

and
$$\int mr \text{ bei } mr \, d \, mr = -mr \text{ ber}' \, mr \quad (20)$$

Since the constant B in (4) is zero, then, from (6),

$$i = A(\text{ber } mr + j \text{ bei } mr) \quad (21)$$

For moderately high frequencies or large radius, so that $mr = 5$ or more, the current density near the surface increases very rapidly as r increases. The current tends to concentrate in the skin of the conductor, hence the name, *skin effect*. The eddy currents flow in straight lines near the surface and return nearer the center and are not like the turbulent flow of a liquid or like a circular eddy.

The constant A and the effective resistance of the wire can be found by calculating the total current I in the wire, using (19) and (20).

---

[1] *Trans. A.I.E.E.*, 1939, p. 787.

[2] "Mathematical Tables," by H. B. Dwight, p. 214, McGraw-Hill Book Company, Inc., New York, 1941.

$$I = \int_0^a 2\pi r A (\text{ber } mr + j \text{ bei } mr)\, dr$$

$$= \frac{2\pi a A}{m} (\text{bei}' \, ma - j \, \text{ber}' \, ma)$$

Then $$i = \frac{Im}{2\pi a} \frac{\text{ber } mr + j \text{ bei } mr}{\text{bei}' \, ma - j \, \text{ber}' \, ma} \qquad (22)$$

The voltage drop in the wire due to magnetic flux outside the wire is in quadrature with I.   Since all the filaments in the wire are in parallel, the voltage drop in the filaments is a constant as r varies.   The voltage drop in any filament, and hence in the wire, due to resistance and to internal flux, is equal to the drop in a surface filament and is $i_a\rho$ since there is no drop due to internal flux at the surface, where $r = a$.   The impedance of the wire due to resistance and internal flux is

$$Z_{eff} = \frac{i_a\rho}{I} = \frac{\rho m}{2\pi a} \frac{\text{ber } ma + j \text{ bei } ma}{\text{bei}' \, ma - j \, \text{ber}' \, ma} \qquad (23)$$

The impedance due to external flux can be computed by well-known methods involving the logarithms of distances.

The power consumed in the wire is the real part of current times voltage drop, that is, of $I^2 Z_{eff}$.   Hence $R_{eff} = R_{ac}$ is the real part of Z_{eff}.   The imaginary part is X_{eff} due to internal flux.

The resistance to direct current is

$$R_{dc} = \frac{\rho}{\pi a^2}$$

$$\frac{R_{ac}}{R_{dc}} = \text{real part of } \frac{ma}{2} \frac{\text{ber } ma + j \text{ bei } ma}{\text{bei}' \, ma - j \, \text{ber}' \, ma} \qquad (24)$$

$$= \frac{ma}{2} \frac{\text{ber } ma \text{ bei}' \, ma - \text{bei } ma \text{ ber}' \, ma}{\text{ber}'^2 \, ma + \text{bei}'^2 \, ma} \qquad (25)$$

This is the *skin-effect resistance ratio*.   Values are given in Table I.

Equation (25) can be expressed as a series in powers of ma.

$$\frac{R_{ac}}{R_{dc}} = 1 + \frac{1}{12}\left(\frac{1}{2} \, ma\right)^4 - \frac{1}{180}\left(\frac{1}{2} \, ma\right)^8 + \cdots \qquad (26)$$

This can be used for values of ma up to about 2.

For values of ma larger than about 5, the following can be used, derived from the asymptotic series:

$$\frac{R_{ac}}{R_{dc}} = \frac{ma}{2\sqrt{2}} + \frac{1}{4} + \frac{3}{16\,ma\,\sqrt{2}} - \frac{63}{256m^3a^3\,\sqrt{2}}$$
$$- \frac{27}{64m^4a^4} - \cdots \quad (27)$$

The value of ma can be found not only from equation (5) but also from the resistance per unit length of the wire. From (5),

$$m^2a^2 = \frac{\omega 4\pi a^2}{\rho} = \frac{8\pi f 10^{-9}}{R_{dc}} \quad (28)$$

where R_{dc} is the d-c resistance of the wire in ohms per centimeter and where f is the frequency.

Using the number of ohms per 1,000 ft, $R_{(1,000\,ft)}$, which is frequently tabulated,

$$m^2a^2 = \frac{8\pi f 10^{-9} \times 12,000 \times 2.540}{R_{(1,000\,ft)}}$$
$$ma = 0.02768 \sqrt{\frac{f}{R_{(1,000\,ft)}}} \quad (29)$$

The conductor may be of any metal and at any temperature.

Penetration Formula. The first two terms of (27) can be represented approximately by assuming that the solid wire is replaced by a tube of the same outside diameter and of thickness

$$\delta_1 = \frac{\sqrt{2}}{m} = \frac{1}{2\pi} \sqrt{\frac{\rho}{f}} = \frac{1}{2\pi} \sqrt{\frac{\rho_1 \times 10^9}{f}} \quad \text{cm} \quad (30)$$

where ρ_1 is the resistivity in ohms per centimeter cube, and by assuming that the total current is uniformly distributed through the section of this tube. The resistance of the tube is then equal to R_{ac}, the effective resistance of the wire to alternating current.

$$\frac{R_{ac}}{R_{dc}} = \frac{\pi a^2}{2\pi(a - \frac{1}{2}\delta_1)\delta_1} = \frac{a}{2\delta_1}\left(1 - \frac{\delta_1}{2a}\right)^{-1}$$
$$= \frac{ma}{2\sqrt{2}}\left(1 - \frac{1}{ma\sqrt{2}}\right)^{-1}$$
$$= \frac{ma}{2\sqrt{2}} + \frac{1}{4} + \frac{1}{4ma\sqrt{2}} + \cdots \quad (31)$$

Formula (31) agrees with the first two terms of (27). For slide-rule accuracy, the penetration formula (30) should not be used when $ma < 5$. Although the penetration formula is a high-frequency formula, its application to round wires cannot be determined by the frequency alone, but by the value of ma, which involves f, ρ, and the radius a.

The penetration depth method can be used, as an approximation, with conductors which are not round but which have rather compact cross section and are rather free from concavities. It is used a great deal with round conductors in communication work at high frequencies but, as shown by equation (42), Chap. 20, if the penetration depth method is used with tubes, as in coaxial conductors, the penetration depth not only should be a small fraction of the outside radius but it should also be a small fraction of the tube thickness.

At power frequencies the penetration depth method has often been incorrectly applied, though its use is proper if care is taken not to go beyond the limits described.

It has been found by measurement that the skin-effect resistance ratio of a concentric stranded cable is practically the same, in ordinary cases, as that of a round wire of the same resistance per unit length, R_{dc}. The mistake should be guarded against of taking a round wire of the same diameter as the cable, in calculating ma and the resistance ratio.

It can be observed from (25) and (26) that the resistance ratio of a round wire depends on the value of ma. By using expression (29) in terms of the conductor resistance, ma can be easily found for any stranded conductor. A stranded conductor is really a mixture of metal and air and has a different value of ρ from the solid metal. The need to compute such a value of resistivity is conveniently avoided by using (29) in terms of $R_{(1,000 \text{ ft})}$.

If the stranded conductor is tubular, its computation may be made to depend in a similar way on R_{dc}, the resistance per unit length of the conductor.

The small difference in a-c resistance between a cable and a wire having the same value of R_{dc} is mainly dependent on the spiraling of the strands. The amount may be read from Fig. 2, Chap. 25. This figure is useful also in indicating when the spirality effect is negligible.

Principle of Similitude. In all the cases of conductors which have been solved mathematically, the skin-effect resistance ratio is found in terms of a quantity involving f/R_{dc}. For a

TABLE I, CHAP. 19.—SKIN-EFFECT RATIO OF ROUND WIRE

ma	R_{ac}/R_{dc}	Diff.	ma	R_{ac}/R_{dc}	Diff.	ma	R_{ac}/R_{dc}	Diff.
0	1.000	..	4.0	1.678		12.5	4.680	
0.1	1.000	..	4.1	1.715	37	13.0	4.856	0.176
.2	1.000	..	4.2	1.752	37	13.5	5.033	.177
.3	1.000	..	4.3	1.789	37	14.0	5.209	.176
.4	1.000	..	4.4	1.826	37	14.5	5.386	.177
					37			.176
0.5	1.000		4.5	1.863		15.0	5.562	
.6	1.001	1	4.6	1.899	36	16.0	5.915	0.353
.7	1.001	0	4.7	1.935	36	17.0	6.268	.353
.8	1.002	1	4.8	1.971	36	18.0	6.621	.353
.9	1.003	1	4.9	2.007	36	19.0	6.974	.353
		2			36			.354
1.0	1.005		5.0	2.043		20.0	7.328	
1.1	1.008	3	5.2	2.114	71	21.0	7.681	0.353
1.2	1.011	3	5.4	2.184	70	22.0	8.034	.353
1.3	1.015	4	5.6	2.254	70	23.0	8.387	.353
1.4	1.020	5	5.8	2.324	70	24.0	8.741	.354
		6			70			.353
1.5	1.026		6.0	2.394		25.0	9.094	
1.6	1.033	7	6.2	2.463	69	26.0	9.447	0.353
1.7	1.042	9	6.4	2.533	70	28.0	10.154	.707
1.8	1.052	10	6.6	2.603	70	30.0	10.861	.707
1.9	1.064	12	6.8	2.673	70	32.0	11.568	.707
		14			70			.707
2.0	1.078		7.0	2.743		34.0	12.275	
2.1	1.094	16	7.2	2.813	70	36.0	12.982	0.707
2.2	1.111	17	7.4	2.884	71	38.0	13.689	.707
2.3	1.131	20	7.6	2.954	70	40.0	14.395	.706
2.4	1.152	21	7.8	3.024	70	42.0	15.102	.707
		23			70			.707
2.5	1.175		8.0	3.094		44.0	15.809	
2.6	1.201	26	8.2	3.165	71	46.0	16.516	0.707
2.7	1.228	27	8.4	3.235	70	48.0	17.223	.707
2.8	1.256	28	8.6	3.306	71	50.0	17.930	.707
2.9	1.286	30	8.8	3.376	70	60.0	21.465	3.535
		32			70			3.536
3.0	1.318		9.0	3.446		70.0	25.001	
3.1	1.351	33	9.2	3.517	71	80.0	28.536	3.535
3.2	1.385	34	9.4	3.587	70	90.0	32.071	3.535
3.3	1.420	35	9.6	3.658	71	100.0	35.607	3.536
3.4	1.456	36	9.8	3.728	70			
		36			71			
3.5	1.492		10.0	3.799				
3.6	1.529	37	10.5	3.975	176			
3.7	1.566	37	11.0	4.151	176			
3.8	1.603	37	11.5	4.327	176			
3.9	1.641	38	12.0	4.504	177			
		37			176			

$$ma = 0.02768 \sqrt{\frac{f}{R_{(1,000\,ft)}}} \qquad \text{equation (23)}$$

given value of f/R_{dc} and a given shape, there is a certain resistance ratio. This is called the *principle of similitude*. Because of this principle, which has been proved mathematically, the results of tests made at high frequencies on small models of conductors can be drawn up as curves of R_{ac}/R_{dc} on a base of f/R_{dc} and used with conductors of large size at 60 cycles. See pp. 1398*ff.* of footnote 2, Chap. 20.

Values of the ratio R_{ac}/R_{dc} are given in Table I which is adapted from the more complete Table XXII, *Bur. Standards Bull.*, Vol. 8, No. 1, 1912. That table was calculated by Professor F. W. Grover, now of Union College, Schenectady, and the values are tabulated here by his permission and that of the National Bureau of Standards.

Values of R_{ac}/R_{dc} for round wire are given also by the left-hand curve of Fig. 1, Chap. 25.

CHAPTER 20

SKIN EFFECT IN CONCENTRIC TUBULAR CONDUCTORS

SKIN EFFECT AT LOW FREQUENCY

Let there be a tubular conductor of inner radius q and outer radius r, as in Fig. 1. Let there be uniform current density a_0 abamp per sq cm in the tube and let there be a current I_p in a

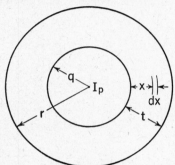

Fig. 1.—Tubular conductor and central wire.

wire at the center of the tube.[1] Following the procedure of footnote 2, beginning at equation (1) of that paper,

Flux density at dx = (current inside dx) $\dfrac{2}{q + x}$

$$= 2\pi a_0 q \left(\frac{2x}{q} - \frac{x^2}{q^2} + \frac{x^3}{q^3} - \frac{x^4}{q^4} + \cdots \right) + \frac{2I_p}{q} \left(1 + \frac{x}{q} \right)^{-1}$$

Integrate from x to t and multiply by $j\omega$ where

$$\omega = 2\pi \times \text{frequency}$$

Put $$\frac{4\pi\omega}{\rho} = m^2 \tag{1}$$

where ρ = resistivity of the metal in abohms per centimeter cube.

[1] Reactance and Skin Effect of Concentric Tubular Conductors, by H. B. Dwight, *Trans. A.I.E.E.*, 1942, p. 513.

[2] Skin Effect in Tubular and Flat Conductors, by H. B. Dwight, *Trans. A.I.E.E.*, 1918, p. 1379.

Reactive drop at dx caused by flux inside radius r due to a_0 and I_p is

$$\frac{jm^2t^2}{2!}\,a_0\rho\left[1-\frac{1}{3}\frac{t}{q}+\frac{1}{4}\frac{t^2}{q^2}-\cdots-\frac{x^2}{t^2}+\frac{1}{3}\frac{x^3}{t^2q}-\frac{1}{4}\frac{x^4}{t^2q^2}+\cdots\right]$$
$$+\frac{j\omega 2I_p t}{q}\left[1-\frac{1}{2}\frac{t}{q}+\frac{1}{3}\frac{t^2}{q^2}-\cdots-\frac{x}{t}+\frac{1}{2}\frac{x^2}{tq}-\frac{1}{3}\frac{x^3}{tq^2}+\cdots\right]$$

$$(2)$$

Let a current density $a_1 + a_1'$ flow, such that its resistance drop will be equal and opposite to the terms in x of (2), in order to keep the voltage drop from all causes uniform over the section, as it is in actual fact.

$$a_1 = \frac{jm^2t^2}{2!}\,a_0\left[\frac{x^2}{t^2}-\frac{1}{3}\frac{x^3}{t^2q}+\frac{1}{4}\frac{x^4}{t^2q^2}-\cdots\right] \qquad (3)$$

$$a_1' = \frac{j\omega 2I_p}{q\rho}\left[x-\frac{1}{2}\frac{x^2}{q}+\frac{1}{3}\frac{x^3}{q^2}-\frac{1}{4}\frac{x^4}{q^3}+\cdots\right] \qquad (4)$$

These currents will in turn produce flux in the metal. From the terms in x of the resulting voltage drops there are obtained values of current densities a_2 and a_2' and so on. The resulting values are

$$a_2 = \frac{(jm^2t^2)^2}{4!}\,a_0\left[\frac{x^4}{t^4}-\frac{2}{5}\frac{x^5}{t^4q}+\frac{3}{10}\frac{x^6}{t^4q^2}\cdots\right]$$

$$a_3 = \frac{(jm^2t^2)^3}{6!}\,a_0\left[\frac{x^6}{t^6}-\frac{3}{7}\frac{x^7}{t^6q}+\frac{9}{28}\frac{x^8}{t^6q^2}\cdots\right]$$

$$a_4 = \frac{(jm^2t^2)^4}{8!}\,a_0\left[\frac{x^8}{t^8}-\frac{4}{9}\frac{x^9}{t^8q}+\frac{1}{3}\frac{x^{10}}{t^8q^2}\cdots\right]$$

$$a_2' = \frac{jm^2t^2}{3!}\frac{j\omega 2I_p}{\rho}\left[\frac{x^3}{t^2q}-\frac{1}{2}\frac{x^4}{t^2q^2}+\frac{7}{20}\frac{x^5}{t^2q^3}-\frac{11}{40}\frac{x^6}{t^2q^4}\cdots\right]$$

$$a_3' = \frac{(jm^2t^2)^2}{5!}\frac{j\omega 2I_p}{\rho}\left[\frac{x^5}{t^4q}-\frac{1}{2}\frac{x^6}{t^4q^2}+\frac{5}{14}\frac{x^7}{t^4q^3}-\frac{2}{7}\frac{x^8}{t^4q^4}\cdots\right]$$

$$a_4' = \frac{(jm^2t^2)^3}{7!}\frac{j\omega 2I_p}{\rho}\left[\frac{x^7}{t^6q}-\frac{1}{2}\frac{x^8}{t^6q^2}+\frac{13}{36}\frac{x^9}{t^6q^3}-\frac{7}{24}\frac{x^{10}}{t^6q^4}\cdots\right]$$

Let the total current in the tube be I. By integrating the complete expression for current density over the cross section of the tube,

$$I = \pi a_0 \, (2qt + t^2) \left[1 + c_1 \frac{jm^2 t^2}{3!} + c_2 \frac{(jm^2 t^2)^2}{5!} + \cdots \right]$$
$$+ I_p \left[d_1 \frac{jm^2 t^2}{2!} + d_2 \frac{(jm^2 t^2)^2}{4!} + d_3 \frac{(jm^2 t^2)^3}{6!} + \cdots \right] \quad (5)$$

where $c_1 = 1 - \dfrac{1}{20} \dfrac{t^2}{q^2} + \dfrac{1}{20} \dfrac{t^3}{q^3} - \dfrac{11}{280} \dfrac{t^4}{q^4} + \cdots$

$\qquad c_2 = 1 - \dfrac{1}{14} \dfrac{t^2}{q^2} + \dfrac{1}{14} \dfrac{t^3}{q^3} - \cdots$

$\qquad c_3 = 1 - \dfrac{1}{12} \dfrac{t^2}{q^2} + \cdots$

$\qquad c_4 = 1 - \dfrac{1}{11} \dfrac{t^2}{q^2} + \cdots \qquad\qquad$ as in footnote 2

$\qquad d_1 = 1 + \dfrac{1}{3} \dfrac{t}{q} - \dfrac{1}{12} \dfrac{t^2}{q^2} + \dfrac{1}{30} \dfrac{t^3}{q^3} - \cdots$

$\qquad d_2 = 1 + \dfrac{2}{5} \dfrac{t}{q} - \dfrac{1}{10} \dfrac{t^2}{q^2} + \dfrac{3}{70} \dfrac{t^3}{q^3} - \cdots$

$\qquad d_3 = 1 + \dfrac{3}{7} \dfrac{t}{q} - \dfrac{3}{28} \dfrac{t^2}{q^2} + \dfrac{1}{21} \dfrac{t^3}{q^3} - \cdots$

$\qquad d_4 = 1 + \dfrac{4}{9} \dfrac{t}{q} - \dfrac{1}{9} \dfrac{t^2}{q^2} + \cdots$

This gives the value of a_0 in terms of I and I_p.

If the tube were not present, the center conductor I_p would supply its resistance loss including its own eddy-current loss. Then, as stated by Waldo V. Lyon at the top of p. 1377, *Trans. A.I.E.E.*, 1921, in his paper on eddy-current losses in armature conductors, if the outer tube and its current I be introduced, it does not change the eddy-current loss in the inner conductor, and the total additional power supplied by the circuits to the two conductors is equal to the resistance loss of the tube. There is a transfer of power from the inner conductor to the tube. These amounts of power can be computed.

In the work so far, magnetic flux outside the tube has not been considered as it would not change any of the current densities. It will be included now in computing the transfer of power and, as would be expected, it will be shown that it has no effect on the expression for eddy-current loss.

The voltage drop in all elements of the tube is the same as that at its outer surface and is

$$j\omega 2(I + I_p) \log_n \frac{s}{r} + \rho \, i_{(t)} \quad (6)$$

where $i_{(t)}$ is the current density at the outer surface and where s is a certain large distance to which flux is counted. Since the expression in s will finally cancel out, the result is the same no matter how large a value of s is chosen.

Let $\hat{I}$ be the conjugate of I, that is, the same complex quantity except with j changed to $-j$. Multiply (6) by $\hat{I}$ and take the real part, to obtain the power delivered to the tube from its own circuit, per centimeter of the tube. This is

$$\text{Re } \hat{I} j\omega 2 \left(I + I_p \right) \operatorname{logn} \frac{s}{r}$$

$$+ \text{ Re } \hat{I} a_0 \rho \left[1 + b_1 \frac{jm^2 t^2}{2!} + b_2 \frac{(jm^2 t^2)^2}{4!} + \cdots \right]$$

$$+ \text{ Re } \hat{I} I_p \frac{j\omega 4 t}{2q + t} \left[e_1 + e_2 \frac{jm^2 t^2}{3!} + e_3 \frac{(jm^2 t^2)^2}{5!} + \cdots \right] \quad (7)$$

where Re denotes the real part of the complete expression following it,

$$b_1 = 1 - \frac{1}{3}\frac{t}{q} + \frac{1}{4}\frac{t^2}{q^2} - \cdots$$

$$= \frac{1}{2} + \frac{q}{t} - \frac{q^2}{t^2} \operatorname{logn} \left(1 + \frac{t}{q} \right)$$

$$b_2 = 1 - \frac{2}{5}\frac{t}{q} + \frac{3}{10}\frac{t^2}{q^2} - \frac{17}{70}\frac{t^3}{q^3} \cdots$$

$$b_3 = 1 - \frac{3}{7}\frac{t}{q} + \frac{9}{28}\frac{t^2}{q^2} - \frac{11}{42}\frac{t^3}{q^3} \cdots$$

$$b_4 = 1 - \frac{4}{9}\frac{t}{q} + \frac{1}{3}\frac{t^2}{q^2} \cdots$$

$$b_5 = 1 - \frac{5}{11}\frac{t}{q} + \frac{15}{44}\frac{t^2}{q^2} \cdots \qquad \text{as in footnote 2}$$

$$e_1 = 1 + \frac{1}{12}\frac{t^2}{q^2} - \frac{1}{12}\frac{t^3}{q^3} + \frac{3}{40}\frac{t^4}{q^4} - \frac{1}{15}\frac{t^5}{q^5} \cdots$$

$$= \left(\frac{1}{2} + \frac{q}{t} \right) \operatorname{logn} \left(1 + \frac{t}{q} \right)$$

$$e_2 = 1 + \frac{1}{10}\frac{t^2}{q^2} - \frac{1}{10}\frac{t^3}{q^3} + \frac{51}{560}\frac{t^4}{q^4} \cdots$$

$$e_3 = 1 + \frac{3}{28}\frac{t^2}{q^2} - \frac{3}{28}\frac{t^3}{q^3} \cdots$$

$$e_4 = 1 + \frac{1}{9}\frac{t^2}{q^2} - \frac{1}{9}\frac{t^3}{q^3} \cdots$$

The total flux caused by the current in the tube, as far as radius s, is

$$2I \operatorname{logn} \frac{s}{r} + 4\pi a_0 t^2 \left[\frac{b_1}{2!} + b_2 \frac{jm^2 t^2}{4!} + b_3 \frac{(jm^2 t^2)^2}{6!} + \cdots \right]$$
$$+ \frac{4I_p t}{2q + t} \left[e_2 \frac{jm^2 t^2}{3!} + e_3 \frac{(jm^2 t^2)^2}{5!} + \cdots \right] \quad (8)$$

Multiply by $j\omega$ to obtain the voltage induced in the central conductor. Then multiply by $\hat{I}_p$ and take the real part to obtain the additional power supplied by the circuit of the central conductor. This power is transferred to the tube and helps supply the resistance loss in the tube. By adding (7), the total resistance loss in the tube is found to be

$$\operatorname{Re} \hat{I} j\omega 2 \operatorname{logn} \frac{s}{r} + \operatorname{Re} \hat{I} a_0 \rho \left[1 + b_1 \frac{jm^2 t^2}{2!} + b_2 \frac{(jm^2 t^2)^2}{4!} + \cdots \right]$$
$$+ \operatorname{Re} \hat{I} I_p \frac{j\omega 4 t}{2q + t} \left[e_1 + e_2 \frac{jm^2 t^2}{3!} + e_3 \frac{(jm^2 t^2)^2}{5!} + \cdots \right]$$
$$+ \operatorname{Re} \hat{I}_p I j\omega 2 \operatorname{logn} \frac{s}{r} + \operatorname{Re} \hat{I}_p a_0 \rho \left[b_1 \frac{jm^2 t^2}{2!} + b_2 \frac{(jm^2 t^2)^2}{4!} + \cdots \right]$$
$$+ \operatorname{Re} \hat{I}_p I_p \frac{j\omega 4 t}{2q + t} \left[e_2 \frac{jm^2 t^2}{3!} + e_3 \frac{(jm^2 t^2)^2}{5!} + \cdots \right] \quad (9)$$

Now $\hat{I} I$ is a real quantity, $|I|^2$, since

$$(a - jb)(a + jb) = a^2 + b^2 + j\,0$$

$\hat{I} I_p + I \hat{I}_p$ is also a real quantity, since

$$(a - jb)(c + jd) + (a + jb)(c - jd) = 2ac + 2bd + j\,0$$

It is the sum of a complex quantity and its conjugate. Therefore, the terms in $\operatorname{logn} \frac{s}{r}$ have no real part and disappear.

The resistance loss in the tube, then, is

$$\operatorname{Re} \hat{I} a_0 \rho + \operatorname{Re} (\hat{I} + \hat{I}_p) a_0 \rho \left[b_1 \frac{jm^2 t^2}{2!} + b_2 \frac{(jm^2 t^2)^2}{4!} + \cdots \right]$$
$$+ \operatorname{Re} \frac{j\omega 4 t}{2q + t} \left[\hat{I} I_p e_1 + I_p (\hat{I} + \hat{I}_p) \right.$$
$$\left. \left\{ e_2 \frac{jm^2 t^2}{3!} + e_3 \frac{(jm^2 t^2)^2}{5!} + \cdots \right\} \right] \quad (10)$$

Note that the real parts of the entire expressions are taken in this chapter.

Equations (5) and (10) can be applied to the three tubes in succession of a three-phase, concentric circuit, thus obtaining the skin-effect resistance ratio of each tube, that is, the ratio of the resistance loss in the tube compared with the loss with direct current of the same amperage.

The power lost in a tube with direct current of amperage I is

$$\frac{|I|^2 \rho}{\pi(2qt + t^2)} \tag{11}$$

The skin-effect resistance ratio of the inner tube is the same as that of an isolated tube, since the surrounding tubes do not affect its current density. In this case, $I_p = 0$. The formulas and curves were published in footnote 2 and are given in Fig. 1, Chap. 25.

Dividing (10) by (11) and substituting the value of a_0 given by (5),

$$\frac{R_{ac}}{R_{dc}} = \operatorname{Re} \frac{1 + b_1 \dfrac{jm^2t^2}{2!} + b_2 \dfrac{(jm^2t^2)^2}{4!} + \cdots}{1 + c_1 \dfrac{jm^2t^2}{3!} + c_2 \dfrac{(jm^2t^2)^2}{5!} + \cdots} \tag{12}$$

for the inner tube.

For the intermediate tube,

$$\frac{R_{ac}}{R_{dc}} = \operatorname{Re} \frac{LM}{Q} + \operatorname{Re} S \tag{13}$$

where

$$L = 1 + \left(1 + \frac{\hat{I}_p}{\hat{I}}\right) \left\{ b_1 \frac{jm^2t^2}{2!} + b_2 \frac{(jm^2t^2)^2}{4!} + \cdots \right\} \tag{14}$$

$$M = 1 - \frac{I_p}{I} \left\{ d_1 \frac{jm^2t^2}{2!} + d_2 \frac{(jm^2t^2)^2}{4!} + \cdots \right\} \tag{15}$$

$$Q = 1 + c_1 \frac{jm^2t^2}{3!} + c_2 \frac{(jm^2t^2)^2}{5!} + \cdots \tag{16}$$

[Same as equation (16) in footnote 2, or the denominator of (12).]

$$S = \frac{I_p}{I} e_1 \frac{jm^2t^2}{1!} + \left(\frac{I_p}{I} + \left|\frac{I_p}{I}\right|^2\right) \left\{ e_2 \frac{(jm^2t^2)^2}{3!} \right.$$
$$\left. + e_3 \frac{(jm^2t^2)^3}{5!} + \cdots \right\} \tag{17}$$

In balanced three-phase circuits, for the two opposite phase rotations,

$$\frac{I_p}{I} = -\frac{1}{2} + j\frac{\sqrt{3}}{2} \quad \text{or} \quad -\frac{1}{2} - j\frac{\sqrt{3}}{2} \qquad (18)$$

$$1 + \frac{\hat{I}_p}{\hat{I}} = \frac{1}{2} - j\frac{\sqrt{3}}{2} \quad \text{or} \quad \frac{1}{2} + j\frac{\sqrt{3}}{2}$$

$$\frac{I_p}{I} + \left|\frac{I_p}{I}\right|^2 = \frac{1}{2} + j\frac{\sqrt{3}}{2} \quad \text{or} \quad \frac{1}{2} - j\frac{\sqrt{3}}{2}$$

The two opposite phase rotations produce slightly different amounts of eddy-current loss, that is, different values of R_{ac},

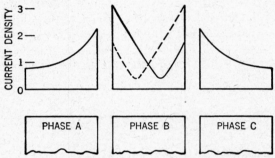

FIG. 2.—Current density in three-phase closely adjacent strap conductors. Current density for same amperage of direct current = 1. $mt = \sqrt{6}$. The dotted line is for opposite phase rotation.

depending on whether the greater current density is produced in the inner or the outer surface of the intermediate tube (see Fig. 2).

For the outer tube, $I_p = -I$, and

$$\frac{R_{ac}}{R_{dc}} = \text{Re} \frac{1 + d_1 \dfrac{jm^2t^2}{2!} + d_2 \dfrac{(jm^2t^2)^2}{4!} + \cdots}{1 + c_1 \dfrac{jm^2t^2}{3!} + c_2 \dfrac{(jm^2t^2)^2}{5!} + \cdots} \qquad (19)$$

Equations (12), (13), and (19) give the skin-effect resistance ratio of the three tubes of a three-phase, concentric, tubular circuit. They are applicable up to about $mt = 4$ and $t/d = 0.2$ ($t/q = \frac{2}{3}$), as in footnote 2.

The values of the ratios are plotted in Fig. 3, Chap. 25, on a base of thickness of copper tube, for standard frequency and temperature. This can save the work of computing by the formulas, in cases where the curves apply. For a frequency f multiply the tube thickness by $\sqrt{f/60}$ before reading from the curves.

In order to show that there is a larger skin-effect ratio for the intermediate tube than for the others, the current density in the three phases is plotted in Fig. 2, as computed by equation (3) and following formulas. The case chosen is that of three flat straps which is the same as that of three concentric tubes with extremely large radii.

The skin-effect resistance ratio of the outer tube of a single-phase concentric circuit is the same as the ratio for the outer tube of a three-phase concentric circuit as given by Fig. 3, Chap. 25, or equation (19), since the total current inside the tube in either case is $-I$. The resistance ratio of the inner tube of a single-phase concentric circuit, and also the ratio of an isolated tube, are the same as that of the inner tube of a three-phase circuit, as given by Fig. 3, Chap. 25 or equation (12) (see also footnotes 2 and 4).

Example 1.   Find the effective resistance at 60 cycles and 75°C of the three copper tubes described in the example in Chap. 16.

The inner tube, whose inside and outside diameters are 1.2 and 3.0 in., has a resistance to direct current of 5.47×10^{-8} ohm per cm.   From Fig. 3, Chap. 25, taking $t = 0.9$ in. and $t/d = 0.3$, the skin-effect resistance ratio is 1.92.   Then R_{ac} for 60 cycles is

$$5.47 \times 10^{-8} \times 1.92 = 1.050 \times 10^{-7} \qquad \text{ohm/cm}$$

This is to be used for resistance drop and copper loss in the inner tube.

For the intermediate tube, with inside and outside diameters 4.0 and 4.5 in. and thickness 0.25 in., the resistance to direct current is 9.74×10^{-8}. From Fig. 3, Chap. 25, $R_{ac}/R_{dc} = 1.059$ and, therefore, $R_{ac} = 1.030 \times 10^{-7}$ ohm per cm.

For the outer tube, the inside and outside diameters are 5.6 and 6.0 in. The resistance ratio, from Fig. 3, Chap. 25, is 1.008 and

$$R_{ac} = 8.92 \times 10^{-8} \times 1.008 = 8.99 \times 10^{-8} \qquad \text{ohm/cm}$$

BESSEL-FUNCTION FORMULAS FOR SINGLE-PHASE CONCENTRIC CIRCUITS AND ISOLATED TUBES

The well-known solution for skin effect in an isolated tube in terms of Bessel functions is as follows:[3,4]

[3] "Electrical Papers," by Oliver Heaviside, Vol. 2, p. 69, equation (50b).

[4] A Precise Method of Calculation of Skin Effect in Isolated Tubes, by H. B. Dwight, *Jour. A.I.E.E.*, August, 1923, p. 827, equations (4) and (10).

$$\frac{R_{ac}}{R_{dc}} = \text{Re} \; \frac{\alpha t(q + r)}{2r} \; \frac{I_0(\alpha r)K_0'(\alpha q) - K_0(\alpha r)I_0'(\alpha q)}{I_0'(\alpha r)K_0'(\alpha q) - K_0'(\alpha r)I_0'(\alpha q)} \qquad (20)$$

where I_0 and K_0 are modified Bessel functions of the first and second kinds, of order zero.   Re denotes "real part of."

r = outside radius.

q = inside radius.

t = thickness of tube = $r - q$.

$\alpha^2 = \dfrac{j4\pi\omega}{\rho} = jm^2.$

$\alpha = me^{j\pi/4}.$

$j = \sqrt{-1}.$

$\omega = 2\pi \times$ frequency.

ρ = resistivity of the metal, in abohms per centimeter cube.

Note that

$$I_0(\alpha r) = \text{ber } mr + j \text{ bei } mr \qquad (21)$$
$$K_0(\alpha r) = \text{ker } mr + j \text{ kei } mr \qquad (22)$$
$$I_0'(\alpha r) = e^{-j\pi/4} (\text{ber}' \; mr + j \text{ bei}' \; mr) \qquad (23)$$
$$K_0'(\alpha r) = e^{-j\pi/4} (\text{ker}' \; mr + j \text{ kei}' \; mr) \qquad (24)$$

Equation (20) is applicable to the inner tube of a concentric circuit and to a nonconcentric circuit in which the conductors are separated by more than a few diameters, and proximity effect is considered negligibly small.

For the outer tube of a concentric circuit, where all the return conductors are within the outer tube,[3,5]

$$\frac{R_{ac}}{R_{dc}} = \text{Re} \; \frac{-\alpha t(q + r)}{2q} \; \frac{I_0(\alpha q)K_0'(\alpha r) - K_0(\alpha q)I_0'(\alpha r)}{I_0'(\alpha q)K_0'(\alpha r) - K_0'(\alpha q)I_0'(\alpha r)} \qquad (25)$$

This is the same as (20) for an isolated tube, except that we interchange q and r and multiply by -1.   Both (20) and (25) may be derived by following the general method used in footnotes 4 and 5.

Equations (20) and (25) may be used for direct computation of numerical problems, using tabulated values from footnote 6 or 7.

[5] "Theory of Alternating Currents," by Alex. Russell, Cambridge University Press, London, ed. of 1914, p. 207.

[6] Bessel Functions for A-C Problems, by H. B. Dwight, *Trans. A.I.E.E.*, July, 1929, p. 812.

[7] "Tables of Integrals and Other Mathematical Data," by H. B. Dwight, The Macmillan Company, New York, p. 211.

For very small or very large values of the argument, or for tubes whose thickness is small compared with their radius, series formulas, as given in this paper, may be shorter to use.

HIGH-FREQUENCY FORMULAS

For frequencies higher than 60 cycles, formulas derived from the asymptotic expansions of Bessel functions are often convenient. Except that they do not give any effect of radiation and that they apply only to the dominant mode of transmission in a coaxial line, they are applicable to very high frequency since they are series with powers of the frequency in the denominators of the terms. As is usual with power series, their applicability depends on the rapidity with which the terms of the series become smaller and smaller.

Formulas of this type for the inner and outer conductors are given here. They are applicable to single-phase concentric circuits and the formula for the inner conductor is applicable also to all the tubular conductors of circuits which are not concentric and in which the conductors are separated by more than a few diameters. With high frequency, such circuits are more likely to occur than three-phase concentric circuits.

To express equation (20) as a power series using asymptotic expansions (see items 810.6, 810.7, 816.1, and 816.2 of footnote 7) we have

$$-\frac{I_0'(\alpha q)}{K_0'(\alpha q)} = \frac{I_1(\alpha q)}{K_1(\alpha q)}$$

$$= \frac{e^{2\alpha q}}{\pi} \frac{1 - \dfrac{3}{1!8\alpha q} - \dfrac{3 \times 5}{2!(8\alpha q)^2} - \dfrac{3^2 \times 5 \times 7}{3!(8\alpha q)^3} \cdots}{1 + \dfrac{3}{1!8\alpha q} - \dfrac{3 \times 5}{2!(8\alpha q)^2} + \dfrac{3^2 \times 5 \times 7}{3!(8\alpha q)^3} \cdots}$$

$$= \frac{e^{2\alpha q}}{\pi}\left[1 - \frac{6}{8\alpha q} + \frac{18}{(8\alpha q)^2} - \frac{204}{(8\alpha q)^3} \cdots\right]$$

$$\frac{Z_{ac}}{R_{dc}} = \frac{\alpha t(q + r)}{2r}\frac{N}{D}$$

where

$$N = e^{\alpha r}\left\{1 + \frac{1}{8\alpha r} + \frac{9}{2(8\alpha r)^2} + \frac{75}{2(8\alpha r)^3}\cdots\right\}$$

$$+ e^{2\alpha q - \alpha r}\left\{1 - \frac{1}{8\alpha r} + \frac{9}{2(8\alpha r)^2} - \frac{75}{2(8\alpha r)^3}\cdots\right\}$$

$$\left\{1 - \frac{6}{8\alpha q} + \frac{18}{(8\alpha q)^2} - \frac{204}{(8\alpha q)^3}\cdots\right\}$$

$$\text{and } D = e^{\alpha r}\left\{1 - \frac{3}{8\alpha r} - \frac{15}{2(8\alpha r)^2} - \frac{105}{2(8\alpha r)^3}\cdots\right\}$$

$$- e^{2\alpha q - \alpha r}\left\{1 + \frac{3}{8\alpha r} - \frac{15}{2(8\alpha r)^2} + \frac{105}{2(8\alpha r)^3}\cdots\right\}$$

$$\left\{1 - \frac{6}{8\alpha q} + \frac{18}{(8\alpha q)^2} - \frac{204}{(8\alpha q)^3}\cdots\right\}$$

$$\text{Then } \frac{Z_{ac}}{R_{dc}} = \frac{\alpha t(q+r)}{2r}\left[1 + \frac{4}{8\alpha r} + \frac{24}{(8\alpha r)^2} + \frac{192}{(8\alpha r)^3}\cdots\right.$$

$$+ 2e^{-2\alpha t}\left\{1 + \frac{6}{8\alpha r} + \frac{42}{(8\alpha r)^2} + \frac{348}{(8\alpha r)^3}\cdots\right\}$$

$$\left\{1 - \frac{6}{8\alpha q} + \frac{18}{(8\alpha q)^2} - \frac{204}{(8\alpha q)^3}\cdots\right\} + \text{terms in } e^{-4\alpha t}\cdots\right]$$

$$= \frac{t(q+r)}{r^2}\left[\frac{\alpha r}{2} + \frac{1}{4} + \frac{3}{16\alpha r} + \frac{3}{16\alpha^2 r^2}\cdots\right.$$

$$+ e^{-2\alpha t}\left\{\alpha r + \frac{3}{4} + \frac{21}{32\alpha r}\cdots\right\}\left\{1 - \frac{3}{4\alpha q} + \frac{9}{32\alpha^2 q^2}\cdots\right\}$$

$$\left. + \text{terms in } e^{-4\alpha t}\cdots\right]$$

omitting the final terms of the last two brackets.

$$\text{Now}\qquad \alpha = me^{j\pi/4} = m\left(\frac{1}{\sqrt{2}} + \frac{j}{\sqrt{2}}\right)$$

$$\frac{1}{\alpha} = \frac{1}{m}e^{-j\pi/4} = \frac{1}{m}\left(\frac{1}{\sqrt{2}} - \frac{j}{\sqrt{2}}\right)$$

$$\frac{1}{\alpha^2} = \frac{1}{m^2}e^{-j\pi/2} = \frac{1}{m^2}(0 - j)$$

$$e^{-2\alpha t} = e^{-mt\sqrt{2}}(\cos mt\sqrt{2} - j\sin mt\sqrt{2})$$

$$\text{(see item 408.05 of footnote 7)}$$

Taking the real part, the resistance ratio for an isolated tube is

$$\frac{R_{ac}}{R_{dc}} = \frac{t(q+r)}{r^2}\left[\frac{mr}{2\sqrt{2}} + \frac{1}{4} + \frac{3}{16mr\sqrt{2}} + \frac{0}{r^2}\cdots\right.$$

$$+ e^{-mt\sqrt{2}}(\cos mt\sqrt{2})\left\{\frac{mr}{\sqrt{2}} - \frac{3}{4}\frac{t}{q} + \frac{3}{32mr\sqrt{2}}\left(7 - 6\frac{r}{q}\right.\right.$$

$$\left.\left. + 3\frac{r^2}{q^2}\right)\cdots\right\}$$

$$+ e^{-mt\sqrt{2}}(\sin mt\sqrt{2})\left\{\frac{mr}{\sqrt{2}} - \frac{3}{32mr\sqrt{2}}\left(7 - 6\frac{r}{q}\right.\right.$$

$$\left.\left. + 3\frac{r^2}{q^2}\right)\cdots\right\} + \text{terms in } e^{-2mt\sqrt{2}}\cdots\right] \qquad (26)$$

The first line is seen to be the series that is applicable to solid wire. Formula (26) was given a number of years ago in his S.M. thesis at Massachusetts Institute of Technology by J. M. Roberts, now Professor of Electrical Engineering at the University of Louisville, Louisville, Ky.

The expansion of (25) for large values of m is not obtained by interchanging q and r in (26), for $e^{-mt\sqrt{2}}$ would become $e^{mt\sqrt{2}}$. The expansion is made by taking $K_0(\alpha q)/K_0'(\alpha q)$ as the initial part. The result is

High-frequency formula for resistance ratio of outer tube,

$$
\begin{aligned}
\frac{R_{ac}}{R_{dc}} = \frac{t(q+r)}{q^2} &\left[\frac{mq}{2\sqrt{2}} - \frac{1}{4} + \frac{3}{16mq\sqrt{2}} + \frac{0}{q^2} \cdots \right. \\
&+ e^{-mt\sqrt{2}}(\cos mt\sqrt{2}) \left\{ \frac{mq}{\sqrt{2}} - \frac{3}{4}\frac{t}{r} + \frac{3}{32mq\sqrt{2}} \left(7 - 6\frac{q}{r} \right. \right. \\
&\left. \left. + 3\frac{q^2}{r^2} \right) \cdots \right\} \\
&+ e^{-mt\sqrt{2}}(\sin mt\sqrt{2}) \left\{ \frac{mq}{\sqrt{2}} - \frac{3}{32mq\sqrt{2}} \left(7 - 6\frac{q}{r} \right. \right. \\
&\left. \left. \left. + 3\frac{q^2}{r^2} \right) \cdots \right\} + \text{terms in } e^{-2mt\sqrt{2}} \cdots \right]
\end{aligned} \qquad (27)
$$

PENETRATION FORMULA

The *penetration formula* is a well-known and useful method for computing the a-c resistance of conductors at moderately high frequencies. However, special precautions should be taken in using it for tubes, and these will now be described.

A convenient statement of the penetration formula, arranged so as to give a close approximation to the Bessel-function solution at high frequencies, is that the alternating current is taken to penetrate, at uniform current density, to a depth δ_1 and the a-c resistance is taken to be equal to the d-c resistance of a tube consisting of the surface layer of metal of thickness δ_1. The formula for the thickness is

$$
\delta_1 = \frac{\sqrt{2}}{m} \qquad \text{cm} \qquad (28)
$$

where $m = \sqrt{4\pi\omega/\rho}$ and where ρ is in abohms per centimeter cube [see equation (1)].

For an isolated round wire or tube of outside radius r, the effective resistance, then, is that of a tube of cross section

$$\pi\{r^2 - (r - \delta_1)^2\} = 2\pi r \delta_1 \left(1 - \frac{\delta_1}{2r}\right)$$

$$= \frac{2\pi r \sqrt{2}}{m} \left(1 - \frac{1}{mr \sqrt{2}}\right) \qquad (29)$$

from equation (28).

The resistance ratio by the penetration formula is the ratio of the two cross sections, which is

$$\frac{\pi(r^2 - q^2)m}{2\pi r \sqrt{2}} \left(1 - \frac{1}{mr\sqrt{2}}\right)^{-1}$$

$$= \frac{t(q + r)}{r^2} \left(\frac{mr}{2\sqrt{2}} + \frac{1}{4} + \frac{1}{4mr\sqrt{2}} + \cdots \right) \qquad (30)$$

by the binomial expansion of $(1 - x)^{-1}$.

The first two terms of the series in (30) are the same as in (26). These two terms give the equation of the straight line which is the asymptote of the curve of R_{ac}/R_{dc} plotted on mt, as in Fig. 3 of footnote 2.

In order for (30) to agree with the corresponding portion of (26) within what might be called "slide-rule accuracy," or about 0.5 per cent, it is necessary for $1/(8m^2r^2)$ to be less than 0.005. That is, mr should be greater than 5. This is equivalent to

$$\frac{\delta_1}{r} < \frac{1}{4} \qquad (31)$$

This is often expressed by stating that the penetration depth δ_1 should be a small fraction of the radius of curvature. Under such a condition it can apply in some cases to conductors that are not round.

In the case of round tubes, another requirement is found from equation (26), namely, that the penetration depth δ_1 should be a small part of the thickness t. Equation (30) plainly does not take care of the terms in $e^{-mt\sqrt{2}}$ of (26) and so, if the penetration formula is to be a good approximation, these terms should be proportionately small. This leads to the condition that

$$\frac{\delta_1}{t} < 0.3 \qquad \text{approximately} \quad (32)$$

It is obvious that if the computed penetration depth is greater than the tube thickness, the result could not be right and penetration depth should not be used. In most cases, if (32) is complied with, then the requirement of (31) also is met.

The penetration formula can be applied to the inner surface of the outer tube of a concentric circuit.

Example 2. Find the skin-effect resistance ratio for an outer tube in which $mt = 3.2$, $mq = 4.8$, and $mr = 8$.

$$\frac{q + r}{2q} = \frac{4}{3}, \qquad \alpha t = mte^{j\pi/4}$$

$$
\begin{aligned}
I_0(\alpha q) &= \text{ber } mq + j \text{ bei } mq \\
&= \text{ber } 4.8 + j \text{ bei } 4.8 \\
&= -5.45 + j\, 0.884
\end{aligned}
$$

$$
\begin{aligned}
K_0'(\alpha r) &= e^{-j\pi/4}(\text{ker}' \; 8.0 + j \text{ kei}' \; 8.0) \\
&= e^{-j\pi/4}(-0.000\,880 - j\, 0.001\,336)
\end{aligned}
$$

$$
\begin{aligned}
\frac{R_{ac}}{R_{dc}} &= \text{Re}\left\{-3.2(0 + j) \times \frac{4}{3}\right\} \frac{-0.447 \times j\, 0.376}{0.629} \\
&= 2.55 \qquad\qquad\qquad\qquad\qquad\qquad \text{by (25)}
\end{aligned}
$$

From equation (27), $\dfrac{t(q + r)}{q^2} = 1.777$

$$
\begin{aligned}
\text{1st line of (27)} &= 1.697 - 0.25 + 0.0276 \\
&= 1.475
\end{aligned}
$$

$$mt\sqrt{2} = 4.525 \qquad e^{-4.525} = 0.010\,83$$

$$\cos 4.525 = -0.1858$$

$$
\begin{aligned}
\text{2d line of (27)} &= 0.010\,83 \times (-0.1858)(3.39 - 0.30 + 0.062 \cdots) \\
&= -0.006\,34
\end{aligned}
$$

$$
\begin{aligned}
\text{3d line of (27)} &= 0.010\,83 \times (-0.983)(3.39 - 0.062) \\
&= -0.0354
\end{aligned}
$$

$$
\begin{aligned}
\frac{R_{ac}}{R_{dc}} &= 1.777(1.475 - 0.0063 - 0.0354) \\
&= 2.55 \qquad\qquad\qquad\qquad\qquad\qquad \text{by (27)}
\end{aligned}
$$

Thickness of tube in inches, for copper at 75°C and 60 cycles,

$$
\begin{aligned}
m^2 &= \frac{4\pi\omega}{\rho} = \frac{4\pi \times 120\pi}{1{,}724} \times \frac{234 + 20}{234 + 75} \\
&= 2.26 \\
m &= 1.504
\end{aligned}
$$

$$\text{Thickness} = \frac{3.2}{1.504} \times \frac{1}{2.54} = 0.838 \text{ in.}$$

$$\frac{t}{d} = \frac{3.2}{2 \times 8} = 0.2$$

$$\frac{R_{ac}}{R_{dc}} = 2.54 \qquad\qquad\qquad\qquad \text{from Fig. 3, Chap. 25}$$

By the penetration formula, the section of the equivalent tube of thickness δ_1 is

$$\pi \left\{ (q + \delta_1)^2 - q^2 \right\} = 2\pi q \delta_1 \left(1 + \frac{\delta_1}{2q} \right) = \frac{2\pi q \sqrt{2}}{m} \left(1 + \frac{1}{mq \sqrt{2}} \right) \quad \text{by (28)}$$

$$\frac{R_{ac}}{R_{dc}} = \frac{\pi t (q + r) m}{2\pi q \sqrt{2} \left(1 + \dfrac{1}{mq \sqrt{2}} \right)} = \frac{3.2 \times 12.8}{2(6.78 + 1)} = 2.63$$

which is 3 % too large.

$$\delta_1 = \frac{\sqrt{2}}{1.504} = 0.94 \qquad\qquad \text{cm or 0.37 in.}$$

$$\frac{\delta_1}{t} = \frac{0.37}{0.838} = 0.44$$

which is somewhat too large for the employment of the penetration formula.

Acknowledgment is made of work done by S. B. Vindsberg in connection with his S.M. thesis under the supervision of the writer at Massachusetts Institute of Technology, especially on the formulas and curves for the outer conductor.

CHAPTER 21

CORELESS INDUCTION FURNACE

A coreless induction furnace usually consists of a cylindrical coil wound rather closely on the outside of a crucible holding the molten charge. It is equivalent to a transformer with a solid metal secondary. Several formulas are available for calculating the electrical characteristics, and it is useful to show the relation between these formulas and the range for which each is suitable. In this chapter the formulas dealing with the Bessel-function solution and the penetration solution for the currents and flux in the charge will be discussed.[1]

In Fig. 1, let a be the average outside radius of the charge in centimeters and b, the radius of the primary coil. Assume that conditions are uniform in the direction of the axis of the cylinder, that the coil and the charge are of equal axial length, and that the permeability of the charge is unity. If the permeability

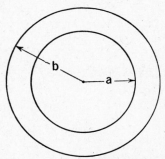

FIG. 1.—Cross section of furnace.

is not unity, then with alternating current and flux the permeability changes during every cycle, and the accuracy of a solution based on assuming constant permeability is greatly reduced.

Let the magnetic flux density between the radii a and b be $H_{(g)}$, produced by the current in the primary coil. As circumferential currents will flow in the charge in the direction opposite to the primary current, the flux density within the charge will be less than $H_{(g)}$. Let H be the flux density and i the current density in the charge in abamperes per square centimeter at radius r. Carry a unit pole so as to move 1 cm axially with the flux $H_{(g)}$ and return 1 cm against H. No work is done moving radially.

[1] Calculations for Coreless Induction Furnaces, by H. B. Dwight and M. M. Bagai, *Trans. A.I.E.E.*, Vol. 54, p. 312, 1935.

Then $$H_{(o)} - H = 4\pi \int_r^a i \, dr \qquad (1)$$

Since $H_{(o)}$ is constant, by differentiating (1),

$$\frac{dH}{dr} = 4\pi i \qquad (2)$$

The total voltage around any circle of radius r due to resistance drop and alternating flux is zero.   That is,

$$2\pi r i \rho + j\omega \int_0^r 2\pi r(-H) \, dr = 0$$

the flux in the direction in which i would drive magnetic flux, being $(-H)$. The resistivity of the charge in abohms per centimeter cube is ρ.

Substituting the value of i given by (2), and multiplying by $2/\rho$,

$$r\frac{dH}{dr} - j\frac{\omega}{\rho} \int_0^r 4\pi r H \, dr = 0$$

Differentiating, $r\dfrac{d^2H}{dr^2} + \dfrac{dH}{dr} - j\dfrac{\omega 4\pi r}{\rho} H = 0$

Put $$p^2 = \frac{-j\omega 4\pi}{\rho}$$

$$\frac{d^2H}{dr^2} + \frac{1}{r}\frac{dH}{dr} + p^2 H = 0$$

Let $pr = z$.

$$\frac{d^2H}{dz^2} + \frac{1}{z}\frac{dH}{dz} + H = 0 \qquad (3)$$

This is the standard form of Bessel's differential equation of order zero. The solution consists of Bessel functions and is

$$H = A \, I_0(mr \sqrt{j}) + B \, K_0(mr \sqrt{j}) \qquad (4)$$

putting $pr = mrj \sqrt{j}$ where $m^2 = \dfrac{4\pi\omega}{\rho}$.

A and B are constants to be determined by the boundary conditions. The function K_0 contains $\log n \, (mr \sqrt{j})$ and so is infinite when r is zero. As the magnetic flux density cannot be infinite at the center of the metallic charge, the constant B is zero. The equation then becomes

$$H = A\, I_0(mr\, \sqrt{j})$$
$$= A\, J_0(mrj\, \sqrt{j})$$
$$= A\, (\text{ber } mr + j \text{ bei } mr) \quad \text{by definition} \quad (5)$$

The constant A is found by putting $r = a$ where $H = H_{(g)}$.

$$A = \frac{H_{(g)}}{\text{ber } ma + j \text{ bei } ma} = \frac{4\pi N I_1}{l(\text{ber } ma + j \text{ bei } ma)} \quad (6)$$

where I_1 = primary current, abamp.

N = turns in the primary.

l = axial length, cm.

The voltage impressed on the primary coil is $I_1 R_{abs} + j\omega\phi N$ where R_{abs} is the resistance in abohms of the primary coil to alternating current of the given frequency and ϕ is the total flux in the circle of radius b, neglecting the thickness of the primary winding.

$$\phi = \int_{r=0}^{a} 2\pi r \frac{4\pi N I_1}{l} \frac{\text{ber } mr + j \text{ bei } mr}{\text{ber } ma + j \text{ bei } ma}\, dr + \int_{r=a}^{b} 2\pi r H_{(g)}\, dr$$
$$= \frac{8\pi^2 N I_1 a}{lm} \frac{\text{bei' } ma - j \text{ ber' } ma}{\text{ber } ma + j \text{ bei } ma} + \pi(b^2 - a^2) H_{(g)} \quad (7)$$

where ber' ma denotes differentiation with respect to ma, using the integrals

$$\int mr \text{ ber } mr\, d\, mr = mr \text{ bei' } mr$$

and

$$\int mr \text{ bei } mr\, d\, mr = -mr \text{ ber' } mr$$

Dividing the voltage by I_1 and noting that $m^2 = \dfrac{4\pi\omega}{\rho}$,

$$Z_{eff} = R_{abs} + \frac{2\pi N^2 \rho ma}{l} \frac{\text{ber' } ma + j \text{ bei' } ma}{\text{ber } ma + j \text{ bei } ma}$$
$$+ j \frac{\omega 4\pi^2 N^2}{l}(b^2 - a^2) \quad \text{abohms} \quad (8)$$

Rationalizing the denominator, and letting R = the a-c resistance of the primary coil in ohms, and ρ_1 = the resistivity of the charge in ohms per centimeter cube,

$$R_{eff} = R + \frac{2\pi N^2 \rho_1 ma}{l} \frac{\text{ber } ma \text{ ber' } ma + \text{bei } ma \text{ bei' } ma}{\text{ber}^2 ma + \text{bei}^2 ma}$$
$$\text{ohms} \quad (9)$$

$$X_{eff} = \frac{2\pi N^2 \rho_1 ma}{l} \frac{\text{ber } ma \text{ bei}' \, ma - \text{bei } ma \text{ ber}' \, ma}{\text{ber}^2 \, ma + \text{bei}^2 \, ma}$$
$$+ \frac{8\pi^3 f N^2}{l} (b^2 - a^2) 10^{-9} \quad \text{ohms} \quad (10)$$

These are in agreement with the expression following (37), p. 31, of *Theory of Eddy-current Heating*, by C. R. Burch and N. R. Davis. Heaviside determined the magnetic field in the metallic core of a solenoid in terms of Bessel functions. See *The Electrician*, May 3, 1884, p. 585, or Heaviside's "Electrical Papers," The Copley Publishers, Boston, Vol. 1, p. 360.

The series for the fractions in Bessel functions in (9) and (10) have been published [2,3] and when they are substituted the following are obtained:

When ma is less than 2,

$$R_{eff} = R + \frac{2\pi N^2 \rho_1}{l} \left(\frac{1}{2} ma\right)^4 \left[1 - \frac{11}{24} \left(\frac{1}{2} ma\right)^4 \right.$$
$$\left. + \frac{473}{2,160} \left(\frac{1}{2} ma\right)^8 - \cdots \right] \text{ohms} \quad (11)$$

$$X_{eff} = \frac{4\pi N^2 \rho_1}{l} \left(\frac{1}{2} ma\right)^2 \left[1 - \frac{1}{3} \left(\frac{1}{2} ma\right)^4 + \frac{19}{120} \left(\frac{1}{2} ma\right)^8 \right.$$
$$\left. - \cdots \right] + \frac{8\pi^3 f N^2}{l} (b^2 - a^2) 10^{-9} \text{ohms} \quad (12)$$

When ma is greater than about 4, for slide-rule accuracy,

$$R_{eff} = R + \frac{\pi N^2 \rho_1 ma \sqrt{2}}{l} \left[1 - \frac{1}{ma \sqrt{2}} - \frac{1}{8m^2 a^2} \right.$$
$$\left. + \frac{25}{128 m^4 a^4} + \cdots \right] \text{ohms} \quad (13)$$

$$X_{eff} = \frac{\pi N^2 \rho_1 ma \sqrt{2}}{l} \left[1 + \frac{1}{8m^2 a^2} + \frac{1}{4 \sqrt{2} m^3 a^3} \right.$$
$$\left. + \frac{25}{128 m^4 a^4} - \cdots \right] + \frac{8\pi^3 f N^2}{l} (b^2 - a^2) 10^{-9} \text{ohms} \quad (14)$$

When ma is between 2 and 4, values of the functions of the ber type should be taken from tables and used in equations (9) and

[2] "Theory of Alternating Currents," by A. Russell, ed. of 1914, Vol. 1, p. 211, equations (29), (30), (35), (36).

[3] Article by H. G. Savidge, *Rept. Brit. Assoc.*, 1916, pp. 114 and 115.

(10). These tables have been published in *Trans. A.I.E.E.*, 1939, p. 787, and in "Mathematical Tables," by H. B. Dwight, pp. 214 to 221, for x up to 20, and elsewhere.

Note that
$$ma = 2\pi a \sqrt{\frac{2f}{\rho_1 \times 10^9}} \tag{15}$$

where a is the radius of the charge in centimeters and ρ_1 is in ohms per centimeter cube.

An accurate experimental check on the first term of (14) has been made.[4] Sufficiently high frequencies were used so that terms in $1/(m^2a^2)$ and higher powers were negligible. Rods of copper and of alloys were used inside the primary coil. The resistivity of these cores was precisely measured with direct current, and the reactance at different frequencies was measured with alternating current. The agreement between measured and computed values was very close.

The current density at radius r in the charge is given by (2), (5), and (6) and is

$$i = \frac{1}{4\pi} \frac{d}{dr} \left[\frac{4\pi N I_1}{l} \frac{\text{ber } mr + j \text{ bei } mr}{\text{ber } ma + j \text{ bei } ma} \right]$$

$$= \frac{N I_1 m}{l} \frac{\text{ber}' mr + j \text{ bei}' mr}{\text{ber } ma + j \text{ bei } ma} \tag{16}$$

$$= \frac{N I_1 m}{l}$$

$$\frac{\text{ber } ma \, \text{ber}' mr + \text{bei } ma \, \text{bei}' mr + j(\text{ber } ma \, \text{bei}' mr - \text{bei } ma \, \text{ber}' mr)}{\text{ber}^2 ma + \text{bei}^2 ma}$$

$$\text{abamp/sq cm} \tag{17}$$

For computing numerical values, the tables of functions of the ber type may be used. If I_1 is in amperes, then i will be also.

The first two terms of the series in (13) for the effective resistance of the charge can be represented by assuming that the charge is replaced by its outermost shell of thickness

$$\delta_1 = \frac{\sqrt{2}}{m} = \frac{1}{2\pi} \sqrt{\frac{\rho_1 \times 10^9}{f}} = 5,030 \sqrt{\frac{\rho_1}{f}} \qquad \text{cm} \tag{18}$$

where ρ_1 is in ohms per centimeter cube, and by assuming that the current density is uniform throughout the shell. The

[4] Measurement of Specific Resistance by Eddy Current Shielding, by W. B. Kouwenhoven and G. P. Daiger, *Rev. Sci. Instruments*, Vol. 5, No. 2, p. 94, February, 1934.

effective resistance of the secondary can then be computed by
the following.

$$R_{eff} = \frac{\delta_1 2\pi(a - \frac{1}{2}\delta_1)}{\delta_1 l} \qquad \text{ohms} \quad (19)$$

referred to the secondary.

Substituting $\delta_1 = \sqrt{2}/m$ in (19) and multiplying by N^2 for
resistance referred to the primary, the first two terms of the
second part of (13) are obtained. This gives the resistance with
slide-rule accuracy for $ma = 6$ or larger. It is necessary to use
$2\pi(a - \frac{1}{2}\delta_1)$ for the mean perimeter of the shell and not $2\pi a$, or an
error as large as 12 per cent will be made when $ma = 6$.

The reactance is not computed by means of the shell of thickness δ_1 but by the Bessel-function calculation. However, it can
be expressed in terms of δ_1, for $ma = 6$ or larger, directly from
(14), as follows:

$$X_{eff} = \frac{2\pi a \rho_1 N^2}{\delta_1 l} + \frac{8\pi^3 f N^2}{l}(b^2 - a^2)10^{-9} \text{ ohms} \quad (20)$$

The first part of this is not quite equal to the secondary resistance,
but is 12 per cent larger when $ma = 6$, and 7 per cent larger when
$ma = 10$.

Even where the frequency is high enough for the penetration
formula to give the effective resistance with desired accuracy,
the coreless induction furnace is not in every way equivalent to a
primary coil and a shell of thickness δ_1. For instance, to assume
such a complete equivalence and to calculate flux density and
exciting current by usual transformer formulas do not seem so
safe as to compute these features by the fundamental equations
given in this chapter.

The penetration formula is used also in calculations of conductors carrying high-frequency current. It is a very useful
device but the limited extent of the equivalence of the shell of
thickness δ_1 to the actual body of metal should always be kept in
mind.

Example. Find the electrical characteristics of the following coreless
induction furnace:

Average diameter of charge, $2a = 18$ in.

Length of charge, $l = 24$ in.

Resistivity of molten iron charge, $\rho_1 = 200 \times 10^{-6}$ ohms/cm cube.

Permeability of charge, $\mu = 1$.

Diameter of coil, $2b = 25$ in.

Number of turns in coil, $N = 12$.
Frequency, 960 cycles/sec.
Resistance of coil for 960 cycles current, 0.0030 ohm.

$$ma = 2\pi \times 9 \times 2.54 \sqrt{\frac{1,920}{200,000}}$$

$$= 14.1 \qquad \text{by (15)}$$

$$R_{eff} = 0.0030 + \frac{\pi \times 144 \times 200 \times 10^{-6} \times 14.1 \times \sqrt{2}}{24 \times 2.54}$$

$$\left[1 - \frac{1}{14.1 \sqrt{2}} - \cdots \right]$$

The series in brackets $= 1 - 0.05 = 0.95$.

$$R_{eff} = 0.0030 + 0.0281 = 0.0311 \qquad \text{ohm, by (13)}$$

From this can be computed the first term of X_{eff}, which is

$$\frac{0.0281}{0.95} = 0.0296 \qquad \text{ohm}$$

$$X_{eff} = 0.0296 + \frac{8\pi^3 \times 960 \times 144 \times 3.5 \times 21.5 \times 6.45 \times 10^{-9}}{24 \times 2.54}$$

putting
$$b^2 - a^2 = (b - a)(b + a)$$
$$X_{eff} = 0.0296 + 0.273 = 0.303 \qquad \text{ohm, by (14)}$$
$$Z_{eff} = \sqrt{0.0311^2 + 0.303^2} = 0.319 \qquad \text{ohm}$$
$$\text{Power factor} = \frac{R_{eff}}{Z_{eff}} = \frac{0.0311}{0.319} = 0.098 \text{ or } 9.8\%$$
$$\text{Efficiency} = \frac{R_2}{R_1 + R_2} = \frac{0.0281}{0.0311} = 0.90 \text{ or } 90\%$$

By the penetration formula, equation (18),

$$\delta_1 = \frac{1}{2\pi} \sqrt{\frac{200,000}{960}} = 2.30 \qquad \text{cm}$$

Resistance of skin depth of charge, by (19)

$$= R_2 = \frac{200 \times 10^{-6} \times 2\pi(9 \times 2.54 - 1.15) \times 144}{2.30 \times 24 \times 2.54}$$

$$= 0.0281 \qquad \text{ohm, referred to the primary side}$$

It is to be noted that all the dimensions in the formulas are in centimeters.

CHAPTER 22

PROXIMITY EFFECT IN A RETURN CIRCUIT OF TWO ADJACENT STRAP CONDUCTORS

When two flat strap conductors, forming a return circuit for alternating current, are close together in parallel planes, that is, in the face-to-face position, the alternating magnetic field produced by their current passes through the metal and a voltage drop is produced which is not the same at all parts of the cross section. As the magnetic lines of force in this case are almost entirely in straight lines, this is one of the simplest cases of skin effect or

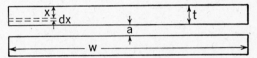

FIG. 1.—Cross section of return circuit.

proximity effect that can be computed for a practical case and compared with a measurement.[1]

Let the current density at dx (Fig. 1) in amperes per square centimeter be

$$i = a_0 + a_1x + a_2x^2 + \cdots + a_nx^n + \cdots \qquad (1)$$

Centimeter units are used. The total current between the top surface and dx is

$$I_1 = w \int_0^x i\,dx \qquad (2)$$

where w is the width of the strap.

This drives magnetic flux along the path dx and along return paths in the surrounding air which can be assumed to have a large cross section and negligible reluctance. This is similar to the case of a long solenoid, in which well-known formulas show that the reluctance for the magnetism in return paths in the

---

[1] Skin Effect of a Return Circuit of Two Adjacent Strap Conductors, by H. B. Dwight, *Elec. Jour.*, April, 1916, p. 157.

surrounding air is practically negligible. Then the flux density
at dx is

$$\frac{4\pi I_1}{10w} = \frac{4\pi}{10}\left(a_0 x + \frac{a_1 x^2}{2} + \frac{a_2 x^3}{3} + \cdots + \frac{a_n x^{n+1}}{n+1} + \cdots\right)$$

$$\text{lines/sq cm} \quad (3)$$

The flux between the inner surface of the strap and dx is

$$\varphi_1 = \int_x^t \frac{4\pi I_1}{10w}\, dx$$

The total drop in volts per centimeter of strap is

$$V = i\rho_1 + j2\pi f\varphi_1 10^{-8}$$

where f is frequency and ρ_1 is resistivity in ohms per centimeter
cube.   Note that

$$\text{Resistivity} \times \text{current density} = \text{volts/cm}$$

The current in a filament of the conductor of cross section A is iA
and the voltage drop in 1 cm of the filament is

$$iA \times \frac{\rho_1}{A} = i\rho_1$$

Performing the integration,

$$V = j8\pi^2 f 10^{-9}\left[\frac{a_0 t^2}{1 \times 2} + \frac{a_1 t^3}{2 \times 3}\right.$$
$$\left. + \cdots + \frac{a_n t^{n+2}}{(n+1)(n+2)} + \cdots\right]$$
$$- j8\pi^2 f 10^{-9}\left[\frac{a_0 x^2}{1 \times 2} + \frac{a_1 x^3}{2 \times 3}\right.$$
$$\left. + \cdots + \frac{a_n x^{n+2}}{(n+1)(n+2)} + \cdots\right]$$
$$+ \rho_1\left[a_0 + a_1 x + a_2 x^2 + \cdots + a_n x^n + \cdots\right]$$

The voltage drop V is the same for all values of x.   The current takes up such a distribution that the drop is the same for all
sections.   All the filaments of the strap in the direction of the
current flow, that is, in the direction of the length of the strap,
being parts of the same solid piece of metal, are electrically in
parallel and have the same voltage drop per centimeter or per 100

meters. Accordingly, the coefficients of x, x^2, etc., may be separately equated to zero. Thus,

$$a_1 = 0$$

$$a_2 = \frac{j8\pi^2 f 10^{-9}}{1 \times 2\rho_1} a_0$$

$$= \frac{jm^2 a_0}{1 \times 2}$$

where

$$m^2 = \frac{4\pi(2\pi f)10^{-9}}{\rho_1} \qquad (4)$$

$$a_3 = 0$$

$$a_4 = \frac{jm^2 a_2}{3 \times 4}$$

$$\dots\dots\dots\dots\dots$$

$$a_{2n} = \frac{jm^2 a_{2n-2}}{(2n-1)(2n)}$$

$$V = a_0\rho_1 + jm^2\rho_1\left[\frac{a_0 t^2}{1 \times 2} + \frac{a_2 t^4}{3 \times 4}\right.$$
$$\left. + \cdots + \frac{a_{2n} t^{2n+2}}{(2n+1)(2n+2)} + \cdots\right]$$

Putting all in terms of a_0,

$$V = a_0\rho_1\left[1 + \frac{jm^2 t^2}{2!} + \frac{(jm^2 t^2)^2}{4!} + \cdots + \frac{(jm^2 t^2)^n}{(2n)!} + \cdots\right] \qquad (5)$$

The total current is found by putting $x = t$ in equation (2) and is

$$I = w\left[a_0 t + \frac{a_2 t^3}{3} + \frac{a_4 t^5}{5} + \cdots + \frac{a_{2n} t^{2n+1}}{2n+1} + \cdots\right]$$

By putting all the coefficients in terms of a_0, we obtain

$$a_0 = \frac{I}{wt\left(1 + \dfrac{jm^2 t^2}{3!} + \dfrac{(jm^2 t^2)^2}{5!} + \cdots + \dfrac{(jm^2 t^2)^n}{(2n+1)!} + \cdots\right)}$$

Therefore, from equation (5),

$$V = \frac{I\rho_1}{wt}\frac{1 + \dfrac{jm^2 t^2}{2!} + \dfrac{(jm^2 t^2)^2}{4!} + \cdots + \dfrac{(jm^2 t^2)^n}{(2n)!} + \cdots}{1 + \dfrac{jm^2 t^2}{3!} + \dfrac{(jm^2 t^2)^2}{5!} + \cdots + \dfrac{(jm^2 t^2)^n}{(2n+1)!} + \cdots} \qquad (6)$$

Now V is the voltage drop per centimeter of length of strap, due to alternating current, and is equal to IZ_{ac} where Z_{ac} is the effective impedance. $I\rho_1/wt$ is equal to IR_{dc}, the drop due to a direct current of I amp, where R_{dc} is the resistance of the strap, per centimeter, for direct current. Therefore,

$$\frac{Z_{ac}}{R_{dc}} = \frac{1 + \dfrac{jm^2t^2}{2!} + \dfrac{(jm^2t^2)^2}{4!} + \cdots + \dfrac{(jm^2t^2)^n}{(2n)!} + \cdots}{1 + \dfrac{jm^2t^2}{3!} + \dfrac{(jm^2t^2)^2}{5!} + \cdots + \dfrac{(jm^2t^2)^n}{(2n+1)!} + \cdots} \quad (7)$$

The real component of this ratio is R_{ac}/R_{dc}, the *skin-effect resistance ratio*, that is, the ratio of the resistance for alternating current to the resistance for direct current. Proximity effect is a special case of skin effect.

The reactance is changed with change of frequency as well as the resistance, the reactance being decreased, while the resistance is increased, by an increase in frequency. The amount of this change may be computed by using the imaginary component of (7), which gives the *skin-effect reactance ratio*. This may be denoted by X_{ac}/R_{dc}, the reactance being due only to flux inside the metal.

The two series of (7) are convergent for all values of the variable and are the same as those used in the expansion of the hyperbolic cosine and sine. For large values of the argument, as with high frequency, the series may not be practically convergent in the first few terms, and in such cases methods of computing the hyperbolic sine and cosine of a complex quantity may be used.

For low frequencies, as at 60 cycles, where m^2t^2 is not greater than about 4, a shorter method than equation (7) may be used. By long division of (7), the following formulas for the ratios can be obtained:

$$\frac{R_{ac}}{R_{dc}} = 1 + \frac{m^4t^4}{45} - \frac{m^8t^8}{4,725} \cdots \quad (8)$$

$$\frac{X_{ac}}{R_{dc}} = \frac{m^2t^2}{3}\left(1 - \frac{2m^4t^4}{315} + \frac{2m^8t^8}{31,185} \cdots \right) \quad (9)$$

In order to obtain an expression for the complete inductance per centimeter of strap, including the effect of flux in the air space, a, between the straps, multiply (9) by $\dfrac{R_{dc}}{2\pi f} = \dfrac{\rho_1}{2\pi fwt}$ and add $\dfrac{2\pi a}{w} 10^{-9}$. The complete inductance, per centimeter of strap, is

$$\frac{2\pi a}{w} 10^{-9} + \frac{4\pi t}{3w} 10^{-9} \left(1 - \frac{2m^4 t^4}{315} + \frac{2m^8 t^8}{31,185} \cdots \right) \text{ henries} \quad (10)$$

using equation (4).

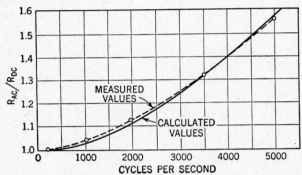

FIG. 2.—Skin-effect ratio, R_{ac}/R_{dc}. Size of copper straps, 0.159 by 3.81 cm.

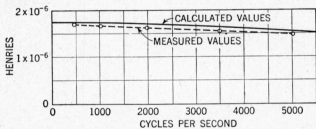

FIG. 3.—Self-inductance of circuit. Size of copper straps, 0.159 by 3.81 cm. Air space between them, 0.05 cm. Total length of strap in return circuit 6638 cm.

Precise measurements of the effective resistance and reactance of two closely adjacent strap conductors at different frequencies are to be found in Experimental Researches on Skin Effect in Conductors, by A. E. Kennelly, F. A. Laws, and P. H. Pierce, *Trans. A.I.E.E.*, 1915, p. 1970. They are shown in Figs. 2 and 3 and are seen to agree closely with values calculated by the formulas that have just been described. Each strap was 3,319 cm long, according to information furnished to the writer by the authors of the paper. That is, the inductance per centimeter of strap, computed from (10), is to be multiplied by 6,638 to obtain the inductance of the loop.

It is seen from Fig. 3 that at several thousand cycles the inductance of the medium-sized conductors is several per cent less than the maximum value, but at 60 cycles the terms in m are almost negligible and the inductance is practically equal to the maximum value.

A set of curves for the reactance of parallel strap conductors at low frequency, plotted on a base of the spacing between them, is given in Chap. 17.   The lower parts of the curves for thin straps in the face-to-face position are straight and are in agreement with equation (10).   As they begin to curve, they show that the straps are then too far apart for equation (10) to be used.

CHAPTER 23

PROXIMITY EFFECT IN WIRES

•• FINITE WIRE AND INFINITESIMAL WIRE

The current density at any point in a finite round wire which carries a current I and is in the neighborhood of an infinitesimal wire carrying I_1 was given by C. Manneback.[1] It is, using absolute electromagnetic units,

$$i_{(r\theta)} = \frac{I}{\pi a^2} \frac{j\alpha a}{2} \frac{J_0(j\alpha r)}{J_1(j\alpha a)} + \frac{I_1}{\pi a^2} j\alpha a \sum_{n=1}^{\infty} \frac{a^n}{s^n} \frac{J_n(j\alpha r)}{J_{n-1}(j\alpha a)} \cos n\theta \quad (1)$$

which r, θ = polar coordinates of the point in the wire.

a = radius of the wire.

$\alpha^2 = j4\pi\omega/\rho$.

$\omega = 2\pi \times$ frequency.

$j = \sqrt{-1}$.

ρ = resistivity in abohms per centimeter cube.

n = an integer.

s = distance from the center of the wire to the infinitesimal wire.

The quantity
$$\begin{aligned} J_n(j\alpha a) &= J_n(bj\sqrt{j}) \\ &= u_n + jv_n \\ &= \text{ber}_n\, b + j\, \text{bei}_n\, b \end{aligned}$$

is a Bessel function of the first kind, order n and argument $j\alpha a$. It can be expressed by algebraic series. If $n = 0$ or 1, tables can be used. A collection of series and tables for x up to 10 is in the author's book "Tables of Integrals and Other Mathematical Data." Values of ber x, bei x, ber' x, and bei' x, for x up to 20, are tabulated in the author's book "Mathematical Tables," pp. 214 to 221.

[1] An Integral Equation for Skin Effect in Parallel Conductors, by C. Manneback, *Jour. Math. Phys.*, April, 1922.

It is seen from equation (1) that, if the small wire is absent, $I_1 = 0$ and the first part of the expression is the current density in an isolated wire.   Since

$$\int_0^{2\pi} \cos n\theta \, d\theta = 0 \tag{2}$$

the net total of the current density caused by I_1, when added up over the section of the wire, is zero, and so the current density due to I_1 does not affect the value of I.   It is a component of current which flows along one side of the wire and back on the other side.   As both parts of expression (1) are based on the fact that the impedance drops at every point of the cross section are equal, these impedance drops remain equal when the second current density is added to the first.   Similarly, the current density due to other concentrated currents may be added.   This is often done by integration, so as to obtain the proximity effect due to conductors of finite size.

By finding an expression for the magnetic field at any point of the surface of the wire and using Poynting's theorem to find the resistance loss in the wire, the following expression for the value of the resistance ratio when $I_1 = \pm I$ is obtained:[2]

$$\frac{R_{ac}}{R_{dc}} = \frac{b}{2} \frac{(u_0 v_0' - u_0' v_0)}{(u_0'^2 + v_0'^2)} + b \sum_{n=1}^{\infty} \frac{a^{2n}}{s^{2n}} \frac{(u_n v_n' - u_n' v_n)}{(u_{n-1}^2 + v_{n-1}^2)} \tag{3}$$

where $u_n' = \dfrac{du_n}{db}$, etc.

$b = |\alpha a| = \sqrt{4\omega / R_{dc}}.$

The first part of (3) is the well-known expression for an isolated wire, and the second part gives the increase in effective resistance due to proximity effect.   When $I_1 = -I$, the two conductors form a return circuit; when $I_1 = I$, they are in parallel and carry equal currents.

• • TWO WIRES IN RETURN CIRCUIT

Let all Bessel functions used have argument

$$j\alpha a = bj \sqrt{j}$$

That is, $b = \sqrt{\dfrac{4\omega}{R_{dc}}}$

[2] For equations (3) to (5) and (7), (8), see Proximity Effect in Wires and Thin Tubes, by H. B. Dwight, *Trans. A.I.E.E.*, 1923, p. 850.

Let
$$A_0 = \frac{bj \sqrt{j}}{2J_1} = \frac{b}{2J_1}\left(\frac{-1}{\sqrt{2}} + \frac{j}{\sqrt{2}}\right)$$

$$A_1 = -\frac{a}{s}\frac{bj \sqrt{j}}{J_0}$$

$$A_2 = -\frac{a^2}{s^2}\frac{bj \sqrt{j}}{J_1}$$

$$\cdots\cdots\cdots\cdots\cdots\cdots\cdots\cdots$$

$$A_n = -\frac{a^n}{s^n}\frac{bj \sqrt{j}}{J_{n-1}} \qquad\qquad [n \neq 0]$$

$$B_n = \sum_{k=1}^{\infty} -A_k \frac{a^{n+k}}{s^{n+k}}\frac{(n+k-1)!}{(n-1)!\,k!}\frac{J_{k+1}}{J_{n-1}}$$

$$C_n = \sum_{k=1}^{\infty} -B_k \frac{a^{n+k}}{s^{n+k}}\frac{(n+k-1)!}{(n-1)!\,k!}\frac{J_{k+1}}{J_{n-1}}$$

$$\cdots\cdots\cdots\cdots\cdots\cdots\cdots\cdots$$

$$N_1 = A_1 + B_1 + C_1 + \cdots$$
$$N_n = A_n + B_n + C_n + \cdots$$

$$\frac{R_{ac}}{R_{dc}} = \frac{2}{b}|A_0|^2(u_0v_0' - u_0'v_0) + \frac{1}{b}\sum_{n=1}^{\infty}|N_n|^2(u_nv_n' - u_n'v_n) \qquad (4)$$

The first part of (4) is seen to be the ratio for an isolated wire. Values of proximity effect for wires are plotted in Fig. 6, Chap. 25.

●—● TWO WIRES IN PARALLEL

Let
$$M_1 = A_1 - B_1 + C_1 - D_1 + \cdots$$
$$M_n = A_n - B_n + C_n - D_n + \cdots$$

$$\frac{R_{ac}}{R_{dc}} = \frac{2}{b}|A_0|^2(u_0v_0' - u_0'v_0) + \frac{1}{b}\sum_{n=1}^{\infty}|M_n|^2(u_nv_n' - u_n'v_n) \qquad (5)$$

Example 1. $b = 10$, $s/a = 4$. Isolated wire, $R_{ac}/R_{dc} = 3.80$. This quantity is tabulated in Table I, Chap. 19, putting $b = ma$.
Two wires in parallel,

$$\frac{R_{ac}}{R_{dc}} = 3.80 + 0.384 = 3.80 \times 1.101$$

Finite wire and infinitesimal wire,

$$\frac{R_{ac}}{R_{dc}} = 3.80 + 0.433 = 3.80 \times 1.114$$

Two wires in return circuit,

$$\frac{R_{ac}}{R_{dc}} = 3.80 + 0.490 = 3.80 \times 1.129$$

•˙• THREE-PHASE CIRCUIT, EQUILATERAL TRIANGULAR SPACING[3]

$$A_0 = \frac{bj\sqrt{j}}{2J_1} = \frac{b}{2J_1}\left(\frac{-1}{\sqrt{2}} + \frac{j}{\sqrt{2}}\right)$$

$$A_n = -\frac{a^n}{s^n}\frac{bj\sqrt{j}}{J_{n-1}}\cos\frac{n\pi}{6}$$

$$F_n = \sqrt{3}\,\frac{a^n}{s^n}\frac{bj\sqrt{j}}{J_{n-1}}\sin\frac{n\pi}{6}$$

$$B_n = \sum_{k=1}^{\infty}\frac{a^{n+k}}{s^{n+k}}\frac{J_{k+1}}{J_{n-1}}\frac{(n+k-1)!}{(n-1)!\,k!}$$

$$\left\{-A_k\cos\frac{(n-k)\pi}{6} + \sqrt{3}\,F_k\sin\frac{(n-k)\pi}{6}\right\}$$

$$G_n = \sum_{k=1}^{\infty}\frac{a^{n+k}}{s^{n+k}}\frac{J_{k+1}}{J_{n-1}}\frac{(n+k-1)!}{(n-1)!\,k!}$$

$$\left\{\sqrt{3}\,A_k\sin\frac{(n-k)\pi}{6} + F_k\cos\frac{(n-k)\pi}{6}\right\}$$

C_n and H_n have the same formulas as B_n and G_n except change A to B and F to G, and so on.

$$M_n = A_n + B_n + C_n + \cdots$$
$$N_n = F_n + G_n + H_n + \cdots$$

$$\frac{R_{ac}}{R_{dc}} = \frac{2}{b}|A_0|^2(u_0v_0' - u_0'v_0) + \frac{1}{b}\sum_{n=1}^{\infty}\{|M_n|^2 + |N_n|^2\}(u_nv_n' - u_n'v_n)$$

$$(6)$$

Example 2. Three-conductor cable, 500,000 circ mils. Frequency, 60 cycles; $s/a = 2.5$; $b = 1.4$. Neglect the effect of the spiraling of the strands.

$$\frac{R_{ac}}{R_{dc}} = 1.020 + 0.054 = 1.074 = 1.020 \times 1.053$$

The value of $b = \sqrt{4\omega/R_{dc}}$ should be computed from R_{dc}, the resistance per centimeter of the conductor, when the conductor is stranded.

[3] See Proximity Effect in Groups of Round Wires, by H. B. Dwight, *Gen. Elec. Rev.*, November, 1927, p. 535.

The spiraling of the strands reduces the proximity effect to some extent. The current tends to follow along the strands and the eddy currents are reduced in the same way as in an armature coil with spiraled strands. It is stated by A. H. M. Arnold in *Jour. I.E.E.* (England), December, 1942, that the proximity-effect losses in stranded cables, in the absence of magnetic material, are reduced by the spirality of the strands to the same extent that they would be if the frequency were lowered 10 per cent.

••• THREE-PHASE CIRCUIT, FLAT SPACING

$$A_0 = \frac{bj \sqrt{j}}{2J_1}$$

In the following, $n \neq 0$:

$$A_{an} = A_{bn} \left\{ \cos \frac{2\pi}{3} + j \sin \frac{2\pi}{3} + \frac{1}{2^n} \left(\cos \frac{4\pi}{3} + j \sin \frac{4\pi}{3} \right) \right\}$$

$$A_{bn} = \frac{bj \sqrt{j}}{J_{n-1}} \frac{a^n}{s^n}$$

$$A_{cn} = A_{bn} \left(\cos \frac{4\pi}{3} + j \sin \frac{4\pi}{3} \right)$$

$$A_{dn} = A_{bn} \left(\frac{1}{2^n} + \cos \frac{2\pi}{3} + j \sin \frac{2\pi}{3} \right)$$

$$B_{an} = \sum_{k=1}^{\infty} \frac{J_{k+1}}{J_{n-1}} \frac{(n+k-1)!}{(n-1)! \, k!}$$

$$\left\{ \left(A_{bk} + A_{ck} \cos k\pi \right) \frac{a^{n+k}}{s^{n+k}} + A_{dk} \frac{a^{n+k}}{(2s)^{n+k}} \right\}$$

$$B_{bn} = \sum_{k=1}^{\infty} \frac{J_{k+1}}{J_{n-1}} \frac{(n+k-1)!}{(n-1)! \, k!} \, A_{ak} \frac{a^{n+k}}{s^{n+k}}$$

$$B_{cn} = \sum_{k=1}^{\infty} \frac{J_{k+1}}{J_{n-1}} \frac{(n+k-1)!}{(n-1)! \, k!} \, A_{dk} \frac{a^{n+k}}{s^{n+k}}$$

$$B_{dn} = \sum_{k=1}^{\infty} \frac{J_{k+1}}{J_{n-1}} \frac{(n+k-1)!}{(n-1)! \, k!}$$

$$\left\{ A_{ak} \frac{a^{n+k}}{(2s)^{n+k}} + \left(A_{bk} \cos k\pi + A_{ck} \right) \frac{a^{n+k}}{s^{n+k}} \right\}$$

C_{an}, C_{bn}, etc., are obtained from the same formulas as B_{an}, B_{bn}, etc., respectively, except that A is changed to B. Similarly for D_{an}, D_{bn}, etc., change B to C. This process can be continued indefinitely.

Outside conductors:

$$\text{Let} \qquad L_n = A_{an} + B_{an} + C_{an} + \cdots$$

$$\frac{R_{ac}}{R_{dc}} = \frac{2}{b} |A_0|^2 (u_0 v_0' - u_0' v_0) + \frac{1}{b} \sum_{n=1}^{\infty} |L_n|^2 (u_n v_n' - u_n' v_n) \qquad (7)$$

Middle conductor:

$$M_n = A_{bn} + B_{bn} + C_{bn} + \cdots$$
$$N_n = A_{cn} + B_{cn} + C_{cn} + \cdots$$

$$\frac{R_{ac}}{R_{dc}} = \frac{2}{b} |A_0|^2 (u_0 v_0' - u_0' v_0)$$

$$+ \frac{1}{b} \sum_{n=1}^{\infty} \{ |M_n|^2 + |N_n|^2 + (\widehat{M}_n N_n + M_n \widehat{N}_n) \cos n\pi \}$$

$$(u_n v_n' - u_n' v_n) \qquad (8)$$

$\widehat{M}_n$ is the conjugate of M_n, that is, the imaginary part of $\widehat{M}_n$ is (-1) times the imaginary part of M_n.

Putting the B's and C's $= 0$ is equivalent to assuming two of the conductors to be infinitesimal.

Example 3. 2,000,000-circ mil single-conductor cables without lead sheaths, flat spacing, 60 cycles. Neglect the effect of spiraling of the strands. $s/a = 5$, $b = 2.7$ for 75°C.

$$R_{ac}/R_{dc} = 1.228 + 0.041 = 1.228 + 1.033 \quad \text{for each outside cable}$$
$$R_{ac}/R_{dc} = 1.228 + 0.167 = 1.228 \times 1.136 \quad \text{for the middle cable}$$

GROUPS OF WIRES

In the cases so far considered, where three-phase current flows in three conductors, the total current in each conductor is known in advance. Where there are wires or conductors in parallel in a phase, the currents I_1, I_2, etc., in the wires of the same phase are not known. It is then necessary to find the voltage drop in each wire in terms of the letters I_1 and I_2. These voltage drops can be equated since the wires are in parallel.

The simplest expression to derive is that for the voltage drop in the central filament of a wire. This is, of course, equal to the drop in any other filament. Taking the case of a finite wire and an infinitesimal wire, the resistance drop in the central filament is $i_0\rho$ where i_0 is the current density at the center. From equation (1) this is equal to

$$\frac{I_1\rho}{\pi a^2}\frac{j\alpha a}{2J_1(j\alpha a)} \tag{9}$$

since $J_0(0) = 1$ and $J_n(0) = 0$ when $n \neq 0$.

The reactive drop in the central filament due to the concentrated current I_2, taking into account flux up to a certain large distance u, is

$$j\omega 2 I_2 \operatorname{logn} \frac{u}{s} \tag{10}$$

where logn denotes natural logarithm.

The reactive drop in the central filament due to the element of current $i_{(r\theta)} r\, d\theta\, dr$ is

$$j\omega 2 i_{(r\theta)}\left(\operatorname{logn}\frac{u}{r}\right) r\, d\theta\, dr = j\omega 2 \frac{I_1}{\pi a^2}\frac{j\alpha a}{2}\frac{J_0(j\alpha r)}{J_1(j\alpha a)}\left(\operatorname{logn}\frac{u}{r}\right) r\, d\theta\, dr$$

$$+ j\omega 2 \frac{I_2}{\pi a^2} j\alpha a \sum_{n=1}^{\infty}\frac{a^n}{s^n}\frac{J_n(j\alpha r)}{J_{n-1}(j\alpha a)}\cos n\theta\left(\operatorname{logn}\frac{u}{r}\right) r\, d\theta\, dr$$

from equation (1)

To find the reactive drop due to the entire current I_1, this expression is integrated from $\theta = 0$ to 2π and from $r = 0$ to a. The integral of the second member of the right-hand side of the equation is 0 and that of the first member of the right-hand side, integrating by parts, is

$$\frac{I_1\rho}{\pi a^2}\frac{j\alpha a}{2}\frac{J_0(j\alpha a)}{J_1(j\alpha a)} + j\omega 2 I_1 \operatorname{logn}\frac{u}{a} - \frac{I_1\rho}{\pi a^2}\frac{j\alpha a}{2J_1(j\alpha a)} \tag{11}$$

The impedance drop in the wire of radius a is the sum of expressions (9) to (11) and is

$$\frac{I_1\rho}{\pi a^2}\frac{j\alpha a}{2}\frac{J_0(j\alpha a)}{J_1(j\alpha a)} + j\omega 2 I_1 \operatorname{logn}\frac{u}{a} + j\omega 2 I_2 \operatorname{logn}\frac{u}{s}$$

Suppose now that in a group of several wires there is a current I_1 in wire A and a current density

$$i_{(r\theta)} = \frac{I_1}{\pi a^2} \frac{j\alpha a}{2} \frac{J_0(j\alpha r)}{J_1(j\alpha a)} + \sum_{n=1}^{\infty} M_n J_n(j\alpha r) \cos n\theta$$

In another equal wire, B, let there be a total current I_2 and a current density

$$i_{(v\varphi)} = \frac{I_2}{\pi a^2} \frac{j\alpha a}{2} \frac{J_0(j\alpha v)}{J_1(j\alpha a)} + \sum_{n=1}^{\infty} N_n J_n(j\alpha v) \cos n\varphi$$

M_n and N_n are expressions involving the unknown currents I_1, I_2, etc., and dimensions of the circuit. The foregoing expressions are of the usual form for current density in proximity effect problems involving round wires.

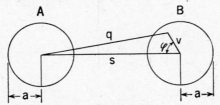

Fig. 1.—Two round wires.

The impedance drop in wire A due to its own current is the sum of (9) and (11) because the integral of the term involving M_n over the section of the wire is zero by (2).

The impedance drop in A due to current in B is

$$j\omega 2 \int_0^a \int_0^{2\pi} \frac{I_2}{\pi a^2} \frac{j\alpha a}{2} \frac{J_0(j\alpha v)}{J_1(j\alpha a)} \left(\operatorname{logn} \frac{u}{q}\right) v \, d\varphi \, dv$$

$$+ j\omega 2 \int_0^a \int_0^{2\pi} \sum_{n=1}^{\infty} N_n J_n(j\alpha v) \cos n\varphi \left(\operatorname{logn} \frac{u}{q}\right) v \, d\varphi \, dv \quad (12)$$

In Fig. 1 $\qquad q^2 = s^2 + v^2 - 2sv \cos \varphi$

$$\operatorname{logn} \left(1 - \frac{v}{s} e^{j\varphi}\right)$$

$$= -\left[\frac{v}{s}(\cos \varphi + j \sin \varphi) + \frac{v^2}{2s^2}(\cos 2\varphi + j \sin 2\varphi) + \cdots \right]$$

$$\operatorname{logn} \left(1 - \frac{v}{s} e^{-j\varphi}\right)$$

$$= -\left[\frac{v}{s}(\cos \varphi - j \sin \varphi) + \frac{v^2}{2s^2}(\cos 2\varphi - j \sin 2\varphi) + \cdots \right]$$

$$\operatorname{logn}\left(1 - \frac{2v}{s}\cos\varphi + \frac{v^2}{s^2}\right) = -2\left[\frac{v}{s}\cos\varphi + \frac{v^2}{2s^2}\cos 2\varphi + \cdots\right]$$

$$= \operatorname{logn}\frac{q^2}{s^2}$$

This gives the well-known proposition,

$$\operatorname{logn} q = \operatorname{logn} s$$
$$-\left[\frac{v}{s}\cos\varphi + \frac{v^2}{2s^2}\cos 2\varphi + \cdots + \frac{v^n}{ns^n}\cos n\varphi + \cdots\right] \quad (13)$$

When the first part of (12) is integrated from 0 to 2π, the only part of logn q that does not vanish is logn s [see equation (2)]. When the second part of (12) is integrated from 0 to 2π, the only parts that do not vanish are those involving $\cos^2 n\varphi$, since

$$\int_0^{2\pi}\cos^2 n\varphi\,d\varphi = \pi$$

Thus, the impedance drop in A due to current in B is

$$j\omega 2I_2\operatorname{logn}\frac{u}{s} + j\omega 2\sum_{n=1}^{\infty} N_n\pi a^2\,\frac{a^n}{ns^n}\,\frac{J_{n+1}(j\alpha a)}{j\alpha a} \quad (14)$$

The impedance drop in A due to all the currents is found and then the impedance drop in B and in as many wires as there are unknown currents I_1, I_2, etc. These drops can be equated and so the ratios of I_1, I_2, etc., to the total current can be found. Having found these ratios, the loss in each wire can be computed.

For any configuration, algebraic formulas are to be found, in terms of I_1, I_2, etc., for the voltage drop in each wire and also for the energy loss in each wire. Then numerical values are inserted, so as to obtain the eddy-current loss or the resistance ratio.

The results of equation (9) and following are given in the author's paper Proximity Effect in Groups of Round Wires, *Gen. Elec. Rev., November,* 1927, p. 531.

Example 4. Four Wires per Phase on a Square, Phases in a Plane. Size of conductors, 1,700,000 circ mils. Frequency, 60 cycles. Conductors have no lead sheaths. Spacing between conductors of the same phase, 3.6 in. Distance between middle and outer phases, 29 in., center to center.

In computing one phase, the currents of the other phases are taken to be concentrated at the center of each phase.

The effect of the spirality of the strands is neglected.   The conductors are called "wires" in the title, in order to indicate this.

The algebraic formulas for the middle phase are given in the paper of November, 1927, just referred to.

Results of computation for the cables of the central phase, which have greater circulating currents than those of the outer phases:

$$\text{Loss in wire 1} = 150\%$$
$$\text{Loss in wire 2} = 137\%$$

where the loss in each wire with direct current of the same amperage for each group of 4 wires = 100 %.

For cables, a value of ρ is not used, but the value of $\rho/(\pi a^2)$ is used, which is equal to the resistance per centimeter of cable.   This can be readily computed.

Example 5.   *Four Wires per Phase on Square, Phases on Equilateral Triangle.*   Conditions same as in previous example.   Distance between phases, 18 in., center to center.

There are four different unknown currents in this problem.

Losses in conductors: No. 1, 103 %; No. 2, 97 %; No. 3, 185 %; No. 4, 202 %.

Example 6.   *Four Wires on Square, in Parallel, Remote from Other Phases.* Conditions same as in previous examples.

Loss in each conductor = 139 % of the loss with direct current of the same amperage.

This is substantially the same as in practical three-phase cases, with the four conductors per phase rotated around the square, so as to transpose them.

Example 7.   *Four Wires per Phase in Plane, Phases on Triangle.*   Size of conductors, 1,700,000 circ mils.   Frequency, 60 cycle.   Conductors have no lead sheaths.   Spacing between conductors of the same phase, 3.6 in. Distance between middle and outer phase, 30 in., center to center.   Height of middle phase above centers of other two, 6 in.

There are four different unknown currents in this problem.

Results of computation for the cables of the central phase:

Losses in conductors: No. 1, 238 %; No. 2, 63 %; No. 3, 64 %; No. 4, 215 %. The loss in each conductor with direct current of the same total amperage for each group of four wires = 100 %.

CHAPTER 24

PROXIMITY EFFECT IN THIN TUBES AND SHEATHS

Thin Tube and Infinitesimal Wire. Let XMP (Fig. 1) be an extremely thin, round tube of radius a and thickness t, and let Y be a very small return conductor. The ratio of the tube thickness to the diameter is taken to be very small, so that the change in current density from the inner to the outer surface is inappreciable compared with the changes from one part of the tube to another caused by the presence of the return conductor. An expression will be derived for the current density in the tube, caused by the proximity of the current in the small wire.

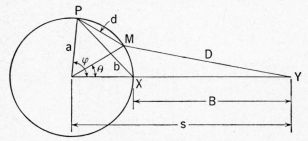

Fig. 1.—Thin tube and infinitesimal wire.

Let the current density at M be $i_{(\theta)}$, absolute electromagnetic units being used throughout. Then the resistance drop at M is $i_{(\theta)}\rho$ abvolts per centimeter, where ρ is the resistivity of the conductor. Also, let i_0 be the current density at X.

The difference between the reactance drops at X and M due to flux caused by current I_1 in the conductor Y is

$$j\omega 2I_1 \operatorname{logn} \frac{D}{B} \qquad \text{abvolts/cm}$$

where $\omega = 2\pi \times$ frequency and the distances D and B are as shown in Fig. 1.

Let the current density at P be $i_{(\varphi)}$ and the element of area of section at P be $at\, d\varphi$. The difference between the reactance

202

drops at X and M due to flux caused by the current $i_{(\varphi)}at\,d\varphi$ at P is

$$j\omega 2 \left(\operatorname{logn}\frac{d}{b}\right) i_{(\varphi)}at\,d\varphi$$

where d and b are as shown in Fig. 1.   Integrating this around the tube, the difference between the reactance drops at X and M due to current in the tube is

$$j\omega 2 \int_{\varphi=0}^{2\pi} \left(\operatorname{logn}\frac{d}{b}\right) i_{(\varphi)}at\,d\varphi$$

Adding the resistance and reactance drops and dividing by ρ,

$$i_{(\theta)} = i_0 + j\,\frac{2\omega}{\rho}\,I_1 \operatorname{logn}\frac{D}{B} + j\,\frac{2\omega}{\rho} \int_{\varphi=0}^{2\pi} \left(\operatorname{logn}\frac{d}{b}\right) i_{(\varphi)}at\,d\varphi \quad (1)$$

This is the same as equation (5) in the paper by C. Manneback on proximity effect in wire.[1]   Let

$$l^2 = \frac{2\pi at\omega}{\rho}$$

Then
$$j\,\frac{2\omega}{\rho} = \frac{jl^2}{\pi at}$$

$$B = XY = s - a$$
$$d^2 = MP^2 = a^2 + a^2 - 2a^2 \cos(\varphi - \theta)$$
$$b^2 = XP^2 = a^2 + a^2 - 2a^2 \cos\varphi$$
$$D^2 = YM^2 = s^2 + a^2 - 2sa \cos\theta$$

From equation (13), Chap. 23,

$$\operatorname{logn}\frac{d}{a} = -\left\{\cos(\varphi - \theta) + \frac{1}{2}\cos 2(\varphi - \theta)\right.$$

$$\left. + \cdots + \frac{1}{n}\cos n(\varphi - \theta) + \cdots\right\} \quad (2)$$

$$\operatorname{logn}\frac{b}{a} = -\left\{\cos\varphi + \frac{1}{2}\cos 2\varphi + \cdots + \frac{1}{n}\cos n\varphi + \cdots\right\} \quad (3)$$

$$\operatorname{logn}\frac{D}{s} = -\left\{\frac{a}{s}\cos\theta + \frac{a^2}{2s^2}\cos 2\theta + \cdots + \frac{a^n}{ns^n}\cos n\theta + \cdots\right\} \quad (4)$$

---

[1] An Integral Equation for Skin Effect in Parallel Conductors, by C. Manneback, *Jour. Math. Phys.*, April, 1922.

First, let the effect of the current I_1 be neglected, and put

$$i_{(\varphi)} = i_0$$

Then $i_{(\theta)} = i_0 + \dfrac{jl^2}{\pi at} \displaystyle\int_{\varphi=0}^{2\pi} \left(\operatorname{logn} \dfrac{d}{a} - \operatorname{logn} \dfrac{b}{a}\right) i_0 at\, d\varphi$

Using series (2) and (3), all the terms of the integrals are zero and $i_{(\theta)} = i_0$, as is expected when the effect of a current I_1 is omitted.

Now, for the present, neglect the effect of i_0 and find a value of $i_{(\theta)}$ which will balance the effect of I_1, making the voltage drop the same at all parts of the section.

$$i_{(\theta)} = \dfrac{jl^2}{\pi at} I_1 \left(\operatorname{logn} \dfrac{D}{s} + \operatorname{logn} \dfrac{s}{s-a}\right) + \dfrac{jl^2}{\pi at} \int_{\varphi=0}^{2\pi} \left(\operatorname{logn} \dfrac{d}{b}\right) i_{(\varphi)} at\, d\varphi$$

The nth term of $\operatorname{logn} \dfrac{D}{s}$ is $-\dfrac{a^n}{ns^n} \cos n\theta$. Find a solution $i_{n(\theta)}$ of the equation

$$i_{n(\theta)} = -\dfrac{jl^2}{\pi at} \dfrac{I_1 a^n}{ns^n} \cos n\theta + \dfrac{jl^2}{\pi at} \int_{\varphi=0}^{2\pi} \left(\operatorname{logn} \dfrac{d}{b}\right) i_{(\varphi)} at\, d\varphi \quad (5)$$

Let $\qquad i_{n(\theta)}{}^{(1)} = -\dfrac{jl^2}{n} \dfrac{I_1}{\pi at} \dfrac{a^n}{s^n} \cos n\theta \quad (6)$

Let $i_{n(\theta)}{}^{(2)} = i_{n(\theta)}{}^{(1)} + \dfrac{jl^2}{\pi at} \displaystyle\int_{\varphi=0}^{2\pi} \left(\operatorname{logn} \dfrac{d}{a} - \operatorname{logn} \dfrac{b}{a}\right) i_{n(\varphi)}{}^{(1)} at\, d\varphi \quad (7)$

$$= i_{n(\theta)}{}^{(1)} + \left(\dfrac{jl^2}{\pi at}\right)^2 \dfrac{I_1 a^n}{ns^n} \int_{\varphi=0}^{2\pi} \cos n\varphi \left[\sum_{k=1}^{\infty} \dfrac{\cos k(\varphi - \theta)}{k} - \sum_{k=1}^{\infty} \dfrac{\cos k\varphi}{k}\right] at\, d\varphi$$

Now $\quad \cos A \cos B = \tfrac{1}{2} \cos (A + B) + \tfrac{1}{2} \cos (A - B)$

The integrals of all the terms are zero except when $k = n$.

$$i_{n(\theta)}{}^{(2)} = i_{n(\theta)}{}^{(1)} + \left(\dfrac{jl^2}{\pi at}\right)^2 \dfrac{I_1 a^n}{ns^n} \int_{\varphi=0}^{2\pi} \left(\dfrac{\cos n\theta}{2n} - \dfrac{1}{2n}\right) at\, d\varphi$$

$$= i_{n(\theta)}{}^{(1)} + \left(\dfrac{jl^2}{\pi at}\right)^2 \dfrac{I_1 a^n}{ns^n} \left(\dfrac{\pi \cos n\theta}{n} - \dfrac{\pi}{n}\right) at$$

$$i_{n(\theta)}{}^{(2)} = i_{n(\theta)}{}^{(1)} - \dfrac{jl^2}{n} i_{n(\theta)}{}^{(1)} - \left(\dfrac{jl^2}{n}\right)^2 \dfrac{I_1}{\pi at} \dfrac{a^n}{s^n} \; \text{[from (6)]} \quad (8)$$

Put $i_{n(\theta)}{}^{(3)} = i_{n(\theta)}{}^{(1)} + \dfrac{jl^2}{\pi at} \displaystyle\int_{\varphi=0}^{2\pi} \left(\operatorname{logn} \dfrac{d}{a} - \operatorname{logn} \dfrac{b}{a}\right) i_{n(\varphi)}{}^{(2)} at\, d\varphi$

$\qquad = i_{n(\theta)}{}^{(2)} - \dfrac{jl^2}{n}\dfrac{jl^2}{\pi at} \displaystyle\int_{\varphi=0}^{2\pi} \left(\operatorname{logn} \dfrac{d}{a} - \operatorname{logn} \dfrac{b}{a}\right) i_{n(\varphi)}{}^{(1)} at\, d\varphi$

$\qquad - \left(\dfrac{jl^2}{n}\right)^2 \dfrac{jl^2}{\pi at} \displaystyle\int_{\varphi=0}^{2\pi} \left(\operatorname{logn} \dfrac{d}{a} - \operatorname{logn} \dfrac{b}{a}\right) \dfrac{I_1}{\pi at}\dfrac{a^n}{s^n}\, at\, d\varphi \quad \text{from (7)}$

The last integral is zero.

$i_{n(\theta)}{}^{(3)} = i_{n(\theta)}{}^{(2)} + \left(\dfrac{jl^2}{n}\right)^2 i_{n(\theta)}{}^{(1)} + \left(\dfrac{jl^2}{n}\right)^3 \dfrac{I_1}{\pi at}\dfrac{a^n}{s^n} \qquad \text{as in} \quad (8)$

$\qquad = i_{n(\theta)}{}^{(1)} \left[1 - \dfrac{jl^2}{n} + \left(\dfrac{jl^2}{n}\right)^2\right] - \left(\dfrac{jl^2}{n}\right)^2 \dfrac{I_1}{\pi at}\dfrac{a^n}{s^n}\left[1 - \dfrac{jl^2}{n}\right] \quad (9)$

Similarly, $i_{n(\theta)}{}^{(4)} = i_{n(\theta)}{}^{(3)} - \left(\dfrac{jl^2}{n}\right)^3 i_{n(\theta)}{}^{(1)} - \left(\dfrac{jl^2}{n}\right)^4 \dfrac{I_1}{\pi at}\dfrac{a^n}{s^n}$

$\qquad = i_{n(\theta)}{}^{(1)} \left[1 - \dfrac{jl^2}{n} + \left(\dfrac{jl^2}{n}\right)^2 - \left(\dfrac{jl^2}{n}\right)^3\right]$

$\qquad\qquad - \left(\dfrac{jl^2}{n}\right)^2 \dfrac{I_1}{\pi at}\dfrac{a^n}{s^n}\left[1 - \dfrac{jl^2}{n} + \left(\dfrac{jl^2}{n}\right)^2\right]$

If this process is continued indefinitely, the value of $i_{n(\theta)}$ is given by infinite series, provided the values of l and n are such as to make the series convergent. Since n is equal to 1 or greater, the series give the value of $i_{n(\theta)}$ for l less than 1. The sum of the infinite series is

$$\frac{1}{1 + \dfrac{jl^2}{n}}$$

Thus, $i_{n(\theta)} = -\dfrac{I_1}{\pi at}\dfrac{a^n}{ns^n}\dfrac{jl^2}{1+\dfrac{jl^2}{n}} \cos n\theta - \dfrac{I_1}{\pi at}\dfrac{jl^2}{n}\dfrac{a^n}{ns^n}\dfrac{jl^2}{1+\dfrac{jl^2}{n}} \quad (10)$

The value of $i_{(\theta)}$ which will balance the effect of I_1 is

$\dfrac{jl^2 I_1}{\pi at} \displaystyle\sum_{n=1}^{\infty} \dfrac{a^n}{ns^n} - \dfrac{jl^2 I_1}{\pi at} \displaystyle\sum_{n=1}^{\infty} \dfrac{a^n}{ns^n}\dfrac{jl^2}{n+jl^2} - \dfrac{I_1}{\pi at} \displaystyle\sum_{n=1}^{\infty} \dfrac{a^n}{ns^n}\dfrac{jl^2}{1+\dfrac{jl^2}{n}} \cos n\boldsymbol{\theta}$

$\qquad\qquad = \dfrac{jl^2 I_1}{\pi at} \displaystyle\sum_{n=1}^{\infty} \dfrac{a^n}{ns^n}\dfrac{1}{1+\dfrac{jl^2}{n}} (1 - \cos n\theta) \quad (11)$

To this must be added the quantity i_0 to obtain the total value of $i_{(\theta)}$.

$$i_{(\theta)} = i_0 + \frac{I_1}{2\pi a t} \sum_{n=1}^{\infty} \frac{a^n}{s^n} \frac{2jl^2}{n + jl^2} (1 - \cos n\theta) \qquad (12)$$

If I_1, the current in the infinitesimal conductor, is a return current for that in the tube, then the latter is

$$I = -I_1 = \int_0^{2\pi} i_{(\theta)} at \, d\theta = 2\pi a t i_0 - I \sum_{n=1}^{\infty} \frac{a^n}{s^n} \frac{2jl^2}{(n + jl^2)}$$

Then, $i_0 = \frac{I}{2\pi a t} \left[1 + \sum_{n=1}^{\infty} \frac{a^n}{s^n} \frac{2jl^2}{(n + jl^2)} \right] \qquad (13)$

and $i_{(\theta)} = \frac{I}{2\pi a t} \left[1 + \sum_{n=1}^{\infty} \frac{a^n}{s^n} \frac{2jl^2}{(n + jl^2)} \cos n\theta \right] \qquad (14)$

This value of $i_{(\theta)}$ should now be checked by writing $i_{(\varphi)}$ in accordance with it and substituting in the original equation (1). The value of i_0 is given by (13) and of $i_{(\varphi)}$ by (14), changing θ to φ.

$$\operatorname{logn} \frac{D}{B} = \operatorname{logn} \frac{D}{s} - \operatorname{logn} \frac{B}{s} = \sum_{n=1}^{\infty} \frac{a^n}{ns^n} (1 - \cos n\theta)$$

$$\operatorname{logn} \frac{d}{b} = \operatorname{logn} \frac{d}{a} - \operatorname{logn} \frac{b}{a} \quad \text{using (2) and (3)}$$

Substituting all these in (1) and carrying out the integration, equation (14) is obtained.

This furnishes a check on (14) and further shows that it applies for all frequencies, that is, for all values of l. Although the expression was derived by means of series which were convergent for l less than 1, the expression (14) itself is a convergent series for all values of l, that is, for all frequencies, so long as a/s is less than 1, and it has been shown to satisfy the fundamental equations of the problem, irrespective of the value of l.

It is now desired to find an expression for R_{ac}/R_{dc}.

$$R_{dc} = \frac{\rho}{2\pi a t}$$

$$R_{ac} = \frac{1}{I^2} \int_{\theta=0}^{2\pi} i_{(\theta)} at \, d\theta \, \hat{\imath}_{(\theta)} at \, d\theta \, \frac{\rho}{at \, d\theta}$$

where $\hat{\imath}_{(\theta)}$ is the conjugate of $i_{(\theta)}$, that is, it is the same except that j is replaced by $-j$. The integration of the product of the two series is similar to that used in deriving (8), all the terms being zero except when the coefficients taken from the two series are alike.

$$\frac{R_{ac}}{R_{dc}} = \frac{2\pi at}{I^2} \frac{I^2 at}{(2\pi at)^2}\left[2\pi + \sum_{n=1}^{\infty} \frac{\pi a^{2n}}{s^{2n}} \frac{2jl^2}{(n+jl^2)} \frac{(-2jl^2)}{(n-jl^2)}\right]$$

$$\frac{R_{ac}}{R_{dc}} = 1 + \sum_{n=1}^{\infty} \frac{a^{2n}}{s^{2n}} \frac{2l^4}{l^4 + n^2} \tag{15}$$

For infinite frequency, $\dfrac{R_{ac}}{R_{dc}} = 1 + \dfrac{2a^2}{s^2 - a^2}$

These formulas apply when the two conductors form a return circuit and also when they carry equal currents in parallel and are remote from other conductors.

Example 1. $s/a = 4$, $l = 1$, $R_{ac}/R_{dc} = 1.0641$.

Two Thin Tubes in Return Circuit.   For the case of two thin tubes, an element of current at P_2 (Fig. 2) is $i_{(\gamma)}at\ d\gamma$.   The

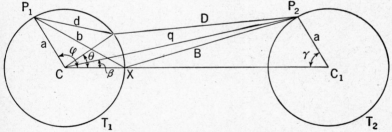

Fig. 2.—Two thin tubes in return circuit.

current density $i_{(\gamma)}$ is taken to be constant at first.   The following series expansions are required:

$$\operatorname{logn} \frac{B}{q} = -\sum_{n=1}^{\infty} \frac{a^n}{nq^n} \cos n\beta$$

$$\operatorname{logn} \frac{D}{q} = -\sum_{n=1}^{\infty} \frac{a^n}{nq^n} \cos n(\beta - \theta)$$

$$\operatorname{logn} \frac{q}{s} = -\sum_{n=1}^{\infty} \frac{a^n}{ns^n} \cos n\gamma$$

$$\frac{\cos n\beta}{q^n} = \frac{1}{s^n}\left[1 + \sum_{k=1}^{\infty} \frac{(n+k-1)!}{(n-1)!\,k!}\frac{a^k}{s^k}\cos k\gamma\right]$$

$$\frac{\sin n\beta}{q^n} = \frac{1}{s^n}\sum_{k=1}^{\infty} \frac{(n+k-1)!}{(n-1)!\,k!}\frac{a^k}{s^k}\sin k\gamma$$

The same process for finding $i_{(\theta)}$ is gone through as for a thin tube and an infinitesimal wire, and when $i_{(\gamma)}$ is constant the same result is obtained, namely, equation (14). This is to be expected, for a round tube or wire with uniform current density has the same external effect as if the current were concentrated at its center.

Now assume that there is the same current density in tube T_2 as has just been computed for tube T_1, and the resulting current density in T_1 can be found. This again can be assumed for T_2. The process gives a symmetrical sequence of expressions. The expression for R_{ac}/R_{dc} is obtained by direct integration, as in the previous case. The result is

$$A_n = \frac{2a^n}{s^n}\frac{(l^4 + jl^2 n)}{(l^4 + n^2)}$$

$$B_n = \frac{1}{2}A_n \sum_{k=1}^{\infty} \frac{a^k}{s^k}A_k\frac{(n+k-1)!}{(n-1)!\,k!}$$

$$C_n = \frac{1}{2}A_n \sum_{k=1}^{\infty} \frac{a^k}{s^k}B_k\frac{(n+k-1)!}{(n-1)!\,k!}$$

$$D_n = \frac{1}{2}A_n \sum_{k=1}^{\infty} \frac{a^k}{s^k}C_k\frac{(n+k-1)!}{(n-1)!\,k!}$$

and so on:

$$N_1 = A_1 + B_1 + C_1 + \cdots$$
$$N_2 = A_2 + B_2 + C_2 + \cdots$$
$$\dots\dots\dots\dots\dots\dots\dots\dots\dots$$
$$N_n = A_n + B_n + C_n + \cdots$$
$$\dots\dots\dots\dots\dots\dots\dots\dots\dots$$

$$\frac{R_{ac}}{R_{dc}} = 1 + \frac{1}{2}|N_1|^2 + \frac{1}{2}|N_2|^2 + \cdots + \frac{1}{2}|N_n|^2 + \cdots \quad (16)$$

The value of 0! is taken to be 1.

Values of proximity effect for two tubes are plotted in Fig. 7, Chap. 25.

Example 2. $s/a = 4$, $l = 1$, $R_{ac}/R_{dc} = 1.0685$. The same value was obtained by the low-frequency computation given by the author in *Trans. A.I.E.E.*, 1922.

Two Thin Tubes in Parallel. This case is the same as the preceding one except that the currents in the two tubes are equal and of the same sign.

Let A_1, B_1, $\cdots$ A_n, B_n, C_n, etc., have the same values as for two thin tubes in a return circuit.

$$M_1 = A_1 - B_1 + C_1 - D_1 + \cdots$$
$$M_2 = A_2 - B_2 + C_2 - D_2 + \cdots$$
$$\cdots\cdots\cdots\cdots\cdots\cdots\cdots\cdots\cdots\cdots\cdots\cdots$$
$$M_n = A_n - B_n + C_n - D_n + \cdots$$
$$\cdots\cdots\cdots\cdots\cdots\cdots\cdots\cdots\cdots\cdots\cdots\cdots$$

$$\frac{R_{ac}}{R_{dc}} = 1 + \frac{1}{2}|M_1|^2 + \frac{1}{2}|M_2|^2 + \cdots + \frac{1}{2}|M_n|^2 + \cdots \quad (17)$$

Example 3. $s/a = 4$, $l = 1$, $R_{ac}/R_{dc} = 1.0600$.

PROXIMITY EFFECT IN OPEN-CIRCUITED SHEATHS OF SINGLE-CONDUCTOR CABLES

Open-circuited Sheaths in Single-phase Circuit. The cable inside the sheath is replaced by a solid wire of the same resistance, of radius a and of resistivity ρ_c. Its current density is taken to be uniform. The return cable and its sheath are represented by an infinitesimal wire.

Mean radius of sheath $= c$
Thickness of sheath $\quad = t$
Resistivity of sheath $\quad = \rho_s$

$$l^2 = \frac{2\pi c t \omega}{\rho_s}$$

$$\frac{\text{Loss in sheath}}{\text{Loss in cable at zero frequency}} = \frac{a^2}{ct}\frac{\rho_s}{\rho_c}\sum_{n=1}^{\infty}\frac{c^{2n}}{s^{2n}}\frac{l^4}{(l^4 + n^2)} \quad (18)$$

Open-circuited Sheaths in Three-phase Circuit, Flat Spacing. Two cables and their sheaths represented by infinitesimal wires. Axial spacing $= s$.

$\odot$ · · *Outside conductors:*

$$\frac{\text{Loss in sheath}}{\text{Loss in cable at zero frequency}}$$

$$= \frac{a^2}{ct}\frac{\rho_s}{\rho_c}\sum_{n=1}^{\infty}\left(1 - \frac{1}{2^n} + \frac{1}{2^{2n}}\right)\frac{c^{2n}}{s^{2n}}\frac{l^4}{(l^4+n^2)} \quad (19)$$

· $\odot$ · *Middle conductor:*

$$\frac{\text{Loss in sheath}}{\text{Loss in cable at zero frequency}}$$

$$= \frac{a^2}{ct}\frac{\rho_s}{\rho_c}\sum_{n=1}^{\infty}(2 - \cos n\pi)\frac{c^{2n}}{s^{2n}}\frac{l^4}{(l^4+n^2)} \quad (20)$$

Example 4.   2,000,000-circ mil single-conductor cables with lead sheaths, 60 cycles.

$$c = 2.97 \text{ cm} \qquad t = 0.357 \text{ cm} \qquad s = 10.7 \text{ cm}$$
$$c/s = 0.278 \qquad \rho_s = 25,000 \text{ at } 75°C$$
$$l^2 = 0.1005 \qquad \rho_c = 2100 \text{ at } 75°C$$

$$\frac{\text{Loss in sheath}}{\text{Loss in cable at zero frequency}} = 2.8\% \text{ for single phase circuit}$$

$$= 2.1\% \text{ for three-phase circuit, flat spacing, outside conductor}$$
$$= 8.4\% \text{ for three-phase circuit, flat spacing, middle conductor}$$

The results in (1) to (20) are from the author's paper Proximity Effect in Wires and Thin Tubes, *Trans. A.I.E.E.* 1923, p. 850.

PROXIMITY EFFECT IN BONDED SHEATHS OF SINGLE-CONDUCTOR CABLES

Bonded Sheaths in Single-phase Circuit.   When the sheaths of single-conductor cables are bonded or grounded at more than one point, they form closed circuits through which may pass comparatively heavy currents, induced by the main currents in the power conductors.   Using the same notation as for (18), let

$$P = \frac{-j\omega \log_n \frac{s}{c}}{j\omega 2 \log_n \frac{s}{c} + \frac{\rho_s}{2\pi ct}}$$

$$A = 0$$

$$F_n = jl^2(1 + 2P)\frac{c^n}{ns^n}$$

$$B = jl^2 \left[-2A \log n \frac{s}{c} + \sum_{k=1}^{\infty} \frac{c^k}{ks^k} F_k \right]$$

$$G_n = jl^2 \left[2A \frac{c^n}{ns^n} - \frac{F_n}{n} + \frac{c^n}{ns^n} \sum_{k=1}^{\infty} \frac{(n+k-1)!}{(n-1)! \, k!} \frac{c^k}{s^k} F_k \right]$$

For C and H_n use the formulas for B and G_n, respectively, except change A to B and F to G.   Similarly for D and I_n change A to C and F to H, and so on.

$$N = P + B + C + \cdots$$
$$Q_n = F_n + G_n + H_n + \cdots$$

$$\frac{\text{Loss in sheath}}{\text{Loss in conductor at zero frequency}}$$

$$= \frac{a^2}{ct} \frac{\rho_s}{\rho_c} \left[2 \, |N|^2 + \sum_{n=1}^{\infty} |Q_n|^2 \right] \quad (21)$$

For an approximate formula, use

$$\frac{2a^2}{ct} \frac{\rho_s}{\rho_c} |P|^2 \quad (22)$$

By writing an expression for $i_{(\varphi)}$ in terms of N and Q_n, inserting in (1), multiplying by ρ_c, and integrating, the effective impedance of the conductor with short-circuited sheath in a single-phase circuit is found to be

$$R_c + jX_c + j\omega 4N \log n \frac{s}{c} - j\omega 2 \sum_{n=1}^{\infty} \frac{c^n}{ns^n} Q_n \qquad \text{abohms/cm} \quad (23)$$

where R_c and X_c are the resistance and reactance of the power conductor without sheath. N and Q_n are complex quantities. If the value of (23) is found in numbers, the real part is the effective resistance and the j part is the effective reactance.   The effective resistance is in agreement with the value of loss in the sheath as given by (21) plus loss in the conductor at zero frequency.

By putting $N = P$ and $Q_n = 0$, the following well-known formulas are obtained, applicable to uniform current density:

$$\text{Effective resistance} = R_c + \frac{R_s X_m{}^2}{R_s{}^2 + X_m{}^2} \tag{24}$$

$$\text{Effective reactance} = X_c - \frac{X_m{}^3}{R_s{}^2 + X_m{}^2} \tag{25}$$

where X_m is the mutual reactance of the sheath and the conductor and is given by

$$X_m = \omega 2 \log n \frac{s}{c} \qquad\qquad \text{abohms/cm}$$

$$= 2\pi f \frac{140}{10^6} \log_{10} \frac{s}{c} \quad \text{ohms/1,000 ft of cable}$$

where f = frequency. The second part of (24) is the same as (22).

Example 5. 2,000,000-circ mil single-conductor cables, single-phase circuit, 60 cycles, $c = 2.97$ cm, $t = 0.357$ cm = thickness of lead sheath, $s = 6.30$ cm (lead sheaths touching), $a = 1.796$ cm, $\rho_c = 2{,}100$, $\rho_s = 25{,}000$, $l^2 = 0.1005$.

$$\frac{\text{Loss in sheath}}{\text{Loss in conductor at zero frequency}} = 49\% \qquad \text{by (21)}$$

The result by the approximate formula (22) or (24) is 41%.

Bonded Sheaths in Three-phase Circuit, Equilateral Triangular Spacing.

$$A_0 = -jl^2 \log n \frac{s}{c}$$

$$A_n = jl^2 \frac{c^n}{ns^n} \left(\frac{1}{2} - j\frac{\sqrt{3}}{2} \right) \qquad\qquad [n \neq 0]$$

$$F_n = jl^2 \frac{c^n}{ns^n} \left(\frac{1}{2} + j\frac{\sqrt{3}}{2} \right)$$

$$B_0 = jl^2 \left[-2A_0 \log n \frac{s}{c} + \left(\frac{1}{2} - j\frac{\sqrt{3}}{2} \right) \sum_{k=1}^{\infty} \frac{c^k}{ks^k} \left(A_k \cos \frac{k\pi}{3} + F_k \right) \right. $$

$$\left. + \left(\frac{1}{2} + j\frac{\sqrt{3}}{2} \right) \sum_{k=1}^{\infty} \frac{c^k}{ks^k} \left(A_k + F_k \cos \frac{k\pi}{3} \right) \right]$$

$$B_n = jl^2 \left[2A_0 \frac{c^n}{ns^n} \left(\frac{1}{2} - j\frac{\sqrt{3}}{2} \right) - \frac{A_n}{n} \right.$$

$$\left. + \left(\frac{1}{2} - j\frac{\sqrt{3}}{2} \right) \frac{c^n}{ns^n} \sum_{k=1}^{\infty} \frac{(n+k-1)!}{(n-1)! \, k!} \frac{c^k}{s^k} \left(A_k \cos \frac{k\pi}{3} + F_k \right) \right]$$

$$G_n = jl^2 \left[2A_0 \frac{c^n}{ns^n} \left(\frac{1}{2} + j \frac{\sqrt{3}}{2} \right) - \frac{F_n}{n} \right.$$

$$\left. + \left(\frac{1}{2} + j \frac{\sqrt{3}}{2} \right) \frac{c^n}{ns^n} \sum_{k=1}^{\infty} \frac{(n+k-1)!}{(n-1)!\,k!} \frac{c^k}{s^k} \left(A_k + F_k \cos \frac{k\pi}{3} \right) \right]$$

In the above formulas n is not equal to zero. For C_0, C_n, and H_n use the formulas for B_0, B_n, and G_n, respectively, except change A to B and F to G. Similarly for D_0, D_n, and I_n change A to C and F to H, and so on.

$$M_0 = A_0 + B_0 + C_0 + \cdots$$
$$M_n = A_n + B_n + C_n + \cdots$$
$$N_n = F_n + G_n + H_n + \cdots$$

$$\frac{\text{Loss in sheath}}{\text{Loss in conductor at zero frequency}} = \frac{a^2}{ct} \frac{\rho_s}{\rho_c} \left[2\,|M_0|^2 \right.$$

$$\left. + \sum_{n=1}^{\infty} \left\{ |M_n|^2 + |N_n|^2 + (\widehat{M}_n N_n + M_n \widehat{N}_n) \cos \frac{n\pi}{3} \right\} \right] \quad (26)$$

$\widehat{M}_n$ is the conjugate of M_n, that is, it is the same as M_n except that j is changed to $-j$.

For an approximate formula, use

$$\frac{2a^2}{ct} \frac{\rho_s}{\rho_c} |A_0|^2 \quad\quad (27)$$

Example 6. 1,000,000-circ mil single-conductor cables, three-phase circuit, equilateral triangular spacing, sheaths short-circuited together, 60 cycles. $c = 2.16$ cm, $t = 0.277$ cm, $s = 4.60$ cm (lead sheaths touching), $c/s = 0.470$, $\rho_c = 2,100$ at 75°C, $\rho_s = 25,000$, $l^2 = 0.0566$, $a = 1.270$ cm.

$$\frac{\text{Loss in sheath}}{\text{Loss in conductor at zero frequency}} = 15.4\%$$

The result by the approximate formula (27) is 11.7%.

Bonded Sheaths in Three-phase Circuit, Flat Spacing. The calculation for flat spacing is based on the sheaths being short-circuited together by bonds but not on there being a ground return. The unbalanced drop results in a slight voltage in the circuit. Because of the large difference between the middle and the outer conductors, the formula for equilateral triangular spacing should not be used for the case of flat spacing.

$$e^{j2\pi/3} = -\frac{1}{2} + j\frac{\sqrt{3}}{2}$$

$$e^{j4\pi/3} = -\frac{1}{2} - j\frac{\sqrt{3}}{2}$$

$$A_{a0} = jl^2 \left[\frac{1}{3} e^{j2\pi/3} \operatorname{logn} 2 + e^{j2\pi/3} \operatorname{logn} \frac{s}{c} + e^{j4\pi/3} \operatorname{logn} \frac{2s}{c} \right]$$

$$A_{b0} = jl^2 \left[\frac{1}{3} e^{j2\pi/3} \operatorname{logn} 2 + \operatorname{logn} \frac{s}{c} + e^{j4\pi/3} \operatorname{logn} \frac{s}{c} \right]$$

$$A_{c0} = jl^2 \left[\frac{1}{3} e^{j2\pi/3} \operatorname{logn} 2 + \operatorname{logn} \frac{2s}{c} + e^{j2\pi/3} \operatorname{logn} \frac{s}{c} \right]$$

$$A_{an} = A_{bn} \left(e^{j2\pi/3} + \frac{1}{2^n} e^{j4\pi/3} \right) \qquad\qquad [n \neq 0]$$

$$A_{bn} = -jl^2 \frac{c^n}{ns^n}$$

$$A_{cn} = A_{bn} e^{j4\pi/3}$$

$$A_{dn} = A_{bn} \left(\frac{1}{2^n} + e^{j2\pi/3} \right)$$

$$K_2 = \frac{2}{3} A_{b0} \operatorname{logn} 2 + \frac{1}{3} \sum_{k=1}^{\infty} \frac{c^k}{ks^k} \left\{ A_{ak} + A_{bk} + A_{ck} + A_{dk} \right.$$
$$\left. + \frac{1}{2^k} (A_{ak} + A_{dk}) + (-1)^k (A_{bk} + A_{ck}) \right\}$$

$$B_{a0} = jl^2 \left[K_2 - 2A_{a0} \operatorname{logn} \frac{s}{c} + 2A_{c0} \operatorname{logn} 2 \right.$$
$$\left. - \sum_{k=1}^{\infty} \frac{c^k}{ks^k} \left\{ A_{bk} + (-1)^k A_{ck} + \frac{A_{dk}}{2^k} \right\} \right]$$

$$B_{b0} = jl^2 \left[K_2 - 2A_{b0} \operatorname{logn} \frac{s}{c} - \sum_{k=1}^{\infty} \frac{c^k}{ks^k} (A_{ak} + A_{dk}) \right]$$

$$B_{c0} = jl^2 \left[K_2 - 2A_{c0} \operatorname{logn} \frac{s}{c} + 2A_{a0} \operatorname{logn} 2 \right.$$
$$\left. - \sum_{k=1}^{\infty} \frac{c^k}{ks^k} \left\{ \frac{A_{ak}}{2^k} + (-1)^k A_{bk} + A_{ck} \right\} \right]$$

$$B_{an} = jl^2 \left[-\frac{2c^n}{ns^n}\left(A_{b0} + \frac{A_{c0}}{2^n}\right) - \frac{A_{an}}{n} \right.$$

$$\left. -\frac{c^n}{ns^n}\sum_{k=1}^{\infty}\frac{(n+k-1)!}{(n-1)!\,k!}\frac{c^k}{s^k}\left\{A_{bk} + (-1)^k A_{ck} + \frac{A_{dk}}{2^{n+k}}\right\} \right]$$

$$B_{bn} = jl^2 \left[-2A_{a0}\frac{c^n}{ns^n} - \frac{A_{bn}}{n} - \frac{c^n}{ns^n}\sum_{k=1}^{\infty}\frac{(n+k-1)!}{(n-1)!\,k!}\frac{c^k}{s^k} A_{ak} \right]$$

$$B_{cn} = jl^2 \left[-2A_{c0}\frac{c^n}{ns^n} - \frac{A_{cn}}{n} - \frac{c^n}{ns^n}\sum_{k=1}^{\infty}\frac{(n+k-1)!}{(n-1)!\,k!}\frac{c^k}{s^k} A_{dk} \right]$$

$$B_{dn} = jl^2 \left[-\frac{2c^n}{ns^n}\left(\frac{A_{a0}}{2^n} + A_{b0}\right) - \frac{A_{dn}}{n} \right.$$

$$\left. -\frac{c^n}{ns^n}\sum_{k=1}^{\infty}\frac{(n+k-1)!}{(n-1)!\,k!}\frac{c^k}{s^k}\left\{\frac{A_{ak}}{2^{n+k}} + (-1)^k A_{bk} + A_{ck}\right\} \right]$$

In the above formulas, n is not equal to 0. K_3, C_{a0}, C_{an}, etc., are obtained from the same formulas as K_2, B_{a0}, B_{an}, etc., respectively, except that A is changed to B. Similarly for K_4, D_{a0}, D_{an}, etc., change A to C, and so on.

Middle cable:

$$M_0 = A_{b0} + B_{b0} + C_{b0} + \cdots$$
$$M_n = A_{bn} + B_{bn} + C_{bn} + \cdots$$
$$N_n = A_{cn} + B_{cn} + C_{cn} + \cdots$$

$$\frac{\text{Loss in sheath of middle cable}}{\text{Loss in conductor at zero frequency}} = \frac{a^2}{ct}\frac{\rho_s}{\rho_c}\left[2\,|M_0|^2 \right.$$

$$\left. + \sum_{n=1}^{\infty}\left\{|M_n|^2 + |N_n|^2 + (-1)^n(\widehat{M}_n N_n + M_n \widehat{N}_n)\right\} \right] \quad (28)$$

The two outside cables have different sheath losses. The one which has the larger loss depends on the phase rotation.

First outside cable:

$$L_0 = A_{a0} + B_{a0} + C_{a0} + \cdots$$
$$L_n = A_{an} + B_{an} + C_{an} + \cdots$$

Loss in sheath of 1st outside cable

Loss in conductor at zero frequency

$$= \frac{a^2}{ct} \frac{\rho_s}{\rho_c} [2 |L_0|^2 + |L_1|^2 + |L_2|^2 + \cdots + |L_n|^2 + \cdots] \quad (29)$$

Second outside cable:

$$P_0 = A_{c0} + B_{c0} + C_{c0} + \cdots$$
$$P_n = A_{dn} + B_{dn} + C_{dn} + \cdots \qquad [n \neq 0]$$

Loss in sheath of 2d outside cable

Loss in conductor at zero frequency

$$= \frac{a^2}{ct} \frac{\rho_s}{\rho_c} [2 |P_0|^2 + |P_1|^2 + |P_2|^2 + \cdots + |P_n|^2 + \cdots] \quad (30)$$

Example 7.   2,000,000-circ mil, single-conductor cables, three-phase circuit, flat spacing, sheaths short-circuited together, 60 cycles. $c = 2.97$ cm, $t = 0.357$ cm $=$ thickness of lead sheath, $s = 10.7$ cm, $\rho_c = 2,100$ at 75°C, $\rho_s = 25,000$, $l^2 = 0.1005$, $a = 1.796$ cm

$$\frac{\text{Loss in sheath of middle conductor}}{\text{Loss in conductor at zero frequency}} = 86\%$$

$$\frac{\text{Loss in sheath of 1st outside conductor}}{\text{Loss in conductor at zero frequency}} = 235\%$$

$$\frac{\text{Loss in sheath of 2d outside conductor}}{\text{Loss in conductor at zero frequency}} = 180\%$$

For references see the author's papers Losses in Grounded Sheaths of Single-conductor Cables, *Elec. Jour.*, February, 1924, p. 62, and Proximity Effect in Cable Sheaths, *Trans. A.I.E.E.*, September, 1931, p. 993.

Eddy-current Loss in Sheath of Three-conductor Three-phase Cable. When three-phase current is carried by three conductors surrounded by a nonmagnetic sheath, the current density in the sheath and the resulting eddy-current loss can be computed.[2,3]

If a small conductor Y is inside a tube, as in Fig. 3, the calculation is the same as when Y is outside the tube, as in the first part of this chapter, as far as equation (4).   Instead of equation (4), we now have

[2] Eddy Currents in Thin Circular Cylinders, by F. W. Carter, *Proc. Phil. Soc. Cambr.*, Vol. 23, p. 901, 1927.

[3] Proximity Effect in Cable Sheaths, by H. B. Dwight, *Trans. A.I.E.E.*, September, 1931, p. 993.

$$\log n \frac{D}{c} = - \left\{ \frac{s}{c} \cos \theta + \frac{s^2}{2c^2} \cos 2\theta + \cdots \right.$$

$$\left. + \frac{s^n}{nc^n} \cos n\theta + \cdots \right\} \quad (31)$$

since $s < c$.   [See the derivation of equation (13), Chap. 23.]

The calculation is the same as the derivation of equation (14), Chap. 24, except that in every case a/s and a^n/s^n become s/c and s^n/c^n. The letter c is here used for the mean radius of the tube or sheath. The quantity l^2 is as defined just before equation (18).

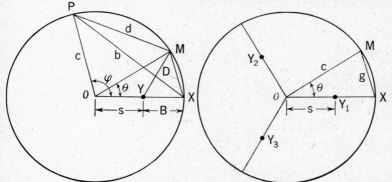

FIG. 3.—Thin tube and enclosed filament.   FIG. 4.—Three-phase cable and sheath.

The current density in the tube due to I at Y (Fig. 3) is obtained by subtracting $I/(2\pi a t)$ from (14), changing a^n/s^n to s^n/c^n and I to $-I$ and is

$$i_{(\theta)} = - \frac{I}{\pi c t} \sum_{n=1}^{\infty} \frac{s^n}{c^n} \left(\frac{jl^2}{n + jl^2} \right) \cos n\theta$$

$$= - \frac{I}{\pi c t} \sum_{n=1}^{\infty} \frac{s^n}{c^n} \left(\frac{l^4 + jl^2 n}{l^4 + n^2} \right) \cos n\theta \quad (32)$$

If three-phase currents are carried by conductors Y_1, Y_2, and Y_3, as in Fig. 4, and the sheath is open-circuited,

$$i_{(\theta)} = - \frac{I}{\pi c t} \sum_{n=1}^{\infty} \frac{s^n}{c^n} \left(\frac{l^4 + jl^2 n}{l^4 + n^2} \right)$$

$$\left[\cos n\theta \left(1 - \cos \frac{2n\pi}{3} \right) + j \sqrt{3} \sin n\theta \sin \frac{2n\pi}{3} \right] \quad (33)$$

The reactive drop in the filament at X due to the element of current $i_{(\theta)}ct\,d\theta$ is

$$j\omega 2cti_{(\theta)}\operatorname{logn}\frac{p}{g}\,d\theta$$

taking account of flux up to a certain large distance p. The distance g is equal to MX (Fig. 4).

Integrating this expression around the circle and adding the drops due to the three power currents and the resistance drop, the drop in the sheath is found to be

$$j\omega I\left[\operatorname{logn}\frac{\left(c+\dfrac{s}{2}\right)^2+\dfrac{3s^2}{4}}{(c-s)^2}\right.$$
$$+\sum_{n=1}^{\infty}\frac{2s^n}{c^n}\left(\frac{-n+jl^2}{n^2+l^4}\right)\left(1-\cos\frac{2n\pi}{3}\right)$$
$$\left.-\sum_{n=1}^{\infty}\frac{2s^n}{nc^n}\left(\frac{l^4+jl^2n}{l^4+n^2}\right)\left(1-\cos\frac{2n\pi}{3}\right)\right]\quad\text{abvolts per cm}\quad(34)$$

where I is in abamperes. This formula gives a result equal to zero in a numerical problem.

The loss in the open-circuited sheath of a three-phase cable is obtained from (33) and is

$$\frac{\text{Loss in open-circuited lead sheath}}{\text{Loss in 3 copper conductors at 0 frequency}}$$
$$=\frac{2a^2}{ct}\frac{\rho_s}{\rho_c}\sum_{n=1}^{\infty}\frac{s^{2n}}{c^{2n}}\left(\frac{l^4}{l^4+n^2}\right)\sin^2\left(\frac{n\pi}{3}\right)\quad(35)$$

where t is the actual thickness of the lead sheath in centimeters, ρ_s is the resistivity of lead and ρ_c that of copper, at the temperatures considered, and where a is the radius in centimeters of a solid copper wire of the same resistance as the stranded copper conductor. The current is assumed to be uniformly distributed over the sections of the copper conductors.

Example 8. Three-conductor three-phase cable, 500,000 cir mils per conductor, sheath open-circuited, $c = 4.5$ cm, $t = 0.40$ cm, $a = 0.898$ cm,

ρ_s = 25,000 abohms/cm cube, ρ_c = 2,100 at 75°C, f = 60 cycles, s = 2.0 cm, l^2 = 0.170.

$$\frac{\text{Loss in open-circuited lead sheath}}{\text{Loss in 3 copper conductors at 0 frequency}} = 0.05 = 5 \text{ per cent.}$$

Example 9.   Three 1,000,000-circ mil unsheathed single-conductor cables in a $\frac{3}{16}$-in. lead sheath or pipe. c = 4.55 cm, t = 0.48 cm, a = 1.27 cm, ρ_s = 25,000, ρ_c = 2,100, f = 60, s = 2.31 cm, l^2 = 0.207.

$$\frac{\text{Loss in open-circuited lead sheath}}{\text{Loss in 3 copper conductors at 0 frequency}} = 0.15 = 15 \text{ per cent.}$$

CHAPTER 25

CURVES FOR SKIN EFFECT AND PROXIMITY EFFECT

For many practical purposes, the values of skin effect and proximity effect may be taken from curves. A collection of such

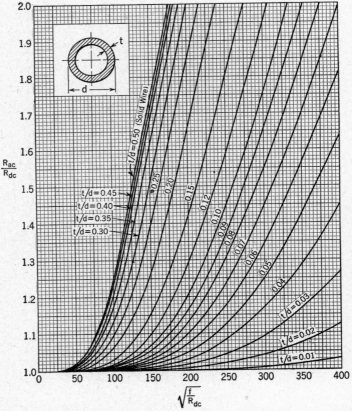

FIG. 1.—Skin effect in isolated round wires and tubes. R_{dc} in ohms per 1,000 ft.

curves is given in this chapter, some being based on computations and some on measurements.

The skin-effect resistance ratio for isolated round conductors, including tubular conductors, may be obtained from Fig. 1, which,[1] being based on R_{dc} of the conductor in question, may be used for stranded conductors, of either the tubular or the concentric type. A concentric stranded conductor is one in which the strands are laid around a central wire or strand. It is the common kind of stranded cable. For ordinary sizes and for power frequencies, its skin-effect ratio is the same as that of a large solid wire having the same value of R_{dc} per unit length, the ratio being given by the left-hand curve of Fig. 1.

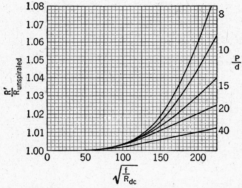

Fig. 2.—Spirality effect ratio in seven-wire cables. P = pitch of spirals; d = diameter of cable; R_{dc} in ohms per 1,000 ft.

When skin effect of a stranded cable becomes pronounced, as at higher frequencies, it is found that the skin effect is greatest when the spiraling is most rapid, that is, when the pitch of the spirals is shortest. It appears that the difference between the skin effect of a stranded cable and a solid wire of the same resistance is due mainly to the spiraling of the strands and is approximately inversely proportional to the pitch of the spiraling. This difference, due to spirality effect, is plotted in the curves of Fig. 2, from high-frequency tests published by A. E. Kennelly and H. A. Affel in *Proc. I. R. E.*, May, 1916, Fig. 17. Measurements below 5,000 cycles published by A. E. Kennelly, F. A. Laws, and P. H. Pierce in *Trans. A.I.E.E.*, 1915, p. 1970, Table VI, show

[1] Skin Effect and Proximity Effect in Tubular Conductors, by H. B. Dwight, *Trans. A.I.E.E.*, 1922, p. 189, Fig. 1. Figures 2, 6, and 7 are also from this paper.

similar results. Figure 2 can be used to give a correction for spirality effect. It is also useful for indicating when the effect of spirality can be expected to be negligible.

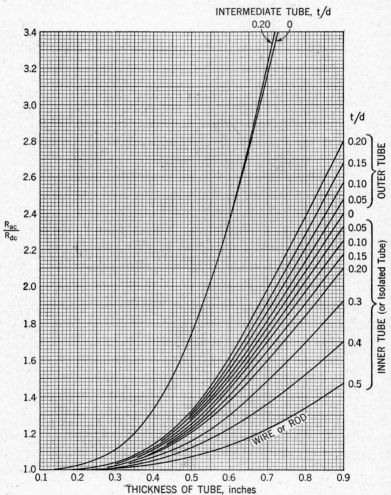

Fig. 3.—Skin-effect ratio for solid copper tubes, 75°C, 60 cycles, 3 phase. Thickness = t and outside diameter = d, of the tube being considered.

The increase in a-c resistance obtained by dividing a conductor into parallel unspiraled strands touching one another is much smaller than the spirality effect, as has been shown by measurements published by Kennelly and Affel in the paper just referred to.

Coaxial tubular conductors, whose skin-effect ratios are given in Fig. 3, are in common use.   Since such tubes, when used for

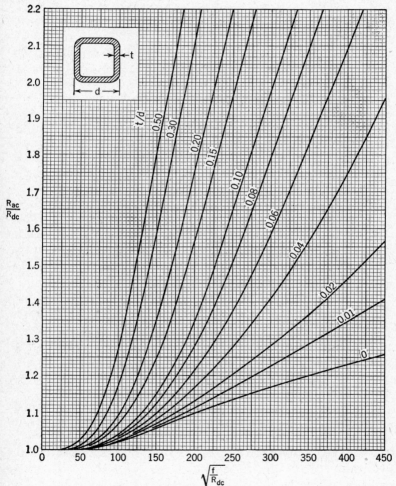

FIG. 4.—Skin effect in isolated square-tubular conductors. R_{dc} in ohms per 1,000 ft.

power applications, are usually of solid metal and are not stranded, the conductivity is definitely known, and the curves have not been drawn on a base of R_{dc} but on the tube thickness, for a frequency of 60 cycles. This arrangement is convenient for cases of tubular bus bars and other coaxial conductors at power frequencies.

The curves of Fig. 3 can be used for other frequencies than 60 cycles, including communication frequencies. For frequency f, multiply the tube thickness by $f/60$ before reading from the curves.

In Fig. 3, the intermediate tube is for the case of three coaxial conductors carrying three-phase current. The curves for the inner and outer tubes apply for both single-phase and three-phase cases of coaxial conductors. The curves marked "inner tube" are the same as for isolated tubes and give the same results as Fig. 1. For explanations and calculations see Chap. 20. Figure 3 is from the author's paper Reactance and Skin Effect of Concentric Tubular Conductors, *Trans. A.I.E.E.*, 1942, p. 513.

For large bus bars, a square tubular shape is used to a considerable extent. Curves for isolated conductors of this type are given[2] in Fig. 4. They were computed from the formulas in A.-C. Resistance of Hollow Square Conductors, by A. H. M. Arnold, *Jour. I.E.E.* (London), Vol. 82, p. 537, 1938. The ratios for square tubes are somewhat larger than for round tubes because the current crowds into the corners of the square conductors as well as into the outside skin.

The curves of Fig. 4 are approximately applicable to bus bars built up in the form of a hollow square tube out of flat straps, channels, or angles, with small openings for ventilation.

The skin-effect resistance ratio of a single, isolated strap conductor is given in Fig. 5 (see footnote 2), which is based on measured values published in the paper by Kennelly, Laws, and Pierce, referred to previously in this chapter.

The resistance ratio of bus bars built up of straps in parallel planes can be approximated to a certain extent. Two straps, separated by an air space and connected in parallel, could be taken to have the same ratio as a rectangular conductor having the same outside dimensions and the same value of R_{dc} as the built-up bus bar. Where the bus bar is composed of three or more straps in parallel planes, the ratio may be approximated by taking the ratio for a solid round conductor having the same

[2] See Temperature Rise of Bus Bars, by H. B. Dwight, G. W. Andrew, and H. W. Tileston, *Gen. Elec. Rev.*, May, 1940, p. 213.

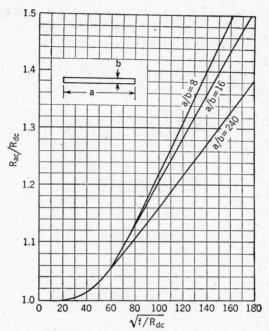

Fig. 5.—Skin effect in isolated rectangular conductors. R_{dc} in ohms per 1,000 ft.

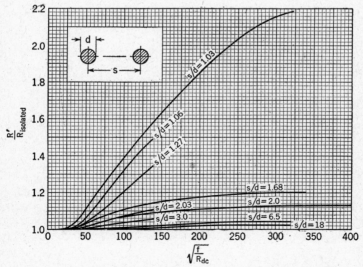

Fig. 6.—Proximity effect ratio in wires. R_{dc} in ohms per 1,000 ft.

value of R_{dc} as the bus bar. This ratio may be read from the left-hand curve of Fig. 1 of this chapter. The ratios for built-up bus bars described in this paragraph are not very precise and are for power frequencies.

The skin-effect ratio is very low for *interleaved construction*, where the straps are close together in parallel planes and where

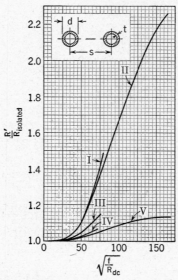

Fig. 7.—Proximity effect ratio in tubes. R_{dc} in ohms per 1,000 ft.

Curve	s/d	t/d	Means Obtained
I	1.0	0	Calculation
II	1.008	0.125	Measurement
III	1.5	0	Calculation
IV	2.0	0	Calculation
V	2.03	0.125	Measurement

neighboring straps have currents that are always either 180 or 120 deg out of phase. For the 180 deg case, the curve for the inner tube, $t/d = 0$, in Fig. 3 of this chapter, gives the ratios. This is the same case as Chap. 22. For adjacent currents at 120 deg, including the arrangement $ABCABC \cdots$, the ratio may be read from the curve for the intermediate tube, $t/d = 0$, in Fig. 3. It can be seen from the curves that in either of these cases, if the straps are $\frac{1}{4}$ in. thick and the frequency is 60 cycles, the increase in resistance is very small.   Figure 5 of this chapter does not apply for interleaved conductors, since the current density in each interleaved strap is kept very uniform by the closely adjacent currents.

With round conductors, proximity effect causes a loss in addition to that which takes place when they are isolated. Values of proximity effect ratio are given in Figs. 6 and 7.   It is seen that if skin effect is noticeable, then proximity effect will also amount to more than a few per cent unless the axial spacing of the conductors is more than three or four times the largest dimension of the cross section.

The proximity effect ratio is the ratio of R', the a-c resistance of the conductor in the presence of the others, to the a-c resistance when isolated.   The proximity-effect ratio and the skin-effect ratio are multiplied together to give the ratio of R' to R_{dc}.

CHAPTER 26

MUTUAL INDUCTANCE OF FINE WIRE CIRCLES

The mutual inductance of two circular, filament conductors with the same axis was given by Maxwell in the following formula in elliptic integrals:[1]

$$M = 4\pi \sqrt{Aa} \left[\left(\frac{2}{k} - k \right) K - \frac{2}{k} E \right] \quad \text{abhenries} \quad (1)$$

where K and E are complete elliptic integrals of the first and second kind, of modulus k.

$$k^2 = 1 - \frac{p^2}{q^2} = \frac{4Aa}{(A + a)^2 + s^2}$$

where A and a are the radii of the two circles, centimeter units being used throughout, and s is the distance between the planes of the circles,

$$p^2 = (A - a)^2 + s^2.$$
$$q^2 = (A + a)^2 + s^2.$$
$$1 \text{ henry} = 10^9 \text{ abhenries.}$$

Maxwell gave also the following formula, obtained by Landen's transformation:

$$M = \frac{8\pi \sqrt{Aa}}{\sqrt{k_1}} [K_1 - E_1] \quad \text{abhenries} \quad (2)$$

where K_1 and E_1 are complete elliptic integrals of modulus k_1 and

$$k_1 = \frac{q - p}{q + p}.$$

The modulus k_1 is smaller than k and (2) sometimes gives more convenient computation from tables than (1).

---

[1] "Electricity and Magnetism," by J. Clerk Maxwell, Vol. II, Par. 701.

A third formula in elliptic integrals is as follows:[2]

$$M = 4\pi \sqrt{Aa} \left[\frac{K_0}{k(1 + k)} - \frac{(1 + k)}{k} E_0 \right] \quad \text{abhenries} \quad (3)$$

where K_0 and E_0 are complete elliptic integrals to modulus k_0, and

$$k_0{}^2 = \frac{4k}{(1 + k)^2}.$$

The value of k_0 is greater than that of k.

The older tables of complete elliptic integrals are based on values of the angle of which the modulus is the sine. This angle, however, has no apparent significance in this problem, and it is generally more convenient to use tables[3] based directly on the square of the modulus. Similarly, Maxwell's table for the mutual inductance of two coaxial circles is based on the angle $\sin^{-1} k$, just mentioned. A newer table for M, Table 2, *Sci. Papers Inst. Phys. Chem. Research* (Tokyo), September, 1927, by Nagaoka and Sakurai, is based on k^2.

The computation of the mutual inductance of two circles by values of elliptic integrals taken from tables is often unsatisfactory, because the result may be the small difference between two large quantities, or because the value of K tends to become infinitely large as the modulus k approaches unity. It is a very common practice to make use of series. For a given case, a series can usually be found which converges with satisfactory rapidity. Where the integral or the derivative of the mutual inductance is desired, the practical method is generally to operate on one of the series, term by term.

For two coaxial circular filaments near together so that p/q is less than about $\frac{1}{4}$, or for two circular coils of negligibly small cross section, with no magnetic material, the mutual inductance is[4]

[2] See equation (4) in Formulas and Tables for the Calculation of Mutual and Self Inductance, by E. B. Rosa and F. W. Grover, *Bur. Standards Sci. Paper* 169, published also as Part 1, Vol. 8, the *Bur. Standards Bull.*, Washington, 1912.

[3] See, for example, "Mathematical Tables," by H. B. Dwight, McGraw-Hill Book Company, Inc., New York, 1941, pp. 199–205.

[4] *Wied. Ann.*, article by Weinstein, Vol. 21, p. 344, 1884, and *Bur. Standards Sci. Paper* 169, equation (7).

$$M = \frac{4\pi N_1 N_2 \sqrt{Aa}}{10^9} \left[\left(\operatorname{logn} \frac{4q}{p} - 1 \right) \left(1 + \frac{3}{4} \frac{p^2}{q^2} + \frac{33}{64} \frac{p^4}{q^4} \right. \right.$$

$$\left. + \frac{107}{256} \frac{p^6}{q^6} + \frac{5,913}{16,384} \frac{p^8}{q^8} + \cdots \right) - \left(1 + \frac{15}{128} \frac{p^4}{q^4} \right.$$

$$\left. \left. + \frac{185}{1,536} \frac{p^6}{q^6} + \frac{7,465}{65,536} \frac{p^8}{q^8} + \cdots \right) \right] \text{henries} \quad (4)$$

where N_1 and N_2 are the numbers of turns in the two coils [taken as 1 in equations (1) to (3)] and where logn denotes natural logarithm.

An alternative series to (4), of about the same rapidity of convergence, is given in equation (16) of *Sci. Paper* 169 and is as follows:

$$M = \frac{\pi N_1 N_2 \sqrt{Dd}}{10^9} \left[\left(\operatorname{logn} \frac{16Dd}{p^2} \right) \left(1 + \frac{3}{4} \frac{p^2}{Dd} - \frac{15}{64} \frac{p^4}{D^2 d^2} \right. \right.$$

$$\left. + \frac{35}{256} \frac{p^6}{D^3 d^3} - \frac{1,575}{16,384} \frac{p^8}{D^4 d^4} + \cdots \right) - 2 - \frac{p^2}{4Dd}$$

$$\left. + \frac{31}{128} \frac{p^4}{D^2 d^2} - \frac{247}{1,536} \frac{p^6}{D^3 d^3} + \frac{7,795}{65,536} \frac{p^8}{D^4 d^4} - \cdots \right]$$

$$\text{henries} \quad (5)$$

where D and d are the diameters of the circles, D being $2A$ and d being $2a$. The other letters are as previously defined.

For circles far apart, where p/q is greater than about $\frac{1}{4}$, the following series may be used:[5]

$$M = \frac{2\pi^2 N_1 N_2 k_1 \sqrt{Aak_1}}{10^9} \left[1 + \frac{3}{8} k_1^2 + \frac{15}{64} k_1^4 + \frac{175}{1,024} k_1^6 \right.$$

$$\left. + \cdots \right] \text{henries} \quad (6)$$

where $$k_1 = \frac{q - p}{q + p}, \qquad \text{as for equation} \quad (2)$$

The general term of the series in the brackets is

$$\frac{n + 1}{2n + 1} \left[\frac{3 \times 5 \times 7 \cdots (2n + 1)}{4 \times 6 \times 8 \cdots (2n + 2)} \right]^2 k_1^{2n}$$

The foregoing series is called "Grover's series formula," in *Bur. Standards Sci. Paper* 492, by H. L. Curtis and C. M. Sparks.

[5] *Bur. Standards Sci. Paper* 169, by E. B. Rosa and F. W. Grover, equation (6).

The mutual inductance of two coaxial circular filaments in the same plane is

$$M = \frac{\pi \sqrt{Dd}}{10^9} \left[\left(\operatorname{logn} \frac{16Dd}{c^2} \right) \left(1 + \frac{3}{4} \frac{c^2}{Dd} - \frac{15}{64} \frac{c^4}{D^2 d^2} \right. \right.$$
$$\left. + \frac{35}{256} \frac{c^6}{D^3 d^3} - \frac{1,575}{16,384} \frac{c^8}{D^4 d^4} + \cdots \right)$$
$$- 2 - \frac{c^2}{4Dd} + \frac{31}{128} \frac{c^4}{D^2 d^2} - \frac{247}{1,536} \frac{c^6}{D^3 d^3} + \frac{7,795}{65,536} \frac{c^8}{D^4 d^4}$$
$$\left. - \cdots \right] \text{ henries} \quad (7)$$

where D and d are the diameters of the two circles and $2c = D - d$. This was obtained by putting the axial distance between the circles equal to zero in equation (16) of *Sci. Paper* 169 or equation (5) of this chapter. It is noteworthy that equation (7), just given, contains only even powers of c. It is equation (13) of footnote 1, Chap. 27.

When the dimensions of the sections of two coils are small compared to their radii and their distance apart, the following extension of Par. 700 of "Electricity and Magnetism," by J. Clerk Maxwell, may be used:

$$\frac{M}{N_1 N_2} = M_0 + \frac{1}{1! \, 3! \, 2^2} \left\{ (b_1{}^2 + b_2{}^2) \frac{\partial^2 M_0}{\partial s^2} + t_1{}^2 \frac{\partial^2 M_0}{\partial A^2} + t_2{}^2 \frac{\partial^2 M_0}{\partial a^2} \right\}$$
$$+ \frac{1}{1! \, 5! \, 2^4} \left\{ (b_1{}^4 + b_2{}^4) \frac{\partial^4 M_0}{\partial s^4} + t_1{}^4 \frac{\partial^4 M_0}{\partial A^4} + t_2{}^4 \frac{\partial^4 M_0}{\partial a^4} \right\}$$
$$+ \frac{1}{3! \, 3! \, 2^4} \left\{ b_1{}^2 b_2{}^2 \frac{\partial^4 M_0}{\partial s^4} + t_1{}^2 (b_1{}^2 + b_2{}^2) \frac{\partial^4 M_0}{\partial A^2 \partial s^2} \right.$$
$$\left. + t_2{}^2 (b_1{}^2 + b_2{}^2) \frac{\partial^4 M_0}{\partial a^2 \partial s^2} + t_1{}^2 t_2{}^2 \frac{\partial^4 M_0}{\partial A^2 \partial a^2} \right\} + \cdots \quad (8)$$

where b_1 and b_2 are the axial lengths of the two coils, t_1 and t_2 are their radial thicknesses, and A and a are their mean radii. The dimension s is the axial distance between the coils.

M_0 is the algebraic expression for the mutual inductance of the central filaments of the two coils, of radii A and a. After the differentiating, the various dimensions are given their numerical values. It is important, however, that in the case of coils of equal radii, A be not put equal to a until after the differentiating has been carried out.

CHAPTER 27

MUTUAL INDUCTANCE OF COAXIAL SOLENOIDS IN AIR[1]

Solenoids are coils, here taken to be circular, which have the shape of a thin tube. One or more layers of wire wound on a cylindrical form make a typical solenoid.

Formulas for the mutual inductance (MI) of solenoids are usually obtained by integrating expressions for the MI of circles.

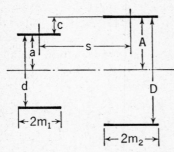

FIG. 1.—Two coaxial solenoids.

Since the integration terminates at the two ends of each of the two coils, four algebraic expressions will normally result. It will be shown in the following paragraphs that the MI of any two coaxial solenoids in any relative position may be expressed in terms of the MI's of four pairs of concentric, coaxial solenoids, in which the outer solenoid is equal in length to the inner.

The MI, M, of two coaxial solenoids, which in general are not equal and not concentric and which have lengths $2m_1$ and $2m_2$ cm and radii a and A (see Fig. 1), is given by

$$\frac{M}{n_1 n_2} = \frac{1}{2} \left[M'_{(x_1)} - M'_{(x_2)} - M'_{(x_3)} + M'_{(x_4)} \right] \quad \text{abhenries} \quad (1)$$

where n_1 and n_2 are the turns per centimeter of the two coils, respectively, and where

$$x_1 = s + m_1 + m_2. \quad (2)$$
$$x_2 = s + m_1 - m_2. \quad (3)$$

[1] Some Series Formulas for Mutual Inductance of Solenoids, by H. B. Dwight and F. W. Grover, *Trans. A.I.E.E.*, 1937, p. 327.

$$x_3 = s - m_1 + m_2. \tag{4}$$
$$x_4 = s - m_1 - m_2. \tag{5}$$

s = axial distance between the central planes. Centimeter units are used throughout this chapter.

$M'_{(x_1)}$ is equal to the MI of two concentric and coaxial solenoids of equal length x_1 cm and of radii a and A, which have one turn per centimeter of axial length, and similarly for x_2, etc. In this chapter the plain letter M represents an actual MI and M' represents an MI where one turn per centimeter is assumed. M' does not represent differentiation.

For comparatively small values of x, for solenoids whose radial thickness can be neglected,

$$
\begin{aligned}
M'_{(x)} = \pi d^2 \sqrt{Dd} &\left[\left\{ \operatorname{logn} \frac{x^2 + c^2}{c^2} \right\} \left\{ \frac{c^2}{d^2} \left(1 + \frac{3}{8} \frac{c^2}{Dd} - \frac{5}{64} \frac{c^4}{D^2 d^2} \right. \right. \right. \\
&\left. + \frac{35}{1{,}024} \frac{c^6}{D^3 d^3} \right) \right\} + \left\{ \operatorname{logn} \frac{16 Dd}{x^2 + c^2} \right\} \left\{ \frac{x^2}{d^2} \left(1 + \frac{3}{4} \frac{c^2}{Dd} - \frac{15}{64} \frac{c^4}{D^2 d^2} \right. \right. \\
&\left. + \frac{35}{256} \frac{c^6}{D^3 d^3} \right) + \frac{x^4}{8 Dd^3} \left(1 - \frac{5}{8} \frac{c^2}{Dd} + \frac{35}{64} \frac{c^4}{D^2 d^2} \right) \\
&\left. - \frac{x^6}{64 D^2 d^4} \left(1 - \frac{7}{4} \frac{c^2}{Dd} \right) + \frac{5}{1{,}024} \frac{x^8}{D^3 d^5} \cdots \right\} \\
&- \frac{4cx}{d^2} \left\{ \tan^{-1} \frac{x}{c} \right\} \left\{ 1 + \frac{c^2}{2 Dd} - \frac{c^4}{8 D^2 d^2} + \frac{c^6}{16 D^3 d^3} \right\} \\
&- \frac{x^2}{d^2} \left(1 - \frac{9}{8} \frac{c^2}{Dd} - \frac{1}{16} \frac{c^4}{D^2 d^2} + \frac{325}{3{,}072} \frac{c^6}{D^3 d^3} \right) \\
&+ \frac{x^4}{16 Dd^3} \left(1 + \frac{3}{2} \frac{c^2}{Dd} - \frac{695}{384} \frac{c^4}{D^2 d^2} \right) \\
&+ \frac{x^6}{48 D^2 d^4} \left(1 - \frac{149}{64} \frac{c^2}{Dd} \right) - \frac{109}{12{,}288} \frac{x^8}{D^3 d^5} \cdots \right]
\end{aligned}
$$
$$\text{abhenries} \quad (6)$$

where logn denotes natural logarithm. Formulas (1) and (6) were obtained by the double integration of equation (5), Chap. 26.

If x is large, say greater than the radius a or if c is comparatively large, say greater than $a/2$, the following expression for $M'_{(x)}$, obtained by integrating equation (56) of *Bur. Standards Sci. Paper* 169 may be used:

$$M'_{(x)} = 4\pi^2 a^2 A \left[\frac{r}{A} - \frac{a^2 A}{8r^3} + \frac{a^4 A}{16r^5} - \frac{5}{64} \frac{a^4 A^3}{r^7} - \frac{5}{128} \frac{a^6 A}{r^7} \right.$$

$$+ \frac{35}{256} \frac{a^6 A^3}{r^9} + \frac{7}{256} \frac{a^8 A}{r^9} - \frac{105}{1,024} \frac{a^6 A^5}{r^{11}} - \frac{189}{1,024} \frac{a^8 A^3}{r^{11}}$$

$$- \frac{21}{1,024} \frac{a^{10} A}{r^{11}} + \frac{693}{2,048} \frac{a^8 A^5}{r^{13}} + \frac{231}{1,024} \frac{a^{10} A^3}{r^{13}} + \frac{33}{2,048} \frac{a^{12} A}{r^{13}}$$

$$- \cdots + \left(-1 + \frac{a^2}{8A^2} + \frac{a^4}{64A^4} + \frac{5}{1,024} \frac{a^6}{A^6} + \frac{35}{16,384} \frac{a^8}{A^8} \right.$$

$$\left. \left. + \frac{147}{128 \times 1,024} \frac{a^{10}}{A^{10}} + \cdots \right) \right] \qquad \text{abhenries} \quad (7)$$

where $\qquad\qquad\qquad r^2 = x^2 + A^2.$ $\qquad\qquad\qquad\qquad$ (8)

By grouping together terms of (7) of the same power of a, the following alternative form is obtained:

$$M'_{(x)} = 4\pi^2 a A^2 \left[C_0 + \frac{a^3}{8r^3} C_2 + \frac{a^5}{64r^5} C_4 + \frac{5}{1,024} \frac{a^7}{r^7} C_6 \right.$$

$$+ \frac{35}{16,384} \frac{a^9}{r^9} C_8 + \frac{147}{128 \times 1,024} \frac{a^{11}}{r^{11}} C_{10} + \cdots$$

$$+ \frac{a}{A} \left(-1 + \frac{a^2}{8A^2} + \frac{a^4}{64A^4} + \frac{5}{1,024} \frac{a^6}{A^6} + \frac{35}{16,384} \frac{a^8}{A^8} \right.$$

$$\left. \left. + \frac{147}{128 \times 1,024} \frac{a^{10}}{A^{10}} + \cdots \right) \right] \qquad \text{abhenries} \quad (9)$$

where $C_0 = \dfrac{ar}{A^2} = \dfrac{a \sqrt{x^2 + A^2}}{A^2}.$

$\qquad C_2 = -1.$

$\qquad C_4 = 2 \left(2 - \dfrac{5}{2} \dfrac{A^2}{r^2} \right).$

$\qquad C_6 = 7 \left(-\dfrac{8}{7} + 4 \dfrac{A^2}{r^2} - 3 \dfrac{A^4}{r^4} \right).$

$\qquad C_8 = \dfrac{9}{5} \left(\dfrac{64}{9} - 48 \dfrac{A^2}{r^2} + 88 \dfrac{A^4}{r^4} - \dfrac{143}{3} \dfrac{A^6}{r^6} \right).$

$\qquad C_{10} = \dfrac{11}{7} \left(-\dfrac{128}{11} + 128 \dfrac{A^2}{r^2} - 416 \dfrac{A^4}{r^4} + 520 \dfrac{A^6}{r^6} - 221 \dfrac{A^8}{r^8} \right).$

Equations (7) and (9) are equivalent to (6) in all respects and give the same numerical result as (6) for any case to which the formulas can be properly applied. The criterion as to whether a series is applicable is that the last terms used shall be almost negligibly small.   In other words, the series shall be practically convergent in the number of terms which are used.

A comparison of the applicability of formulas (6) and (7) is given in Fig. 2.   This depends on the rapidity of convergence. Formula (6) gives the MI of two thin solenoids with slide-rule accuracy, for values of c/d up to 0.25 and of x/d up to about 0.8, as is indicated by the vertical dotted line of Fig. 2.   The convergence is most rapid for small values of these ratios.   Formula (7) is for the larger values of x/d and its range extends to the left as far as the approximate location of the curved dotted line. The range of (9) is the same as that of (7).   Their terms being the same, their higher order terms will become negligible at the same stage.   It is seen that there is a considerable range, between

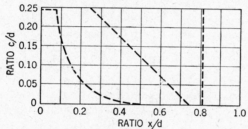

FIG. 2.—Ranges of application of formulas (6) and (7).

the vertical line and the curved line, in which both formulas can be used.   The sloping dotted line shows the approximate boundary to the left of which formula (6) is more rapidly convergent than the others.

Equation (6) is given in terms of diameters and (7) and (9) in terms of radii so that the numbers in the coefficients will be as small as possible.

It is to be noted that the four values of $M'_{(x)}$ in (1) need not necessarily be computed all by (6) or all by (7) or by (9), but some can be computed by one expression and some by another. This may be necessary in some cases, for x_1 may be so large that (6) cannot be used, and for the same pair of coils x_4 may be so small that only (6) can be employed.

There is an advantage in using (7) or (9) for all four cases of (1), namely, that then the round bracket of (7) or (9) need not be computed, for it is like a constant of integration and would cancel out when the two positive and two negative values were added.

The round bracket of (7) and (9) was put in for the purpose of making (7) and (9) equivalent to (6). All these expressions have the same physical interpretation: they are equal to the MI of two equal and concentric coils of length x and with one turn per centimeter, see equation (12). Thus, (9) is the same, term for term, as the well-known MI formula (36), *Sci. Paper* 169, p. 53. A considerable number of additional terms of (7) and (9) can be written down by inspection, from this corresponding formula (36). The terms of (7) and (9) are the same as those in Mechanical Forces in Transformers by J. E. Clem, *Trans. A.I.E.E.*, Vol. 46, p. 577, 1927. The general term of the round bracket of (7) and (9) is given in a paper by T. H. Havelock, and is quoted in footnote 1 following equation 36A and on p. 56 of *Sci. Paper* 169.

Where a is considerably smaller than A, the grouping in (9) according to powers of a is convenient but, if x and therefore r are relatively large, the grouping according to powers of r, as in (7) and (22), is convenient. That is, in general, (7) is for long coils and (9) for short coils, though not so short as those for which (6) is used. However, there is very little difference between (7) and (9) for they contain the same terms and the terms which are not negligible must be computed while those that are negligible will be omitted.

When the two coils are concentric as well as coaxial, $s = 0$. It is to be noted that only even powers of x are involved in (6), (7), and (9) and so

$$M'_{(x)} = M'_{(-x)} \tag{10}$$

Therefore, for concentric coils of unequal length,

$$\frac{M}{n_1 n_2} = M'_{(m_1+m_2)} - M'_{(m_1-m_2)} \tag{11}$$

Equation (11), using (6), (7), or (9) of this chapter as convenient, is thus equivalent to Ròiti's formula [equation (39)], or Searle and Airey's formula extended [equation (43)], *Bur. Standards Sci. Paper* 169.

A further simplification results when the two concentric coils are of equal length, in which case only one expression is required.

$$\frac{M}{n_1 n_2} = M'_{(2m_1)} \tag{12}$$

For (6), (7) and (9), $M'_{(0)} = 0$ (13)

The round bracket of (7) and (9) was inserted to make this so. As previously mentioned, equation (12), using (7) or (9), is the same as equation (36) of *Sci. Paper* 169. It is equivalent to equation (38) of that paper, or other formulas which are given for this type of problem.

Each dimension of the cross section of a coil should be taken to be the number of wires in a row along that dimension, multiplied by the center-to-center distance between adjacent wires.

An experimental check on formulas (6) and (7) was made by winding up two solenoids of equal length and placing them in the concentric position. Their length was 4.29 cm. The smaller coil had 95 turns and a mean diameter of 7.68 cm. The larger one had 91 turns and a mean diameter of 11.20 cm. The measured MI was 0.437 milhenries and the calculated value was 0.450 milhenries.

Another simplification of the problem of MI occurs when the two coils are not concentric but have equal radii. This means that $c = 0$ and $A = a$. Formula (6) then becomes a self-inductance formula, namely, (71), p. 117 of *Sci. Paper* 169. Formulas (7) and (9) similarly become the self-inductance formula (11) of the paper published in *Trans. A.I.E.E.*, Vol. 38, p. 1688, 1919 by the author. Equation (1) of this chapter becomes the same as equation (51) of *Bur. Standards Sci. Paper* 169, as follows:

$$M_{AB} = \tfrac{1}{2}[L_{ACB} - L_{AC} - L_{BC} + L_C] \qquad (14)$$

where A and B denote the two coils of equal radius whose MI M_{AB} is desired, L_C denotes the self-inductance of a fictitious coil C which fills the space between coils A and B and has the same radius and turns per centimeter that they have. L_{ACB}, L_{AC}, and L_{BC} denote the self-inductances of uniform coils composed of coils $A + C + B$, $A + C$, and $B + C$, the plus signs denoting that the coils are joined together end to end.

If coils A and B have unequal turns per centimeter, n_1 and n_2, but equal thickness or negligible thickness, first find the MI of two coils of n_1 turns per centimeter by (14) and then multiply by n_2/n_1.

Equation (1) of this chapter was derived by integration, for infinitely thin solenoids. It can be shown that (14) is applicable to thick coils, if they have the same radial thickness, as follows:

For thick coils,

$$L_{ACB} = L_A + L_B + L_C + 2M_{AB} + 2M_{BC} + 2M_{CA}$$

This can be seen by assuming an alternating current i to flow in all the turns. Then the voltage drop is $2\pi f\, i\, L_{ACB}$ where f is the frequency. This drop can be equated to the sum of the drops in

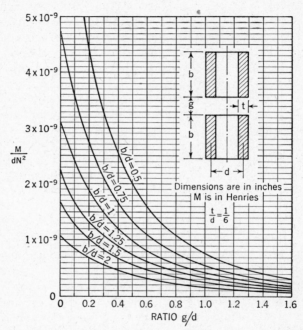

Fig. 3.—Mutual inductance of reactance coils with the same axis.

the three groups of turns of A, C, and B, and the foregoing equation is obtained.

Similarly,
$$L_{AC} = L_A + L_C + 2M_{AC}$$
$$L_{CB} = L_C + L_B + 2M_{BC}$$

Eliminating M_{AC} and M_{BC} from the above three equations gives (14).

When two coaxial coils have equal radius and thickness, their MI can be computed by (14) using well-known self-inductance formulas (see Chap. 31). These may include corrections for the thickness of the winding.

For engineering problems, when the MI of two equal coils placed end to end is desired, an approximate value may be read from the curves of Fig. 3.

It is seen from equations (1) to (5) that if in the dimensions of the lengths, $2m_1$ and $2m_2$ are interchanged, the MI and also the force [see equation (12), Chap. 33] are not changed. This can be called the *principle of interchange of lengths*. It has been pointed out previously for the MI of concentric solenoids and for a solenoid and a circle. See *Sci. Paper* 169, pp. 68 and 101. Since it applies to each thin cylindrical element of thick solenoids or coils, it applies to the entire coils.

An inspection of the formulas of Chaps. 30 and 34 shows that the principle of interchange of lengths applies also to MI and force of coils with parallel axes.

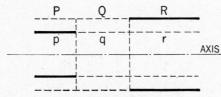

Fig. 4.—Coaxial solenoids.

Equation (14) has been derived in the preceding paragraphs from the knowledge of the properties of self-inductance and MI of coils, including thick coils. Equation (1) was derived from the integration for infinitely thin solenoids. From it the principle of interchange of lengths was obtained and this has been shown to apply to thick coils.

The following derivation of equation (1) for thick coils, written by Dr. F. W. Grover, is obtained by using the principle of interchange of lengths. Besides extending equation (1) to thick coils, it clarifies the physical meaning of the formula.

Suppose that in addition to the two thin solenoids of Fig. 1, there are four others as in Fig. 4, the turns per centimeter being the same for all coils of a given radius. Since these touch each other end to end, they form longer solenoids. For instance, the three solenoids P, Q, and R form one long solenoid which can be called $P + Q + R$. Let the coils have appreciable thickness that is uniform for a given radius.

$$M_{(P+Q+R)(p+q+r)} = M_{Pp} + M_{Pq} + M_{Pr} + M_{Qp} + M_{Qq} + M_{Qr}$$
$$+ M_{Rp} + M_{Rq} + M_{Rr}$$

Using the principle of interchange of lengths, by which $M_{Qp} = M_{Pq}$, etc., this becomes

$$M_{Pp} + M_{Qq} + M_{Rr} + 2M_{Pq} + 2M_{Qr} + 2M_{Rp}$$

Similarly, $\quad M_{(P+Q)(p+q)} = M_{Pp} + M_{Qq} + 2M_{Pq}$

and $\quad M_{(Q+R)(q+r)} = M_{Qq} + M_{Rr} + 2M_{Qr}$

Solving these equations simultaneously in such a way as to leave only pairs of coils that are concentric and of equal length on the right-hand side of the equation,

$$2M_{Rp} = M_{(P+Q+R)(p+q+r)} - M_{(P+Q)(p+q)} - M_{(Q+R)(q+r)} + M_{Qq} \quad (1a)$$

The lengths of the concentric coils are evidently x_1, x_2, x_3, and x_4. This equation is the same as (1) and has thus now been derived for thick coils.

In a similar way, equation (11) can be treated, so that it also applies to thick coils. It is a special case of equation $(1a)$.

In order to find the MI of two thick coils of equal length, as needed for equation $(1a)$, for example $M_{(P+Q+R)(p+q+r)}$, equation (14) may be employed, using formulas for self-inductance of thick coils given in Chap. 31. In this application of equation (14), the coils A, C, and B are not placed end to end along the axis, but they are concentric. They are of equal length but different radii. Coils A and B are the two actual thick coils, and coil C is a fictitious coil of the same length and filling the space between them.

If the densities of turns in the two coils are not the same, the computation is first made on the basis of their being the same, and then the MI is multiplied by the ratio of the turn densities, as described following equation (14).

An alternative method of computing MI's like $M_{(P+Q+R)(p+q+r)}$, if the coils are not very short, is to use the extension in Chap. 28, of equation (7) of this chapter, giving the correction terms for thickness.

The preceding paragraphs cover the numerical computation of the general case of the MI of two thick coaxial solenoids, of rectangular cross section of winding, in the position indicated in Fig. 1.

In the general formula (11) for concentric solenoids, the mutual inductance is given by the difference of two series. In the formula of Searle and Airey [formula 43, *Sci. Paper* 169] a single series of terms suffices for its calculation. Searle and Airey's formula may be derived from (11) and (7) by expanding the two values of r in powers of the ratios of the solenoid lengths to the diagonal drawn from the center to the end of the longer solenoid and combining terms.

This formula does not converge well when the solenoids are of nearly equal radii, and their lengths are small compared with their radii. In such cases formula (6) must be used in connection with (11).

On the other hand, when the lengths of the coils are large compared with their radii, the coefficients X_n and L_n may become very large, rendering the use of this formula uncertain and unsatisfactory (see pp. 63 and 222 of *Sci. Paper* 169).

The following formula (17), derived by F. W. Grover [equation (17) of footnote 1], is an alternative to (43) of *Sci. Paper* 169. Its coefficients λ_n and ξ_n are always less than unity and so it is possible to tell by inspection from the value of δ/ρ how rapid is the convergence of the series (17), which is a power series in δ/ρ. The change also lowers the powers of some of the letters making up the terms.

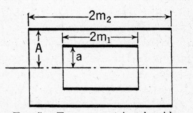

Fig. 5.—Two concentric solenoids.

By putting
$$\delta^2 = a^2 + l^2 = a^2 + m_1^2 \tag{15}$$
and
$$\rho^2 = A^2 + x^2 = A^2 + m_2^2 \tag{16}$$

we can replace l^2 by $\delta^2 - a^2$ and x^2 by $\rho^2 - A^2$ in (43) of *Sci. Paper* 169, giving for the coils of Fig. 5:

$$M = \frac{2\pi^2 a^2 N_1 N_2}{\rho}\left[1 - \frac{A^2 \delta^2}{2\rho^4}\left\{\lambda_2 + \frac{\delta^2}{\rho^2}\lambda_4\xi_2 \right.\right.$$
$$\left.\left. + \frac{\delta^4}{\rho^4}\lambda_6\xi_4 + \frac{\delta^6}{\rho^6}\lambda_8\xi_6 + \cdots \right\}\right] \quad \text{abhenries} \tag{17}$$

where N_1 and N_2 are the turns per coil of the two coils, respectively, and where

$$\lambda_2 = 1 - \frac{7}{4}\frac{a^2}{\delta^2}.$$

$$\lambda_4 = 1 - \frac{9}{2}\frac{a^2}{\delta^2} + \frac{33}{8}\frac{a^4}{\delta^4}$$

$$\lambda_6 = 1 - \frac{33}{4}\frac{a^2}{\delta^2} + \frac{143}{8}\frac{a^4}{\delta^4} - \frac{715}{64}\frac{a^6}{\delta^6}.$$

$$\lambda_8 = 1 - 13\frac{a^2}{\delta^2} + \frac{195}{4}\frac{a^4}{\delta^4} - \frac{1,105}{16}\frac{a^6}{\delta^6} + \frac{4,199}{128}\frac{a^8}{\delta^8}.$$

$$\lambda_{10} = 1 - \frac{75}{4}\frac{a^2}{\delta^2} + \frac{425}{4}\frac{a^4}{\delta^4} - \frac{8,075}{32}\frac{a^6}{\delta^6} + \frac{33,915}{128}\frac{a^8}{\delta^8} - \frac{52,003}{512}\frac{a^{10}}{\delta^{10}}.$$

$$\xi_2 = 1 - \frac{7}{4}\frac{A^2}{\rho^2}.$$

$$\xi_4 = 1 - \frac{9}{2}\frac{A^2}{\rho^2} + \frac{33}{8}\frac{A^4}{\rho^4}.$$

The coefficients ξ_6, ξ_8, etc., are functions of A^2/ρ^2 and can be written down by inspection from the similar expressions for λ_6, λ_8, etc.

Although formulas (17) and (43), previously referred to, are given for the case of the MI of a short solenoid and a longer one outside it as in Fig. 5, these formulas can be used for the case when the shorter solenoid is outside, by first applying the principle of interchange of lengths.

Gray's formula[2] expresses the MI of two coaxial solenoids, not concentric, as the difference of two series of terms. It may be derived from the general formulas (1) and (7) by expressing the four distances r in terms of the distances measured from the center of the coil of smaller radius to the ends of the winding of the other coil. In spite of its smaller number of terms, however, the convergence of Gray's formula is not so good as that of (7), except for coils far apart.

Since Gray's formula contains the same coefficients as (43) of *Sci. Paper* 169, it is subject to the same disadvantage that for certain proportions of coils the coefficients become large, and it cannot be told by inspection how satisfactory is the convergence of the series. By making the same type of substitution as was

[2] "Absolute Measurements in Electricity and Magnetism," by Andrew Gray, ed. of 1893, Vol. 2, part 1, p. 274, equation (53), and *Bur. Standards, Sci. Paper* 169, by E. B. Rosa and F. W. Grover, p. 59, equations (40) and (40a).

used for obtaining (17), the following alternative form of Gray's formula, for two coils as in Fig. 1, is obtained:

$$M = \frac{4\pi^2 a^2 n_1 n_2 m_1 q_2}{\rho_2} \left[1 - \frac{A^2 \delta^2}{2\rho_2^4} \left\{ \lambda_2 + \left(\frac{\delta}{\rho_2}\right)^2 \lambda_4 \xi_4'' \right. \right.$$
$$\left. \left. + \left(\frac{\delta}{\rho_2}\right)^4 \lambda_6 \xi_6'' + \cdots \right\} \right]$$
$$- \frac{4\pi^2 a^2 n_1 n_2 m_1 q_1}{\rho_1} \left[1 - \frac{A^2 \delta^2}{2\rho_1^4} \left\{ \lambda_2 + \left(\frac{\delta}{\rho_1}\right)^2 \lambda_4 \xi_4' \right. \right.$$
$$\left. \left. + \left(\frac{\delta}{\rho_1}\right)^4 \lambda_6 \xi_6' + \cdots \right\} \right] \quad \text{abhenries} \quad (18)$$

where $q_1 = s - m_2$
$\qquad q_2 = s + m_2$
$\qquad \rho_1^2 = A^2 + q_1^2$
$\qquad \rho_2^2 = A^2 + q_2^2$
$\qquad \delta^2 = a^2 + m_1^2$

where λ_2, λ_4, etc., are the same as for (17), where ξ_n' is the same function of A/ρ_1 that λ_n is of a/δ, and where ξ_n'' is the same function of A/ρ_2 that λ_n is of a/δ. The quantities n_1 and n_2 are the numbers of turns per centimeter of the two coils, respectively.

Since the coefficients in (18) are less than unity, the rapidity of convergence of the series is evident at once from the values of δ/ρ_1 and δ/ρ_2. The formula also has been simplified to some extent.

If the two coils of Fig. 1 are concentric, $s = 0$, $\rho_1 = \rho_2$, and (18) becomes the same as (17).

The convergence of (18) may be improved by employing the principle of interchange of lengths if, by so doing, a smaller value of δ results.

The convergence of Gray's formula and the alternative form (18), like that of (7) and (9), improves as the distance between the two solenoids is increased, but for loosely coupled coils this advantage is offset by the difficulty that the MI is obtained as the small difference of much larger terms. Thus each series has to be calculated to a much higher accuracy than that required in the value of the MI.

This difficulty may be avoided by the use of the following formula derived from (18) by F. W. Grover [equation (19) in footnote 1]:

Writing $\rho_1 = q_1 \sqrt{1 + \dfrac{A^2}{q_1^2}}$ and $\rho_2 = q_2 \sqrt{1 + \dfrac{A^2}{q_2^2}}$ and expanding powers of ρ_1 and ρ_2 in (18) by the binomial theorem, there results the expression:

$$
\begin{aligned}
M = \frac{2\pi^2 a^2 A^2 N_1 N_2 s}{q_1^2 q_2^2} &\left[1 + \frac{2\delta^2}{q_1^2}\left(\lambda_2 - \frac{3}{4}\frac{A^2}{\delta^2}\right)\left(1 + \frac{m_2^2}{s^2}\right)\frac{s^2}{q_2^2} \right.\\
&+ \frac{3\delta^4}{q_1^4}\left(\lambda_4 - \frac{5}{2}\frac{A^2}{\delta^2}\lambda_2 + \frac{5}{8}\frac{A^4}{\delta^4}\right)\left(1 + \frac{10}{3}\frac{m_2^2}{s^2} + \frac{m_2^4}{s^4}\right)\frac{s^4}{q_2^4}\\
&+ \frac{4\delta^6}{q_1^6}\left(\lambda_6 - \frac{21}{4}\lambda_4\frac{A^2}{\delta^2} + \frac{35}{8}\frac{A^4}{\delta^4}\lambda_2 - \frac{35}{64}\frac{A^6}{\delta^6}\right)\left(1 + 7\frac{m_2^2}{s^2}\right.\\
&\left.\left. + 7\frac{m_2^4}{s^4} + \frac{m_2^6}{s^6}\right)\frac{s^6}{q_2^6} + \cdots \right] \quad (19)
\end{aligned}
$$

in which N_1 and N_2 are the total numbers of turns on the coils.

This formula is simpler and more accurate the looser the coupling of the coils, that is, in just those cases where formulas (1) and (7) require the greatest care. The coefficients of $\dfrac{\delta^n}{q_1^n}$ are less than unity.

Here also the principle of interchange of lengths should be employed so that δ may have the smaller of the two lengths that are possible.

Solenoid and Single Turn. The MI of a solenoid and a coaxial circular filament in its end plane is of interest in connection with problems of inductance and of force between coils.

If in Fig. 4, R is of length x, and if P becomes a small element of length dx and Q becomes 0, then by equation (1a),

$$2M_{Rp} = M_{(R+P)(r+p)} - M_{Rr} - M_{Pp}$$

Mutual inductance is proportional to the voltage developed in one coil by one unit of alternating current in the other ($V = j2\pi f M$). $M_{(R+P)(r+p)} - M_{Rr}$ is the change in MI due to the addition of P and p. It is closely proportional to twice the voltage developed in P by current in r, while M_{Pp} is proportional to the voltage developed in P by current in p and so is negligible compared with the former quantity when p becomes very small. The turns in P are $n_2\,dx$. Then

$$2M_{Rp} = dM_{Rr} = d[n_1 n_2 M'_{(x)}] \qquad \text{by} \quad (12)$$

If p has only one turn,

$$2M_{Rp} = \frac{d[n_1 n_2 M'_{(x)}]}{n_2 dx} = n_1 \frac{d}{dx} M'_{(x)}$$

That is, the MI of a solenoid with n turns per centimeter and a coaxial circular filament in its end plane is

$$M = \frac{n}{2} \frac{d}{dx} M'_{(x)} \tag{20}$$

Note that this is equal to $4m_1 m_2 n G_{(x)}$ where $G_{(x)}$ is the expression used in computing force between two solenoids (Chap. 33).

For small values of x, the derivative of (6) may be taken from the first step of the integration by which (6) was obtained. This gives, for a short solenoid of n turns per centimeter and a circle lying near it in its end plane,

$$
\begin{aligned}
M = \pi n x \sqrt{Dd} &\left[\left\{ \log n \frac{16Dd}{x^2 + c^2} \right\} \left\{ 1 + \frac{3}{4} \frac{c^2}{Dd} - \frac{15}{64} \frac{c^4}{D^2 d^2} \right. \right. \\
&+ \frac{35}{256} \frac{c^6}{D^3 d^3} + \frac{x^2}{4Dd} \left(1 - \frac{5}{8} \frac{c^2}{Dd} + \frac{35}{64} \frac{c^4}{D^2 d^2} \right) - \frac{3}{64} \frac{x^4}{D^2 d^2} \\
&\times \left(1 - \frac{7}{4} \frac{c^2}{Dd} \right) + \frac{5}{256} \frac{x^6}{D^3 d^3} \cdots \left. \right\} - \left\{ \frac{2c}{x} \tan^{-1} \frac{x}{c} \right\} \\
&\times \left\{ 1 + \frac{c^2}{2Dd} - \frac{c^4}{8D^2 d^2} + \frac{c^6}{16D^3 d^3} \right\} + \left(-2 + \frac{c^2}{2Dd} \right. \\
&+ \frac{15}{64} \frac{c^4}{D^2 d^2} - \frac{151}{768} \frac{c^6}{D^3 d^3} \right) + \frac{x^2}{Dd} \left(\frac{c^2}{4Dd} - \frac{209}{768} \frac{c^4}{D^2 d^2} \right) \\
&+ \frac{x^4}{D^2 d^2} \left(\frac{5}{64} - \frac{43}{256} \frac{c^2}{Dd} \right) - \frac{31}{768} \frac{x^6}{D^3 d^3} \cdots \left. \right] \quad \text{abhenries} \tag{21}
\end{aligned}
$$

where the letters have the same meanings as in (6).   Note that logn denotes natural logarithm.

The fact that (21) is unchanged when D and d are interchanged, furnishes a proof of the principle of interchange of lengths for the special case of a solenoid and a circular filament, as given at the top of p. 101 of *Bur. Standards Sci. Paper* 169.

By putting $x^2 = r^2 - A^2$ and collecting like terms together, a change may be made in (56) of *Sci. Paper* 169, similar to that made in obtaining (17) and (18).   The same result may be obtained by differentiating (7) with respect to x.   This gives the following alternative formula to (56) of the above-mentioned paper, for the MI of a solenoid and a circular filament in its end plane. It may be useful for long coils where it might be undesirable to have the large quantity x in the numerators of the terms. In (22), A^2/r^2 and a^2/r^2 are always less than unity.

Mutual inductance of a solenoid of radius A, length x, and turns per centimeter n, and a coaxial circle of radius a in the plane of one end of the solenoid:

$$
\begin{aligned}
M = \frac{2\pi^2 a^2 x n}{r} &\left[1 + \frac{3}{8} \frac{a^2 A^2}{r^4} - \frac{5}{16} \frac{a^4 A^2}{r^6} + \frac{35}{64} \frac{a^4 A^4}{r^8} \right. \\
&+ \frac{35}{128} \frac{a^6 A^2}{r^8} - \frac{315}{256} \frac{a^6 A^4}{r^{10}} - \frac{63}{256} \frac{a^8 A^2}{r^{10}} + \frac{1{,}155}{1{,}024} \frac{a^6 A^6}{r^{12}} \\
&+ \frac{2{,}079}{1{,}024} \frac{a^8 A^4}{r^{12}} + \frac{231}{1{,}024} \frac{a^{10} A^2}{r^{12}} - \frac{9{,}009}{2{,}048} \frac{a^8 A^6}{r^{14}} - \frac{3{,}003}{1{,}024} \frac{a^{10} A^4}{r^{14}} \\
&\left. - \frac{429}{2{,}048} \frac{a^{12} A^2}{r^{14}} + \cdots \right] \quad \text{abhenries} \quad (22)
\end{aligned}
$$

where $r^2 = x^2 + A^2$. The dimension A may be greater or less than a. See equation (1) in Mechanical Forces in Transformers, by J. E. Clem, *Trans. A.I.E.E.*, 1927, p. 577.

It is to be noted that the expression for the force between two coaxial solenoids is given by the same algebraic series as is the MI between a solenoid and a single turn of wire.

Equations (21) and (22) are to be used twice when the plane of the circle does not pass through one end of the solenoid. In appropriate cases, (21) may be used for a short part of a solenoid and (22) for a long part.

By the principle of interchange of lengths, M is the same for a solenoid of radius A and a single turn of radius a, as for a solenoid of radius a and a single turn of radius A. In other words, the radius of the single turn may be larger or smaller than that of the solenoid, as has been stated.

For equations (1), (6), (1a) and (17) to (22), see footnote 1.

Example 1. A M.I. problem where both (6) and (7) can be used to check each other.

$$A = 25, \qquad m_2 = 3, \qquad a = 20, \qquad m_1 = 2, \qquad s = 30 \quad \text{centimeters}$$
$$x_1 = 35, \qquad x_2 = 29, \qquad x_3 = 31, \qquad x_4 = 25$$

$\frac{1}{2} M'_{(x1)}$ by (6) = $10{,}000\pi \sqrt{12.80}$ [0.0614 + 2.6824 − 0.6290 − 0.7549 + 0.0299 + 0.0058 − 0.0016]

= 156,700   abhenries

$\frac{1}{2}M'_{(x1)}$ by (7) $= 20{,}000\pi^2[(1.7205 - 0.0157 + 0.0017 - 0.0007 - 0.0002$
$+ 0.0003 - 0.0001 - 0.0001) + (-1.0000 + 0.0800 + 0.0064$
$+ 0.0013 + 0.0004)]$
$= 20{,}000\pi^2(1.7057 - 0.9119)$
$= 156{,}700$ abhenries

In a case such as this, where both (6) and (7) are applicable, not many significant figures can be obtained. However, if (6) is used for a much smaller value of x, or (7) for a larger value, the last terms may be smaller than 10^{-7} and so 7 or more significant figures can be obtained.

Example 2. M for a solenoid of one turn per centimeter and a circle in its end plane, with dimensions as in Example 1.

By (21), $M = 35\pi \sqrt{2{,}000}\ [3.721 - 0.411 - 1.994 + 0.002 + 0.029$
$$- 0.009] = 6{,}580$$

By (22), $M = \dfrac{2\pi^2 \times 400 \times 35}{\sqrt{1{,}850}}\ [1 + 0.0274 - 0.0049 + 0.0029 + 0.0009$
$- 0.0014 - 0.0002 + 0.0004 + 0.0005 - 0.0004 - 0.0002]$
$= 6{,}580$ abhenries

Example 3. Two concentric, coaxial coils. Inner solenoid, $a = 2$. $2m_1 = 2$. Outer solenoid, $A = 10$, $2m_2 = 5$. (Example 39, p. 84, *Sci. Paper* 169.)

$$\frac{M}{n_1 n_2} = 160\pi^2(1.055\ 268 - 1.006\ 331) = 77.279 \qquad \text{by (7)}$$

Equation (43) of *Sci. Paper* 169 gives 77.27980. It is a better series for this case, in which the coils are too short for more than five significant figures to be given by (7), and in which $c^2/(Dd) = 0.8$ is too large for (6) to be used. However, equation (7) is applicable to coils that are not concentric, while (43) is not.

Example 4. Two concentric, coaxial solenoids. Inner solenoid, $a = 10$, $2m_1 = 20$. Outer solenoid, $A = 15$, $2m_2 = 200$. (Example 43, p. 91, *Sci. Paper* 169.)

By (7), $M'_{(110)} = 6{,}000\pi^2(7.401\ 200 - 0.000\ 137 + 0.000\ 001)$
$= 6{,}000\pi^2 \times 7.401\ 064$
$M'_{(90)} = 6{,}000\pi^2(6.082\ 762 - 0.000\ 247 + 0.000\ 001)$
$= 6{,}000\pi^2 \times 6.082\ 516$

$$\frac{M}{n_1 n_2} = 6{,}000\ \pi^2(7.401\ 064 - 6.082\ 516) \qquad\qquad (10)$$

$$\frac{M}{4\pi n_1 n_2} = 6{,}213.51$$

This agrees with the values given on p. 91 of *Sci. Paper* 169. On p. 92, a solution that occupies more than a page is given by means of (45) on p. 65 of that paper, which is a formula for two coaxial solenoids that may or may not be concentric. As stated on p. 91, if a series formula can give the accuracy required, it is usually preferable to (45). It is evident that, by using more terms of (7) of this paper, more than six significant figures could be obtained in this case.

Example 5.   As an example of the use of formula (19) there may be taken the case where $a = 2$, $A = 3$, $2m_1 = 10$, $2m_2 = 6$, $s = 18$. Assuming further that $n_1 = n_2 = 10$, it follows that the coils have 100 turns and 60 turns, respectively. $q_1 = 15$, $q_2 = 21$, $\delta^2 = 29$.

Then (19) gives

$$M = \frac{7.776\pi^2 10^6}{(315)^2} \left[1 + 0.102\ 358 - 0.002\ 076 - 0.001\ 039 \cdots \right]$$
$$= 850.17$$

A more rapidly convergent series is obtained if the lengths are interchanged, giving $2m_1 = 6$, $2m_2 = 10$, $s = 18$, $q_1 = 13$, $q_2 = 23$ and $\delta^2 = 13$. The MI is then

$$M = \frac{7.776\pi^2 10^6}{(299)^2} \left[1 - 0.005\ 855 - 0.004\ 150 + 0.000\ 392 + \cdots \right]$$
$$= 850.19$$

If the solution be carried through by (18),

$$M = 8,000\pi^2[0.989\ 447 - 0.978\ 679] = 850.21$$

with $2m_1 = 10$ and $2m_2 = 6$ and, if the lengths be interchanged,

$$M = 4,800\pi^2[0.991\ 508 - 0.973\ 561] = 850.22$$

CHAPTER 28

AN EXTENSION OF A MAXWELL MUTUAL-INDUCTANCE FORMULA TO APPLY TO THICK SOLENOIDS

The formula for the mutual inductance (MI) of two concentric solenoids which is used probably more than any other is the one originally given by Maxwell. Since the solenoids were taken to have negligible thickness in that formula and since the effect of the thickness is often appreciable in practical cases, additional terms to give the effect of the thickness have been calculated and are given in this chapter.[1]

As given by Maxwell,[2] the formula included terms as far as the one in a^4/A^4 of equation (4) of this chapter. The term in a^6/A^6 was added by E. B. Rosa and L. Cohen.[3] The formula was further extended to include the term in a^{14}/A^{14} by E. B. Rosa and F. W. Grover.[4]

The effect of the thickness of two coaxial solenoids on their MI may be found in accordance with the general method described by Maxwell.[5]

The MI of two coils may be described as being proportional to the voltage at the terminals of one coil when unit alternating current flows in the other coil. In the case of cylindrical coils, it may be derived from an expression for the MI of two circular turns of fine wire by summing up the voltage in every turn of one coil, produced by the current in every turn of the other. If the space for insulation is assumed to have negligible effect, the summation may be done by integrating.

If M_p is the MI of two coils of equal length and of radii $a + y_1$ $A + y_2$, whose thickness is negligible and whose numbers of

---

[1] See the paper by H. B. Dwight and S. H. Chen, *Physics*, Vol. 4, p. 323, 1933.

[2] "Electricity and Magnetism," by Maxwell, Vol. II, Par. 678.

[3] *Bur. Standards Bull.*, Vol. 3, No. 2, 1907.

[4] *Bur. Standards Bull.*, Vol. 8, No. 1, equation (36), 1912, or *Bur. Standards Sci. Paper* 169.

[5] "Electricity and Magnetism," by Maxwell, Vol. II, Par. 700.

turns are N_1 and N_2, then the MI of two coils as in Fig. 1, of thickness t_1 and t_2, is

$$M = \frac{1}{t_1 t_2} \int_{y_1 = -\frac{1}{2}t_1}^{\frac{1}{2}t_1} \int_{y_2 = -\frac{1}{2}t_2}^{\frac{1}{2}t_2} M_p \, dy_2 \, dy_1 \tag{1}$$

Now $M_p = f(a + y_1, A + y_2)$ and this, by Taylor's theorem, when expressed symbolically, is equal to

$$f(a,A) + (y_1 D_a + y_2 D_A)f(a,A) + \left(\frac{1}{2!}\right)(y_1 D_a + y_2 D_A)^2 f(a,A)$$

$$+ \cdots + \left(\frac{1}{n!}\right)(y_1 D_a + y_2 D_A)^n f(a,A) + \cdots \tag{2}$$

where $f(a,A) = M_s$, the MI of the central solenoids of infini-

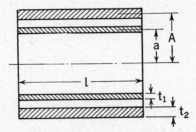

Fig. 1.—Two concentric coaxial solenoids of equal length.

tesimal thickness. Performing the integrations indicated in (1), there is obtained[6]

$$M = M_s + \frac{t_1^2}{3! \, 1! \, 2^2}\frac{\partial^2 M_s}{\partial a^2} + \frac{t_2^2}{1! \, 3! \, 2^2}\frac{\partial^2 M_s}{\partial A^2} + \frac{t_1^4}{5! \, 1! \, 2^4}\frac{\partial^4 M_s}{\partial a^4}$$

$$+ \frac{t_1^2 t_2^2}{3! \, 3! \, 2^4}\frac{\partial^4 M_s}{\partial a^2 \partial A^2} + \frac{t_2^4}{1! \, 5! \, 2^4}\frac{\partial^4 M_s}{\partial A^4} + \frac{t_1^6}{7! \, 1! \, 2^6}\frac{\partial^6 M_s}{\partial a^6}$$

$$+ \frac{t_1^4 t_2^2}{5! \, 3! \, 2^6}\frac{\partial^6 M_s}{\partial a^4 \partial A^2} + \frac{t_1^2 t_2^4}{3! \, 5! \, 2^6}\frac{\partial^6 M_s}{\partial a^2 \partial A^4} + \frac{t_2^6}{1! \, 7! \, 2^6}\frac{\partial^6 M_s}{\partial A^6} + \cdots \tag{3}$$

The series can be extended by inspection. With t_1^8 one writes $1/9!$; with t_1^6, $1/7!$; with t_1^4, $1/5!$; with t_1^2, $1/3!$ and similarly with powers of t_2, according to the arrangement in equation (3).

See corresponding formulas in (7), Chap. 26; (47), Chap. 32; and (10), Chap. 33.

[6] *Trans. A.I.E.E.*, 1919, paper by H. B. Dwight, equation (12), p. 1689.

The formula for M_s in abhenries, from *Bur. Standards Sci. Paper* 169, equation (36), is

$$M_s = \frac{4\pi^2 N_1 N_2 a^2 A}{l^2}\left[Q_1 + \frac{a^2}{8A^2} Q_3 + \frac{a^4}{64A^4} Q_5 \right.$$
$$\left. + \frac{5}{1{,}024}\frac{a^6}{A^6} Q_7 + \cdots \right] \quad (4)$$

where dimensions are in centimeters and are as in Fig. 1. N_1 and N_2 are the numbers of turns in the two coils,

$$r^2 = l^2 + A^2 \tag{5}$$

$$\mu = \frac{A}{r} \tag{6}$$

$$Q_1 = \frac{r}{A} - 1 \tag{7}$$

$$Q_3 = 1 - \mu^3 \tag{8}$$
$$Q = 1 + 4\mu^5 - 5\mu^7 \tag{9}$$
$$Q_7 = 1 - 8\mu^7 + 28\mu^9 - 21\mu^{11} \tag{10}$$

Derivatives of M_s with respect to a and A can be directly written down and substituted in (3) and the following terms giving the correction for thickness are obtained:

$$M = M_s + \Delta M \tag{11}$$

$$\Delta M =$$
$$\frac{4\pi^2 N_1 N_2}{l^2}\left[\frac{t_1^2 A}{24}\left(2Q_1 + \frac{3}{2}\frac{a^2}{A^2} Q_3 + \frac{15}{32}\frac{a^4}{A^4} Q_5 + \frac{35}{128}\frac{a^6}{A^6} Q_7 + \cdots \right) \right.$$
$$+ \frac{t_2^2 \bar{A}}{24}\left(\frac{a^2}{A^2} R_1 + \frac{a^4}{4A^4} R_3 + \frac{a^6}{16A^6} R_5 + \frac{5}{1{,}024}\frac{a^8}{A^8} R_7 + \cdots \right)$$
$$+ \frac{t_1^4}{1{,}920 A}\left(3Q_3 + \frac{45}{8}\frac{a^2}{A^2} Q_5 + \frac{525}{64}\frac{a^4}{A^4} Q_7 + \cdots \right)$$
$$+ \frac{t_1^2 t_2^2}{576 A}\left(2R_1 + 3\frac{a^2}{A^2} R_3 + \frac{15}{8}\frac{a^4}{A^4} R_5 + \frac{35}{128}\frac{a^6}{A^6} R_7 + \cdots \right)$$
$$+ \frac{t_2^4}{1{,}920 A}\left(3\frac{a^2}{A^2} S_3 + \frac{3}{8}\frac{a^4}{A^4} S_5 + \frac{45}{64}\frac{a^6}{A^6} S_7 + \frac{105}{128}\frac{a^8}{A^8} S_9 + \cdots \right)$$
$$\left. + \text{terms in } t_1^6, \text{ etc.} \right] \quad (12)$$

where Q_1 to Q_7 are given by equations (7) to (10),

$$R_1 = \mu - \mu^3 \tag{13}$$
$$R_3 = 1 - \mu^3 + \tfrac{15}{2}\mu^5 - \tfrac{15}{2}\mu^7 \tag{14}$$

$$R_5 = 3 + 2\mu^5 - 40\mu^7 + \tfrac{455}{4}\mu^9 - \tfrac{315}{4}\mu^{11} \tag{15}$$

$$R_7 = 30 - 16\mu^7 + 616\mu^9 - 3{,}402\mu^{11} + 5{,}775\mu^{13} - 3{,}003\mu^{15} \tag{16}$$

$$S_3 = -\mu^3 + 6\mu^5 - 5\mu^7 \tag{17}$$

$$S_5 = 8 + 12\mu^5 - 195\mu^7 + 490\mu^9 - 315\mu^{11} \tag{18}$$

$$S_7 = 8 - 8\mu^7 + 252\mu^9 - 1{,}253\mu^{11} + 2{,}002\mu^{13} - 1{,}001\mu^{15} \tag{19}$$

$$S_9 = 10 + 8\mu^9 - 414\mu^{11} + 3{,}399\mu^{13} - \frac{77{,}649}{8}\mu^{15} + \frac{45{,}045}{4}\mu^{17}$$

$$- \frac{36{,}465}{8}\mu^{19} \tag{20}$$

As a numerical example of (12), the pair of coils described on page 77 of *Sci. Paper* 169[4] may be used, giving each coil a thickness of 1 cm. We have

$$a = 5, \quad A = 10, \quad t_1 = t_2 = 1, \quad l = 200, \quad M_s = \left(\frac{4\pi^2 N_1 N_2}{l^2}\right) \times 4{,}764.3$$

$$r = 200.25, \quad Q_1 = 19.025, \quad Q_3 = 0.9999, \quad Q_5 = 1.000,$$

$$R_1 = 0.0498, \quad R_3 = 0.9999, \quad R_5 = 3.00$$

The series involving $t_1{}^2$ in the square bracket of (12) is

$$\left(\frac{10}{24}\right)(38.050 + 0.375 + 0.029 + 0.004 + \cdots) = \frac{38.46}{2.4} = 16.02$$

The corresponding series in $t_2{}^2$ is

$$\left(\frac{10}{24}\right)(0.012 + 0.016 + 0.003 + \cdots) = \frac{0.031}{2.4} = 0.01$$

$$\Delta M = \left(\frac{4\pi^2 N_1 N_2}{l^2}\right)[16.02 + 0.01 + \cdots]$$

$$\frac{\Delta M}{M_s} = \frac{16.0}{4{,}764.3} = 0.0034 \text{ or } 0.34\%$$

An alternative method of computation of the MI of two thick concentric coils of equal length is to use equation (14) of Chap. 27, as described in that chapter following equation (1a).

CHAPTER 29

MUTUAL INDUCTANCE OF TWO ADJACENT THIN DISK COILS IN AIR

When the axial length, b, of the coaxial coils of Fig. 3, Chap. 27, becomes very small, the coils become thin disk coils and equation (14), Chap. 27, becomes unworkable. The following formula[1] for two infinitely thin, coaxial, duplicate, disk coils (see Fig. 1) may be used.

$$
M = \frac{\pi d N_1 N_2}{0.3937 \times 10^9} \left[\left(\operatorname{logn} \frac{16d^2}{s^2 + t^2} \right) \left(1 + \frac{3}{4} \frac{s^2}{d^2} + \frac{t^2}{24d^2} \right. \right.
$$
$$
\left. - \frac{15}{64} \frac{s^4}{d^4} + \frac{7}{64} \frac{s^2 t^2}{d^4} + \frac{11}{2,880} \frac{t^4}{d^4} \cdots \right)
$$
$$
+ \left(\frac{s^2}{t^2} \operatorname{logn} \frac{s^2 + t^2}{s^2} \right) \left(1 + \frac{5}{8} \frac{s^2}{d^2} - \frac{161}{576} \frac{s^4}{d^4} + \frac{5}{8} \frac{s^2 t^2}{d^4} \cdots \right)
$$
$$
- 4 \left(\frac{s}{t} \tan^{-1} \frac{t}{s} \right) \left(1 + \frac{2}{3} \frac{s^2}{d^2} - \frac{2}{5} \frac{s^4}{d^4} + \frac{2}{9} \frac{s^2 t^2}{d^4} \cdots \right)
$$
$$
\left. - 1 + \frac{37}{24} \frac{s^2}{d^2} + \frac{43}{144} \frac{t^2}{d^2} - \frac{301}{360} \frac{s^4}{d^4} - \frac{s^2 t^2}{720 d^4} + \frac{t^4}{75 d^4} \cdots \right]
$$
$$
\text{henries} \quad (1)
$$

where d = mean diameter of the coils.
t = their radial depth.
s = axial spacing.
N_1, N_2 = numbers of turns in the two coils.
The dimensions are in inches. If they are in centimeters, omit the number 0.3937.

The formula for mutual inductance (MI) of two circles which was integrated twice in order to obtain (1), was given by Clerk Maxwell in "Electricity and Magnetism," Vol. 2, Par. 705, and was extended to a considerable number of terms by E. B. Rosa and L. Cohen in *Bur. Standards Bull.*, Vol. 2, 1906, p. 366 [see equation (14) *Sci. Paper* 169].

[1] Mutual Inductance and Repulsion of Two Adjacent Disk Coils, by H. B. Dwight and T. Y. Lu, *Jour. Math. Phys.*, Vol. 9, p. 315, 1930.

A very complete collection of MI formulas is given in *Bur. Standards Sci. Paper* 169, by E. B. Rosa and F. W. Grover. Four formulas applicable to disk-shaped coils are given, and their characteristics are compared. Three of these formulas, namely, (21) due to Rowland, (24) due to Rayleigh, and (28) due to Lyle, are for coils at a considerable distance apart, and the formulas become more accurate, the greater the distance between the coils.

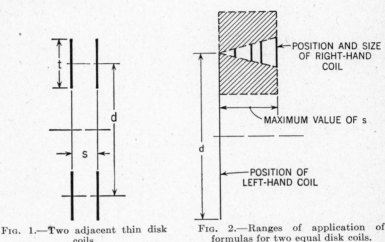

Fig. 1.—Two adjacent thin disk coils.

Fig. 2.—Ranges of application of formulas for two equal disk coils.

A fourth formula, (29) by E. B. Rosa, contains terms in $\dfrac{t^2 s^2}{d^4}$ and $\dfrac{b^2 s^2}{d^4}$, using the notation of this chapter, b being axial length. Consequently, as stated on p. 40 of *Sci. Paper* 169, formula (29) becomes less exact as s is greater. However, it does not follow that (29) is suitable for small values of s in many cases. It contains a series of terms in $\dfrac{t^2}{s^2}, \dfrac{t^4}{s^4}, \dfrac{t^6}{s^6}, \cdots$, and accordingly it is unsuitable for very small values of s such as would be obtained in the case of two thin, flat coils close together, as in Fig. 1. Formula (29) contains terms of the second, fourth, and sixth degrees. In order that the formula should give a precise result, the terms of the sixth degree should be practically negligible and should be distinctly smaller than similar terms of the fourth degree. Some terms of the sixth degree, namely those in $1/a^6$, are not included in this formula, a being the mean radius, and so the terms in $1/a^4$ should be practically negligible.

Although it is desirable that each user of a formula determine the degree of precision being obtained by watching the values of terms of different degrees, an approximate idea of the range in which ordinary accuracy can be obtained is given in Fig. 2.

For equation (29) of *Sci. Paper* 169, the ratio t/s should not be greater than about $\frac{1}{2}$ and the ratio s/d should not be greater than about $\frac{1}{3}$. The cross section of the right-hand coil should, therefore, lie within the unshaded volume indicated in Fig. 2. A few possible sizes are indicated.

Formula (1) of this paper contains no terms with s in the denominator, and so the smaller s is, the more precise is the result. The ratio s/d should not be greater than about $\frac{1}{3}$ and t/d should not be more than about $\frac{1}{2}$. The increase in the range which can be covered is shown by the shaded area in Fig. 2.

In using formula (1), terms of the fourth degree should be practically negligible and should be distinctly smaller than those of the second degree.

A direct check on some of the terms of formula (1) can be obtained by putting $s = 0$, in which case it becomes a self-inductance formula, namely, the formula for thin disk coils derived by T. R. Lyle.[2] It is allowable, in this way, to add two terms to formula (1), namely a term $\dfrac{103}{105 \times 1,024} \dfrac{t^6}{d^6}$ to the bracket following $\log_n \dfrac{16d^2}{s^2 + t^2}$ and a term $\dfrac{98,579}{88,200 \times 512} \dfrac{t^6}{d^6}$ to be added after $- \dfrac{301}{360} \dfrac{s^4}{d^4}$. These terms may improve the accuracy when the coils are very close together and s/d is very small. However, in general the additional terms are not very useful unless the corresponding terms in $\dfrac{t^4 s^2}{d^6}$, etc., are available.

A comparison of the numerical results given by formulas (1) of this chapter and (29) of *Sci. Paper* 169 can be made in cases where both series are rapidly convergent. For instance, when $s/d = \frac{1}{4}$, $t/s = \frac{1}{2}$, and $b = 0$, both formulas give $M = 1.737 \pi d N_1 N_2$.

[2] See *Phil. Trans.* of the Royal Soc., Vol. 213A, p. 421, 1914, *Bur. Standards Sci. Paper* 320, p. 557, and *Sci. Paper* 455, equation (26).

When the coils are closer together, as $s/d = \frac{1}{10}$ and $t/s = \frac{1}{2}$, more significant figures can be obtained. In this case, both formulas give $M = 3.3893\pi d N_1 N_2$.

Formula (1) has been checked by a laboratory measurement on two duplicate disk-shaped coils for which $d = 23.56$ cm, $t = 8.32$ cm, $s = 4.68$ cm, and $N = 516$. The tested value of MI was 0.0374 henry. The calculated value by (1) is 0.0366 henry, the difference being 2 per cent.

CHAPTER 30

MUTUAL INDUCTANCE OF COILS WITH PARALLEL AXES

The common method of mounting reactance coils is with parallel axes, that is, side by side, and it is desirable to have formulas which apply to coils in this position. The values of

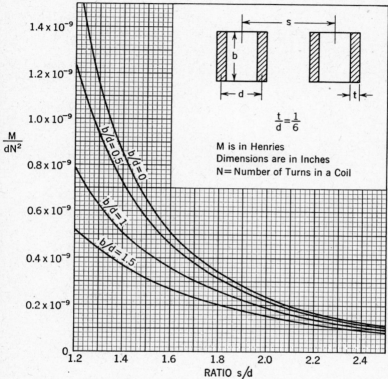

Fig. 1.—Mutual inductance of reactance coils with parallel axes.

mutual inductance (MI) derived in the following paragraphs are useful for calculating the unbalance in voltage and the means for correcting it, when three coils are placed side by side and connected in a three-phase circuit. The calculation is very exact for widely separated coils, and it has an accuracy within a small percentage for coils placed as close together as it is usual to mount reactance coils. For usual engineering problems where precise accuracy is not required, it is not necessary to calculate the results, but values for equal coils may be read from the curves of Fig. 1, thus saving the labor of computation. The calculations for equal, or duplicate, coils will be taken up first.[1]

A formula for the MI of two circles formed of one turn of infinitesimally thin wire has been given by S. Butterworth [*Bur. Standards Sci. Paper* 320, June, 1918, equation (10*A*) and in *Phil. Mag.*, Vol. 31, p. 443, 1916] for the case when the axes of the circles are parallel and when the distance between the centers of the circles is somewhat larger than their diameters. In order to obtain a formula suitable for commercial reactance coils of many turns, the above-mentioned formula has been integrated four times over the rectangular section of a cylindrical coil, with the following result, for two equal coils placed as in Fig. 1:

$$
\begin{aligned}
M = \frac{2\pi^2 a^3 N^2}{0.3937 b^2 10^9} &\left[\frac{a}{r}\left(\frac{r}{s} - 1\right)\left(1 + \frac{c^2}{6a^2} + \frac{c^4}{144a^4}\right) \right.\\
&+ \frac{a^3}{2r^3}\left(1 - \frac{3}{2}\frac{s^2}{r^2} + \frac{r^3}{2s^3}\right)\left(1 + \frac{7}{12}\frac{c^2}{a^2} + \frac{13}{240}\frac{c^4}{a^4} + \frac{c^6}{960a^6}\right)\\
&- \frac{5}{8}\frac{a^5}{r^5}\left(1 - \frac{5s^2}{r^2} + \frac{35}{8}\frac{s^4}{r^4} - \frac{3}{8}\frac{r^5}{s^5}\right)\\
&\left(1 + \frac{17}{15}\frac{c^2}{a^2} + \frac{169}{600}\frac{c^4}{a^4} + \frac{41}{2,800}\frac{c^6}{a^6} + \frac{113}{672,000}\frac{c^8}{a^8}\right)\\
&+ \frac{35}{32}\frac{a^7}{r^7}\left(1 - \frac{21}{2}\frac{s^2}{r^2} + \frac{189}{8}\frac{s^4}{r^4} - \frac{231}{16}\frac{s^6}{r^6} + \frac{5}{16}\frac{r^7}{s^7}\right)\\
&\left(1 + \frac{155}{84}\frac{c^2}{a^2} + \frac{2167}{2,520}\frac{c^4}{a^4} + \frac{541}{4,704}\frac{c^6}{a^6} + \frac{2,129}{3,136 \times 180}\frac{c^8}{a^8}\right.\\
&\left.\left. + \frac{197}{1,960 \times 3,456}\frac{c^{10}}{a^{10}}\right) + \cdots \right] \quad \text{henries} \quad (1)
\end{aligned}
$$

where $r^2 = s^2 + b^2$.

$a = \frac{1}{2}d =$ the mean radius of the coil.

$N =$ number of turns in each coil. See Fig. 1 for the meanings of the letters.

The dimensions are assumed to be given in inches; if they are given in centimeters, the factor 0.3937 should be omitted. In measuring the coil, each dimension should be taken as the number of wires or cables in that dimension times their pitch. The actual measured dimension over the copper should not be used, as it is slightly too small.

[1] Some New Formulas for Reactance Coils, by H. B. Dwight, *Trans. A.I.E.E.*, 1919, p. 1675.

It will be noted that formula (1) is indeterminate when $b = 0$ and therefore $r = s$. For such a case, the following formula should be used:

$$
\begin{aligned}
M = \frac{\pi^2 a^4 N^2}{0.3937 s^3 10^9} &\left[\left(1 + \frac{c^2}{6a^2} + \frac{c^4}{144a^4} \right) \right. \\
&+ \frac{9}{4}\frac{a^2}{s^2} \left(1 + \frac{7}{12}\frac{c^2}{a^2} + \frac{13}{240}\frac{c^4}{a^4} + \frac{c^6}{960a^2} \right) \\
&+ \frac{375}{64}\frac{a^4}{s^4} \left(1 + \frac{17}{15}\frac{c^2}{a^2} + \frac{169}{600}\frac{c^4}{a^4} + \frac{41}{2,800}\frac{c^6}{a^6} + \frac{113}{672,000}\frac{c^8}{a^8} \right) \\
&+ \frac{8,575}{512}\frac{a^6}{s^6} \left(1 + \frac{155}{84}\frac{c^2}{a^2} + \frac{2,167}{2,520}\frac{c^4}{a^4} + \frac{541}{4,704}\frac{c^6}{a^6} \right. \\
&\left.\left. + \frac{2,129}{3,136 \times 180}\frac{c^8}{a^8} + \frac{197}{1,960 \times 3,456}\frac{c^{10}}{a^{10}} \right) + \cdots \right] \text{henries} \quad (2)
\end{aligned}
$$

This gives the MI of two flat disks in the same plane.

The case outlined in Fig. 1, in which the two coils with parallel axes are alike and stand on the same plane, is the simplest for calculation. However, the formula for their MI is not very complicated, if the coils have parallel axes and are alike, and one stands on a plane a distance e higher than the other. It is as follows:

$$
\begin{aligned}
M = \frac{\pi^2 N^2}{0.3937 b^2 10^9} &\left[a^4 \left(\frac{1}{p} - \frac{2}{q} + \frac{1}{r} \right) \left(1 + \frac{c^2}{6a^2} + \frac{c^4}{144a^4} \right) \right. \\
&- \frac{a^6}{2} \left\{ \left(\frac{1}{p^3} - \frac{2}{q^3} + \frac{1}{r^3} \right) - \frac{3s^2}{2} \left(\frac{1}{p^5} - \frac{2}{q^5} + \frac{1}{r^5} \right) \right\} \left(1 + \frac{7}{12}\frac{c^2}{a^2} \right. \\
&\left. + \frac{13}{240}\frac{c^4}{a^4} + \frac{c^6}{960a^6} \right) + \frac{5a^8}{8} \left\{ \left(\frac{1}{p^5} - \frac{2}{q^5} + \frac{1}{r^5} \right) \right. \\
&- 5s^2 \left(\frac{1}{p^7} - \frac{2}{q^7} + \frac{1}{r^7} \right) + \frac{35s^4}{8} \left(\frac{1}{p^9} - \frac{2}{q^9} + \frac{1}{r^9} \right) \right\} \left(1 + \frac{17}{15}\frac{c^2}{a^2} \right. \\
&\left. + \frac{169}{600}\frac{c^4}{a^4} + \frac{41}{2,800}\frac{c^6}{a^6} + \frac{113}{672,000}\frac{c^8}{a^8} \right) - \frac{35a^{10}}{32} \left\{ \left(\frac{1}{p^7} - \frac{2}{q^7} + \frac{1}{r^7} \right) \right. \\
&- \frac{21s^2}{2} \left(\frac{1}{p^9} - \frac{2}{q^9} + \frac{1}{r^9} \right) + \frac{189s^4}{8} \left(\frac{1}{p^{11}} - \frac{2}{q^{11}} + \frac{1}{r^{11}} \right) \\
&\left. - \frac{231s^6}{16} \left(\frac{1}{p^{13}} - \frac{2}{q^{13}} + \frac{1}{r^{13}} \right) \right\} \left(1 + \frac{155}{84}\frac{c^2}{a^2} \right. \\
&+ \frac{2,167}{2,520}\frac{c^4}{a^4} + \frac{541}{4,704}\frac{c^6}{a^6} + \frac{2,129}{3,136 \times 180}\frac{c^8}{a^8} \\
&\left.\left. + \frac{197}{1,960 \times 3,456}\frac{c^{10}}{a^{10}} \right) + \cdots \right] \quad \text{henries} \quad (3)
\end{aligned}
$$

where $p^2 = s^2 + (b - e)^2$.

$\quad q^2 = s^2 + e^2$.

$\quad r^2 = s^2 + (b + e)^2$.

This formula includes the case of two duplicate coaxial coils, when the coils are not near to each other. When the coils are coaxial, the MI is opposite in sign to the value when the coils are side by side. There is a position, when two coils with parallel axes are diagonally from each other, for which the MI is zero.

Formulas (1) to (3) are not very rapidly convergent for s/d less than about 1.2.

Example 1. Find the voltage drop due to MI in each of three coils placed side by side in a row and carrying three-phase, 60-cycle current, 400 amp per phase, the data being as follows:

Mean radius of coils...................... $a = 12.76$ in.
Length of coils........................... $b = 30.87$ in.
Thickness of winding...................... $c = 4.87$ in.
Number of turns........................... $N = 114$
Distance between centers.................. 45 in.

Let the three coils in a row be called A, B, and C. For A and B, $s = 45$ in.

$$M_{AB} = 0.001\,42\,(0.0508 + 0.0061 + 0.0007 + 0.000\,08)$$
$$= 8.2 \times 10^{-5} \qquad\qquad \text{henry}$$

or using Fig. 1, $\qquad\qquad \dfrac{s}{d} = \dfrac{45}{25.52} = 1.76$

and $\qquad\qquad\qquad \dfrac{b}{d} = \dfrac{30.87}{25.52} = 1.21$

$$M_{AB} = 0.25 \times 10^{-9} \times 114^2 \times 25.52 = 8.3 \times 10^{-5} \qquad \text{henry}$$
$$\text{Using a spacing } s = 90 \text{ in.}$$
$$M_{AC} = 1.1 \times 10^{-5} \qquad\qquad \text{henry}$$

Let the currents in the three coils A, B, and C, which are 120 deg apart in phase, be

$$I_A = 400$$
$$I_B = -200 + j\,200\,\sqrt{3}$$
and $\qquad\qquad I_C = -200 - j\,200\,\sqrt{3}$

The drop in A due to MI is

$$2\pi \times 60j(I_B M_{AB} + I_C M_{AC}) = -9.3 - j\,7.0 \qquad \text{volts}$$

The drop in B due to MI is

$$2\pi \times 60j(I_A M_{AB} + I_C M_{BC}) = 10.7 + j\,6.2 \qquad \text{volts}$$

The drop in C due to MI is

$$2\pi \times 60j(I_A M_{AC} + I_B M_{BC}) = 10.7 - j\,4.5 \qquad \text{volts}$$

UNEQUAL COILS

In a group of reactors mounted in a power station there are sometimes more than one size of coil, and so it becomes of practical value to have methods of calculating the force and MI of unequal solenoids with parallel axes.[2]

The basis of this calculation, as in the former cases in this chapter, is the formula given by S. Butterworth for the MI of two unequal circles each formed of one turn of infinitesimally fine wire, the axes of the circles being parallel and separated by a distance larger than the sum of their radii. This expression has been integrated four times, so as to take account of the thicknesses of the solenoids as well as their lengths, the following result for unequal circular solenoids with parallel axes (Fig. 2) being obtained:

$$
\begin{aligned}
M = {} & \frac{\pi^2 A^2 a^2 N_1 N_2}{0.3937 B b 10^9} \left[\left(\frac{1}{G_1} - \frac{1}{G_2} - \frac{1}{G_3} + \frac{1}{G_4} \right) \left(1 + \frac{T^2}{12A^2} \right) \right. \\
& \left(1 + \frac{t^2}{12a^2} \right) - \frac{1}{8} \left\{ 2 \left(\frac{1}{G_1^3} - \frac{1}{G_2^3} - \frac{1}{G_3^3} + \frac{1}{G_4^3} \right) \right. \\
& \left. - 3s^2 \left(\frac{1}{G_1^5} - \frac{1}{G_2^5} - \frac{1}{G_3^5} + \frac{1}{G_4^5} \right) \right\} \left\{ A^2 \left(1 + \frac{T^2}{2A^2} + \frac{T^4}{80A^4} \right) \right. \\
& \left. \left(1 + \frac{t^2}{12a^2} \right) + a^2 \left(1 + \frac{T^2}{12A^2} \right) \left(1 + \frac{t^2}{2a^2} + \frac{t^4}{80a^4} \right) \right\} \\
& + \frac{1}{64} \left\{ 8 \left(\frac{1}{G_1^5} - \frac{1}{G_2^5} - \frac{1}{G_3^5} + \frac{1}{G_4^5} \right) \right. \\
& - 40s^2 \left(\frac{1}{G_1^7} - \frac{1}{G_2^7} - \frac{1}{G_3^7} + \frac{1}{G_4^7} \right) \\
& \left. + 35s^4 \left(\frac{1}{G_1^9} - \frac{1}{G_2^9} - \frac{1}{G_3^9} + \frac{1}{G_4^9} \right) \right\} \\
& \left\{ A^4 \left(1 + \frac{5}{4} \frac{T^2}{A^2} + \frac{3}{16} \frac{T^4}{A^4} + \frac{1}{448} \frac{T^6}{A^6} \right) \left(1 + \frac{t^2}{12a^2} \right) \right. \\
& + 3A^2 a^2 \left(1 + \frac{T^2}{2A^2} + \frac{T^4}{80A^4} \right) \left(1 + \frac{t^2}{2a^2} + \frac{t^4}{80a^4} \right) \\
& \left. \left. + a^4 \left(1 + \frac{T^2}{12A^2} \right) \left(1 + \frac{5}{4} \frac{t^2}{a^2} + \frac{3}{16} \frac{t^4}{a^4} + \frac{1}{448} \frac{t^6}{a^6} \right) \right\} \right] \text{ henries} \quad (4)
\end{aligned}
$$

---

[2] The Force between Unequal Reactance Coils Having Parallel Axes, by H. B. Dwight and R. W. Purssell, *Gen. Elec. Rev.*, July, 1930, p. 401.

where N_1, N_2 = turns in each coil.

$$G_1 = \left\{ s^2 + \left(u + \frac{B+b}{2} \right)^2 \right\}^{\frac{1}{2}}.$$

$$G_2 = \left\{ s^2 + \left(u - \frac{B-b}{2} \right)^2 \right\}^{\frac{1}{2}}.$$

$$G_3 = \left\{ s^2 + \left(u + \frac{B-b}{2} \right)^2 \right\}^{\frac{1}{2}}.$$

$$G_4 = \left\{ s^2 + \left(u - \frac{B+b}{2} \right)^2 \right\}^{\frac{1}{2}}.$$

The dimensions are as in Fig. 2 and are assumed to be given in inches; if they are given in centimeters, the factor 0.3937 should

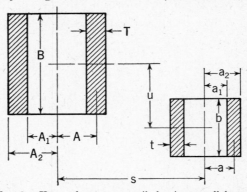

Fig. 2.—Unequal reactance coils having parallel axes.

be omitted. Each dimension of the coil should be taken equal to the number of wires or cables in that dimension times their pitch, the values of the dimensions thus being slightly greater than the actual lengths measured over the copper.

If the two coils are alike, so that $A = a$, $B = b$, $T = t$, and $N_1 = N_2$, this formula becomes the same as equation (1).

Formula (4) includes the case of two coaxial coils, when they are not near together. When the coils are coaxial, the MI is opposite in sign to the value when the coils are side by side.

Example 2. Two reactance coils with parallel axes, as shown in Fig. 2. Dimensions in inches. $A = 3.08$, $B = 5.62$, $T = 0.55$, $N_1 = 1142$, $a = 4.635$, $b = 0.95$, $t = 1.635$, $N_2 = 516$, $s = 12.20$, $u = 2.90$.

$$M = \frac{\pi^2 \times 3.08^2 \times 4.635^2 \times 1142 \times 516}{0.3937 \times 5.62 \times 0.95 \times 10^9} (0.00220 + 0.00030 + 0.00004)$$

$$= 1.43 \times 10^{-3} \qquad \text{henry (calculated)}$$

The MI was measured by passing 60-cycle current through one coil and reading the emf induced in the other. This gave

$$M = 1.47 \times 10^{-3} \qquad \text{henry (measured)}$$

Example 3. This example illustrates the use of the formulas with two unequal reactance coils of dimensions such as might be encountered in practical engineering. Dimensions are in inches.

Large coil, $A_1 = 26.1$, $A_2 = 38.1$, $B = 80$
Small coil, $a_1 = 5$, $a_2 = 9$, $b = 10$, $s = 59.5$, $u = 31$
Mutual inductance, $2.4 N_1 N_2 \times 10^{-9}$ henry

CHAPTER 31

SELF-INDUCTANCE OF CIRCULAR COILS WITHOUT IRON

Long Coils, $b/d >$ **Approximately 0.75.** By putting $A = a$ in equation (7), Chap. 27, the two solenoids merge together and the expression for mutual inductance becomes a formula for self-inductance of one solenoid.   The result is

$$L_s = \frac{\pi^2 d^3 N^2}{0.3937 \times 10^9 \times 2b^2} \left[\frac{1}{m} - \frac{8}{3\pi} - \frac{m^3}{8} + \frac{m^5}{16} - \frac{15}{128} m^7 \right.$$
$$\left. + \frac{21}{128} m^9 - \frac{315}{1,024} m^{11} + \frac{297}{512} m^{13} - \frac{39,039}{32,768} m^{15} + \cdots \right]$$
$$\text{henries} \quad (1)$$

where $m^2 = \dfrac{d^2}{d^2 + 4b^2} = \dfrac{a^2}{r^2}.$

$d = 2a =$ mean diameter of the solenoid.

$b =$ length of the solenoid.

$N =$ number of turns.

Dimensions are in inches; if in centimeters, omit 0.3937.

L_s is the inductance of a thin solenoid whose radial thickness is neglected.   Equation (1) is a current-sheet formula.

The inductance of a coil of appreciable radial thickness t is

$$L = L_s - \Delta L \quad (2)$$

$$\Delta L = \frac{\pi^2 d^3 N^2}{0.3937 \times 10^9 \times 2b^2} \left[\frac{4}{3} \frac{bt}{d^2} - \frac{2}{3} \frac{bt^2}{d^3} \right.$$
$$- \frac{t^2}{d^2} \left\{ \frac{2}{3\pi} \left(\operatorname{logn} \frac{4d}{t} - \frac{23}{12} \right) + \frac{m}{3} - \frac{5}{12} m^3 + \frac{2}{3} m^5 - \frac{95}{64} m^7 \right.$$
$$+ \frac{217}{64} m^9 - \frac{2,135}{256} m^{11} + \frac{21,571}{1,024} m^{13}$$
$$\left. - \frac{13 \times 68,915}{16,384} m^{15} + \cdots \right\} + \frac{t^4}{d^4} \left\{ \frac{1}{30\pi} \left(\operatorname{logn} \frac{4d}{t} - \frac{1}{20} \right) \right.$$
$$- \frac{m}{18} + \frac{17}{90} m^3 - \frac{53}{48} m^5 + \frac{1,265}{288} m^7 - \frac{38,857}{2,304} m^9 + \frac{3,913}{64} m^{11}$$

$$- \frac{231 \times 9{,}551}{10{,}240} \, m^{13} + \frac{143 \times 10{,}625}{2{,}048} \, m^{15} - \cdots \Big\}$$

$$+ \frac{t^6}{d^6} \left\{ \frac{1}{336\pi} \left(\frac{23}{20} \operatorname{logn} \frac{4d}{t} - \frac{4{,}547}{5{,}600} \right) + \frac{m^3}{60} - \frac{15}{56} \, m^5 \right.$$

$$+ \frac{1{,}117}{336} \, m^7 - \frac{1{,}183}{48} \, m^9 + \frac{21 \times 3{,}641}{512} \, m^{11}$$

$$- \frac{11 \times 367{,}621}{5{,}120} \, m^{13} + \frac{143 \times 109{,}353}{4{,}096} \, m^{15} - \cdots \Big\}$$

$$+ \cdots - \frac{4b^2}{\pi q d^2 N} \left(\operatorname{logn} \frac{p}{w} + 0.15 \right) \Big] \quad \text{henries} \quad (3)$$

The last term of (3) represents the effect of the air and insulation space between the conductors. The number of conductors in parallel is q. Dimension w is the conductor diameter and p is the pitch. It is assumed that the coil is wound with round wire or cable. If square wire is used, the constant 0.15 in the last term should be omitted. Therefore, with uniform current distribution over the section of the coil, as, for example, with square wire and infinitely thin insulation, the last term becomes zero. For precise work the constant 0.15, which is an average value, should be changed in accordance with the table in the *Bur. Standards Bull.*, Vol. 8, No. 1, p. 141, 1912.

As with mutual inductance, each dimension of the section of the coil should be taken to be the number of conductors along that dimension times the center-to-center distance, in that direction, between the conductors. The derivation of (1) and (3) is described in *Trans. A.I.E.E.*[1] Although (3) appears long, that is because a large number of terms have been worked out. For most practical purposes, only the first few terms are needed. As is usual with convergent series formulas, terms should be computed until they are found to be negligibly small.

For long coils of considerable thickness, extending to the case of coils of internal diameter equal to zero, the following formula may be used:[2]

[1] Some New Formulas for Reactance Coils, by H. B. Dwight, *Trans. A.I.E.E.*, 1919, p. 1675.

[2] Self-inductance of Long Reactance Coils, by H. B. Dwight, *Elec. World*, Feb. 9, 1918, equation (5), p. 301.

$$L = \frac{2\pi N^2 10^{-9}}{0.3937bt^2}\left[\frac{r^4}{3} - \frac{4}{3}rs^3 + s^4 - \frac{1}{b}\left(0.244\ 127\ 2\ r^5 - \frac{2}{3}r^2s^3\right.\right.$$

$$+ 0.427\ 755\ 9\ s^5 + \frac{s^5}{10}\operatorname{logn}\frac{r}{s}\Bigg) + \frac{s^5}{b}\left(0.004\ 464\ \frac{s^2}{r^2}\right.$$

$$+ 0.000\ 543\ \frac{s^4}{r^4} + 0.000\ 129\ \frac{s^6}{r^6} + \cdots\ \Bigg) + \frac{1}{9b^2}(r^3 - s^3)^2$$

$$- \frac{1}{30b^4}(r^3 - s^3)(r^5 - s^5) + \frac{1}{84b^6}(r^3 - s^3)(r^7 - s^7)$$

$$+ \frac{3}{200b^6}(r^5 - s^5)^2 - \frac{5}{864b^8}(r^3 - s^3)(r^9 - s^9)$$

$$- \frac{3}{112b^8}(r^5 - s^5)(r^7 - s^7)\cdots + \frac{bt^2(r+s)}{\pi qN}\left(\operatorname{logn}\frac{p}{w} + 0.15\right)\Bigg]$$

$$\text{henries}\quad(4)$$

where r = the outer radius.

s = the inner radius.

The constant 0.3937 indicates that the dimensions are in inches.

Short Coils, $b/d <$ Approximately 0.75. The following current-sheet formula for negligible radial thickness applies to short coils. It was published in *Bur. Standards Sci. Paper* 169, p. 117, equation (71).

$$L_s = \frac{2\pi dN^2}{0.3937 \times 10^9}\left[\left(\operatorname{logn}\frac{4d}{b}\right)\left(1 + \frac{b^2}{8d^2} - \frac{b^4}{64d^4} + \frac{5}{1,024}\frac{b^6}{d^6}\right.\right.$$

$$\left.- \frac{35}{16,384}\frac{b^8}{d^8}\cdots\right) - \frac{1}{2} + \frac{b^2}{32d^2} + \frac{b^4}{96d^4} - \frac{109}{24,576}\frac{b^6}{d^6}$$

$$+ \frac{431}{196,608}\frac{b^8}{d^8}\cdots\ \Bigg]\quad\text{henries}\quad(5)$$

For short coils, when $t < b$ [see equation (2)],

$$\Delta L = \frac{2\pi dN^2}{0.3937 \times 10^9}\left[\frac{\pi}{3}\frac{t}{b} - \frac{25}{72}\frac{t^2}{b^2} - \frac{t^2}{8d^2} + \frac{19}{768}\frac{b^2t^2}{d^4} - \frac{t^4}{180b^4}\right.$$

$$+ \frac{67}{7,200}\frac{t^4}{b^2d^2} - \frac{17}{3,840}\frac{t^4}{d^4}\cdots - \left(\operatorname{logn}\frac{4d}{b}\right)\left(\frac{t^2}{24d^2} + \frac{7}{384}\frac{b^2t^2}{d^4}\right.$$

$$+ \frac{11}{2,880}\frac{t^4}{d^4}\cdots\ \Bigg) - \left(\operatorname{logn}\frac{b}{t}\right)\left(\frac{t^2}{6b^2} - \frac{t^4}{120b^2d^2}\cdots\right)$$

$$- \frac{1}{qN}\left(\operatorname{logn}\frac{p}{w} + 0.15\right)\Bigg]\quad\text{henries}\quad(6)$$

The value of L_s, the self-inductance of an infinitely thin cylindrical solenoid, can be conveniently taken from the table of

Nagaoka, Table 21, p. 224. *Bur. Standards Bull.* Vol., 8, No. 1 (also published as *Sci. Paper* 169). This table applies to both long and short solenoids. The table extends over the range— diameter/length = 0 to 10. An extension of the table to larger values of this ratio is given in Table 2 of Tables for the Calculation of the Inductance of Circular Coils of Rectangular Cross Section, by F. W. Grover, *Bur. Standards Sci. Paper* 455.

Columns of first and second differences are given in Table 21 of *Sci. Paper* 169, so that precise values of inductance may be computed. In order to use the differences, a standard interpolation formula and a table of numerical values of coefficients are given in Table 14, pp. 213 and 214, of *Sci. Paper* 169.

For thin, flat, disk-shaped coils, in which the axial length is considered negligible and the radial distance across the face of the coil = t, the current-sheet formula for self-inductance is

$$L_{s1} = \frac{2\pi dN^2}{0.3937 \times 10^9}\left[\left(\operatorname{logn}\frac{4d}{t}\right)\left(1 + \frac{t^2}{24d^2} + \frac{11}{2,880}\frac{t^4}{d^4} + \cdots\right) \right.$$
$$\left. - \frac{1}{2} + \frac{43}{288}\frac{t^2}{d^2} + \frac{t^4}{150d^4}\cdots\right] \quad \text{henries} \quad (7)$$

The inductance of a flat coil of appreciable axial length b is

$$L = L_{s1} - \Delta L$$

where $\Delta L = \dfrac{2\pi dN^2}{0.3937 \times 10^9}\left[\dfrac{\pi}{3}\dfrac{b}{t}\left(1 + \dfrac{b^2}{5d^2} + \dfrac{b^2 t^2}{15d^4} - \dfrac{2}{35}\dfrac{b^4}{d^4}\cdots\right)\right.$

$\left. - \left(\operatorname{logn}\dfrac{4d}{t}\right)\left(\dfrac{b^2}{8d^2} - \dfrac{b^4}{64d^4} + \dfrac{7}{384}\dfrac{b^2 t^2}{d^4}\cdots\right)\right.$

$\left. - \dfrac{b^2}{6t^2}\left(\operatorname{logn}\dfrac{t}{b}\right)\left(1 + \dfrac{b^2}{4d^2} + \dfrac{b^2 t^2}{4d^4}\cdots\right) - \dfrac{b^2}{8d^2} - \dfrac{25}{72}\dfrac{b^2}{t^2} + \dfrac{b^2 t^2}{2,304d^4}\right.$

$\left. - \dfrac{b^4}{180t^4} - \dfrac{23}{288}\dfrac{b^4}{t^2 d^2} - \dfrac{31}{2,304}\dfrac{b^4}{d^4}\cdots - \dfrac{1}{qN}\left(\operatorname{logn}\dfrac{p}{w} + 0.15\right)\right]$

$$\text{henries} \quad (8)$$

For (6) and (8), see Self Inductance of Short Reactance Coils, by H. B. Dwight, *Elec. World*, 1918, p. 1078.

Where precise accuracy is not required, the self-inductance of round cylindrical coils of any proportions may be obtained from Figs. 1 and 2 (from footnote 1, page 1692), the quantity $Lb/(d^2N^2)$ being plotted and the dimensions being in inches.

Example 1. Find the self-inductance of a coil having 1,000 turns of round wire in 10 layers of 100 turns each. The diameter of the insulated wire is $p = 0.1$ cm and the diameter of the bare wire is $w = 0.08$ cm. The mean diameter of the coil is $d = 10$ cm, the length is $b = 10$ cm, and the

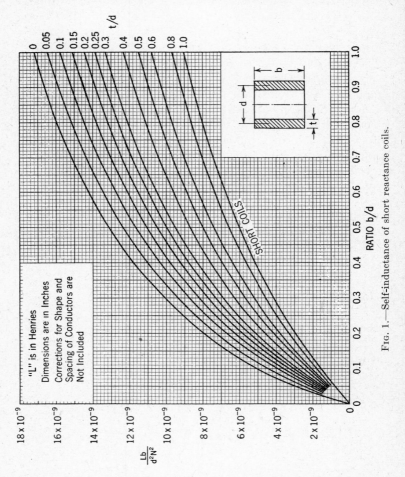

FIG. 1.—Self-inductance of short reactance coils.

thickness is $t = 1$ cm. (Example 1, *Bur. Standards Bull.*, Vol. 4, No. 3, p. 374.)

$$m = 1/\sqrt{5}$$
$$L_s = \pi^2 \times 10N^2 \times 10^{-9} \times 0.688\,422$$

using 9 terms of (1)

Table **21** of *Sci. Paper* 169 gives

$$\pi^2 \times 10N^2 \times 10^{-9} \times 0.688\,423$$

By (3), $$\Delta L = \pi^2 \times 10N^2 \times 10^{-9} \times 0.060\,624$$
$$L = L_s - \Delta L = \pi^2 \times 10^{-2} \times 0.627\,798$$
$$= 0.061\,962$$ henry

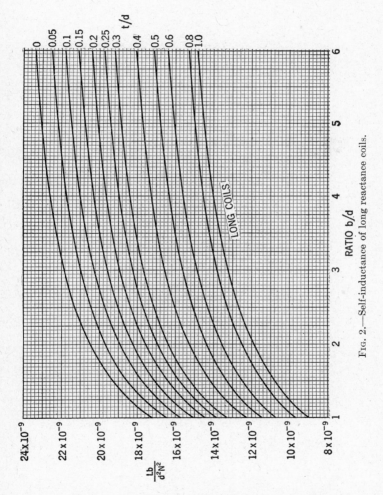

Fig. 2.—Self-inductance of long reactance coils.

As this is a relatively short coil for this formula, having $b = d$, a large number of terms is needed to obtain five significant figures.

Although the ratio $b/d = 1$ is somewhat outside the recommended range for them, formulas (5) and (6) can be used for this problem, as follows:

$L_s = 2\pi \times 10 \times 10^6 \times 10^{-9}[1.386(1 + 0.125 - 0.0156 + 0.0049$
$- 0.0021 + \cdots) - 0.5 + 0.0312 + 0.0104 - 0.0044 + 0.0022 \cdots]$
$= \pi \times 10^{-2} \times 2.162$ henry, by (5)
$\Delta L = 2\pi \times 10^{-2}[0.1047 - 0.0035 - 0.0012 + 0.0002$
$- 1.386 (0.000\ 42 + 0.000\ 18) + 0.0038 - 0.0004]$
$= \pi \times 10^{-2} \times 0.190$ by (6)
$$L = L_s - \Delta L = \pi \times 10^{-2} \times 1.972$$
$$= 0.061\ 94$$ henry

Example 2. Find the self-inductance of a coil of square wire with very thin insulation, in which

$$\frac{b}{d} = 2, \qquad \frac{c}{d} = \frac{1}{10}, \qquad \text{and} \qquad \frac{\pi^2 d^3 N^2}{2b^2} = 4 \times 10^6$$

(Example 9, p. 559, *Bur. Standards Sci. Paper* 320.)

By (1), $$L_s = \frac{\pi^2 d^2 N^2}{b} \times 0.818\ 135\ 7$$ abhenries

Six terms of the series are required. This result is in agreement with Table 21, *Sci. Paper* 169, which gives

$$L_s = \frac{\pi^2 d^2 N^2}{b} \times 0.818\ 136$$

By (3), $$\Delta L = \frac{\pi^2 d^2 N^2}{b} \times 0.062\ 205$$ abhenries

ΔL, in millihenries, 0.995 286

The value of ΔL given by (29A), *Bur. Standards Sci. Paper* 320, is 0.99526 millihenries.

Example 3. The following problem relates to a current-limiting reactor without iron and of usual proportions for that service. $d = 50$ in., $b = 75$ in., $t = 10$ in., $N = 375$. There are 10 layers of stranded conductors, 75 conductors per layer. The number of conductors in parallel is $q = 2$. The diameter of the stranded cable is $w = 0.5$ in. and the distance from center to center of cables is $p = 1$ in.

By equation (1), four terms of the series being needed,

$$L_s = \frac{\pi^2 \times 50^3 \times 375^2}{0.3937 \times 10^9 \times 2 \times 75^2} \times 2.3097$$

By (3), $$\Delta L = \frac{\pi^2 \times 50^3 \times 375^2}{0.3937 \times 10^9 \times 2 \times 75^2} \times 0.3439$$

$$L = L_s - \Delta L = 0.077\ 00$$ henry

The self-inductance of this coil given by (4) is 0.076 99 henry.

Example 4. Find the self-inductance of a coil of mean diameter $d = 10$ in. axial length $b = 2$ in., and of radial thickness of winding $t = 2$ in. It is wound with 400 turns of square wire with very thin insulation.

By (5),

$$L_s = \frac{2\pi \times 10 \times 160{,}000}{0.3937 \times 10^9} [2.996(1 + 0.0050) - 0.5 + 0.001\ 25 - \cdots]$$
$$= 0.064\ 14 \qquad\qquad\qquad\qquad\qquad\qquad\qquad\qquad \text{henry}$$

By (6),

$$\Delta L = \frac{2\pi \times 10 \times 160{,}000}{0.3937 \times 10^9} [1.0472 - 0.3472 - 0.005 - 0.0056 + 0.0004$$
$$- 2.996 \times 0.0017]$$
$$= 0.017\ 49 \qquad\qquad\qquad\qquad\qquad\qquad\qquad\qquad \text{henry}$$
$$L = L_s - \Delta L = 0.046\ 65 \qquad\qquad\qquad\qquad \text{henry}$$

$$L_{s1} = \frac{2\pi \times 10 \times 160{,}000}{0.3937 \times 10^9} [2.996(1 + 0.0017) - 0.5 + 0.0060 + 0.0056]$$
$$= 0.064\ 15 \qquad\qquad\qquad\qquad\qquad\qquad \text{by (7), henry}$$

By (8),

$$\Delta L = \frac{2\pi \times 10 \times 160{,}000}{0.3937 \times 10^9} [1.0472(1 + 0.008) - 2.996 \times 0.005 - 0.005$$
$$- 0.3472 - 0.0032]$$
$$= 0.017\ 50 \qquad\qquad\qquad\qquad\qquad\qquad\qquad\qquad \text{henry}$$
$$L = L_{s1} - \Delta L = 0.046\ 65 \qquad\qquad\qquad\qquad \text{henry}$$

CHAPTER 32

MAGNETIC FIELD STRENGTH NEAR A CYLINDRICAL COIL IN AIR

The magnetic field strength at any given point near a circular cylindrical coil or solenoid in a nonmagnetic medium requires various formulas for its determination, depending on the shape of the solenoid and the position of the point. Formulas are required for the axial component of the magnetic field, called H_x in this chapter, and other formulas are needed for the radial component, H_r.

A number of formulas were given in "Absolute Measurements in Electricity and Magnetism," by Andrew Gray, editions of 1893 and 1921. Others have been published in other articles, as indicated in the footnotes and references of this chapter. A collection of formulas for this problem was published by the author in The Magnetic Field of a Circular Cylindrical Coil, *Phil. Mag.*, Vol. XI, p. 948, April, 1931.

In this chapter, an additional group of formulas is given,[1] suitable particularly for points close to the coil section and for short coils. A device is also given [see paragraphs following equation (3)] by which formulas for the flux density in the end plane only of a solenoid are listed. This greatly increases the range in which the flux density of solenoids under all conditions can be precisely and quickly calculated. It is shown in Fig. 5 that the formulas listed in this chapter cover the entire field of a solenoid.

This chapter contains equipment for computing the magnetic field of a solenoid at any point, including points within the cross section of the winding. The effect of insulation space between conductors, however, is not considered, but the rectangular cross section of the solenoid is assumed to have uniform current distribution.

[1] See Formulas for the Magnetic Field Strength near a Cylindrical Coil, by H. B. Dwight, *Trans. A.I.E.E.*, 1942, p. 327.

One application of the formulas and methods listed in this chapter is in finding the mutual inductance of a solenoid and a comparatively small coil, particularly when the latter is irregular in its shape or position. In many cases the mutual inductance is equal to the magnetic field of the solenoid at the center of the small coil, multiplied by the projected area of the small coil crossing the field. This is of use in problems of electromagnetic interference and shielding.

LOGARITHMIC FORMULAS

The group of logarithmic formulas for points close to the coil section may be derived from a mutual-inductance formula for

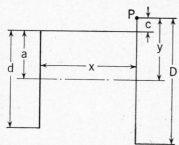

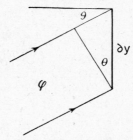

FIG. 1.—Magnetic field at P near a circle of radius a.

FIG. 2.—Flux passing through an area of width ∂y.

two circles which was published by E. B. Rosa and F. W. Grover in equation (16), of *Bur. Standards Sci. Paper* 169. It is given in equation (5), Chap. 26.

If we let a circle of radius $y = a + c$ on the same axis as the circle of radius a, pass through P (Fig. 1) then by differentiating equation (5), Chap. 26, for the mutual inductance of the two circles, with respect to y or c, the change in mutual inductance for an increase in y is found. This is the change in flux passing through the circle of radius y when y is increased, caused by a continuous current in the circle of radius a. The increment in flux passes through the ring of width ∂y and circumference $2\pi y$.

If a certain amount of flux φ, for 1 cm perpendicular to the paper, passes through an area of width ∂y, at an angle θ to the normal to ∂y, as in Fig. 2, then the flux density, or force on a unit magnetic pole, is $\dfrac{\varphi}{\partial y \cos \theta}$. The horizontal component of the flux density is obtained by multiplying by $\cos \theta$ and is $\varphi/\partial y$.

Therefore, in the case of Fig. 1, the axial component of flux density at radius y, or at P, is

$$\frac{1}{2\pi y}\frac{\partial M}{\partial y} \tag{1}$$

Putting $2a = d$ and $2y = D$, as in Fig. 1, in order to make the numerical coefficients smaller, the following expression is obtained for the axial component of flux density at P due to a current of I amp in a circular coil of N turns and of diameter d, assuming that the dimensions of the cross section of the coil are so small that they may be neglected.

$$
\begin{aligned}
H_{x(\text{circle})} &= \frac{NI}{10} \times \frac{1}{2\pi y}\frac{\partial M}{\partial y} \\
&= \frac{NI}{10}\frac{\sqrt{d}}{D\sqrt{D}}\left[\left\{\operatorname{logn}\frac{16Dd}{u^2}\right\}\left\{1 - \frac{3}{4}\frac{u^2}{Dd}\right.\right. \\
&\quad \left.+ \frac{45}{64}\frac{u^4}{D^2d^2}\cdots + \frac{c}{d}\left(\frac{3}{2} - \frac{15}{16}\frac{u^2}{Dd}\cdots\right)\right\} \\
&\quad - \frac{2cD}{u^2} - \left(2 - 2\frac{u^2}{Dd} + \frac{123}{64}\frac{u^4}{D^2d^2}\cdots\right) \\
&\quad \left.+ \frac{c}{d}\left(\frac{5}{2} - \frac{77}{32}\frac{u^2}{Dd}\cdots\right)\right] \quad \text{lines/sq cm} \tag{2}
\end{aligned}
$$

where $u^2 = x^2 + c^2$ and where logn denotes natural logarithm.

Dimensions throughout this chapter are in centimeters, and electromagnetic cgs units are used, except where otherwise stated.

The current is assumed to be in such a direction around the circle that the flux density at the center of the circle is to the right. If the flux density given by equation (2) is a minus quantity, as it usually is when y is greater than a in Fig. 1, that indicates that the direction of the flux at P is to the left. If y is less than a in Fig. 1, the flux density is given by equation (2), but c has a negative numerical value.

Equation (2) and practically all the formulas of this chapter are infinite series and should be used for a given case only if the last term used in each series is almost negligibly small and is smaller than the preceding term. Otherwise, the succeeding terms that are neglected are probably of importance and the formula should not be used for such a case.

To obtain the axial component of flux density at P due to an infinitely thin solenoid, multiply expression (2) by $n\,dx/N$ and integrate from x_1 to x_2, taking these lengths to be positive values (see Fig. 3).   The quantity n is the number of turns per centimeter of axial length of the solenoid.   The expression is 0 when x is 0 and so, by putting $x_1 = 0$ and $x_2 = x$, there is obtained the following formula (3) for the axial field at a point P in the end plane of a solenoid of length x, which is the only type of formula that needs to be listed for solenoids whose length is given:

$$
\begin{aligned}
H_{x(s)} = \frac{nI}{10}\Bigg[&\left\{ \operatorname{logn} \frac{32yd}{x^2 + c^2} \right\} \left\{ \frac{x}{d}\left(1 - \frac{3}{2}\frac{c}{d} + \frac{9}{4}\frac{c^2}{d^2} - \frac{55}{16}\frac{c^3}{d^3}\right.\right. \\
&+ \frac{345}{64}\frac{c^4}{d^4}\cdots\Bigg) - \frac{x^3}{d^3}\left(\frac{1}{4} - \frac{15}{16}\frac{c}{d} + \frac{75}{32}\frac{c^2}{d^2}\cdots\right) \\
&+ \frac{9}{64}\frac{x^5}{d^5}\cdots \Bigg\} - 2\tan^{-1}\frac{x}{c} + \frac{x}{d}\left(\frac{1}{2}\frac{c}{d} - \frac{1}{2}\frac{c^2}{d^2}\right. \\
&- \frac{3}{32}\frac{c^3}{d^3} + \frac{115}{64}\frac{c^4}{d^4}\cdots\Bigg) + \frac{x^3}{d^3}\left(\frac{1}{2} - \frac{61}{32}\frac{c}{d} + \frac{151}{32}\frac{c^2}{d^2}\cdots\right) \\
&- \frac{21}{64}\frac{x^5}{d^5}\cdots \Bigg] \quad \text{lines/sq cm} \quad (3)
\end{aligned}
$$

The letter s in $H_{x(s)}$ denotes an infinitely thin solenoid or current sheet.   This formula has been shortened somewhat by expressing D in terms of d, the mean diameter of the coil.

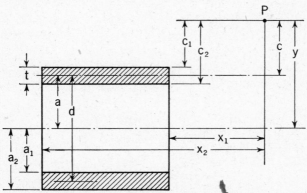

FIG. 3.—Magnetic field at point P near a solenoid.

It is evident from Fig. 3 that the magnetic flux density at P due to the actual solenoid of length $(x_2 - x_1)$ is equal to the difference between the field densities of two solenoids of lengths x_2 and x_1, respectively, of the same thickness, for both of which

P is in the end plane. A physical meaning is thus given to the value of expression (3) for x_1 and x_2 separately, when integration is carried between these limits for the case shown in Fig. 3.

It is, therefore, possible to calculate the value for x_1 by one formula, suitable for short coils, and that for x_2 by another formula if desired, suitable for long coils. The use of this device greatly increases the capability of calculating the flux density due to a solenoid under various conditions, with ease and precision.

A similar device for mutual inductance of solenoids was given in Chap. 27 [see the fourth paragraph following equation (9) of that chapter], and it produced a corresponding increase in the capacity to calculate the mutual inductance of coils of various shapes in various positions.

A correction for the thickness, t, of the coil is desirable. Following Maxwell, "Electricity and Magnetism," Par. 700, and noting that the differential of d is twice the differential of a radial distance,

$$H_{(coil)} = H_{(s)} + \frac{t^2}{3!}\frac{\partial^2 H_{(s)}}{\partial d^2} + \frac{t^4}{5!}\frac{\partial^4 H_{(s)}}{\partial d^4} \cdots \tag{4}$$

where $H_{(s)}$ is the magnetic field density, either axial or radial, at a given point P in the end plane due to the infinitely thin central solenoid whose diameter is d (see Fig. 3).

Expressing equation (3) in terms of $D = 2y$ instead of d, so that c is the only variable, and differentiating, we obtain the term in t^2 of (4).

$$H_{x(coil)} = H_{x(s)} + \Delta H_x$$

$$\begin{aligned}
\text{where } \Delta H_x = \frac{nI}{10}\frac{t^2}{D^2}\Bigg[&\left\{ \log n\,\frac{16D^2}{x^2+c^2} \right\}\left\{ \frac{x}{D}\left(\frac{1}{12} + \frac{1}{16}\frac{c}{D} \right.\right. \\
&\left.\left. -\frac{7}{32}\frac{c^2}{D^2} \cdots \right) - \frac{9}{32}\frac{x^3}{D^3} \cdots \right\} \\
&-\frac{xD}{(x^2+c^2)}\left\{ \frac{1}{3} + \frac{1}{2}\frac{c}{D} + \frac{5}{12}\frac{c^2}{D^2} + \frac{7}{48}\frac{c^3}{D^3} - \frac{21}{64}\frac{c^4}{D^4} \cdots \right. \\
&-\frac{x^2}{D^2}\left(\frac{1}{12} + \frac{9}{16}\frac{c}{D} + \frac{45}{32}\frac{c^2}{D^2} \cdots \right) + \frac{3}{64}\frac{x^4}{D^4} \cdots \Big\} \\
&-\frac{xcD^2}{(x^2+c^2)^2}\left\{ \frac{2}{3} - \frac{2}{3}\frac{c}{D} - \frac{1}{3}\frac{c^2}{D^2} - \frac{1}{6}\frac{c^3}{D^3} - \frac{1}{24}\frac{c^4}{D^4} \right. \\
&+\frac{7}{96}\frac{c^5}{D^5} \cdots + \frac{x^2c}{D^3}\left(\frac{1}{6} + \frac{3}{8}\frac{c}{D} + \frac{9}{16}\frac{c^2}{D^2} \cdots \right)
\end{aligned}$$

$$- \frac{3}{32} \frac{x^4 c}{D^5} \cdots \bigg\} - \frac{x}{D}\bigg(\frac{1}{2} + \frac{121}{96}\frac{c}{D}$$

$$+ \frac{175}{96}\frac{c^2}{D^2} \cdots \bigg) + \frac{33}{32}\frac{x^3}{D^3} \cdots \bigg] \quad (5)$$

Equation (5) should be used only for thin solenoids where t is small and where the correction ΔH_x is a small percentage. For somewhat thicker coils, the following formula may be used, obtained by putting (3) in terms of $D = 2y$ and then integrating over the cross section of the coil:

$$
\begin{aligned}
H_{x(\text{coil})} = \frac{nI}{10}\bigg[& \bigg\{\frac{c}{t}\operatorname{logn}\frac{16D^2}{x^2+c^2}\bigg\}\bigg\{\frac{x}{D}\bigg(1 + \frac{1}{4}\frac{c}{D} + \frac{1}{12}\frac{c^2}{D^2} \\
& + \frac{1}{64}\frac{c^3}{D^3} - \frac{7}{320}\frac{c^4}{D^4}\cdots\bigg) - \frac{x^3}{D^3}\bigg(\frac{1}{4} + \frac{9}{32}\frac{c}{D} \\
& + \frac{9}{32}\frac{c^2}{D^2}\cdots\bigg) + \frac{9}{64}\frac{x^5}{D^5}\cdots\bigg\} \\
& - \bigg\{\frac{x}{t}\operatorname{logn}\frac{x^2+c^2}{D^2}\bigg\}\bigg\{1 + \frac{1}{4}\frac{x^2}{D^2} - \frac{19}{64}\frac{x^4}{D^4}\cdots\bigg\} \\
& + \bigg\{\tan^{-1}\frac{c}{x}\bigg\}\bigg\{\frac{2c}{t} - \frac{x}{t}\bigg(2\frac{x}{D} - \frac{2}{3}\frac{x^3}{D^3} + \frac{4}{5}\frac{x^5}{D^5}\cdots\bigg)\bigg\}\bigg\} \\
& - \frac{c}{t}\bigg\{\pi - \frac{x}{D}\bigg(2 - \frac{1}{2}\frac{c}{D} - \frac{4}{9}\frac{c^2}{D^2} - \frac{59}{192}\frac{c^3}{D^3} \\
& - \frac{917}{4,800}\frac{c^4}{D^4}\cdots\bigg) - \frac{x^3}{D^3}\bigg(\frac{1}{6} - \frac{1}{6}\frac{c}{D} - \frac{103}{120}\frac{c^2}{D^2}\cdots\bigg) \\
& + \frac{151}{320}\frac{x^5}{D^5}\bigg\}\Bigg]_{c=c_1}^{c_2} \quad \text{lines/sq cm} \quad (6)
\end{aligned}
$$

If y is less than a_1 then c_1 and c_2 are negative. If y lies in value between a_1 and a_2, then c_1 is negative and c_2 is positive.

Corresponding formulas are required for the radial component of magnetic field. Using equation (5), Chap. 26, for the mutual inductance of two circles, the radial field at P (Fig. 1) due to a circle or coil of N turns of very small cross section, is

$$-\frac{NI}{10} \times \frac{1}{2\pi y}\frac{\partial M}{\partial x} = H_{r(\text{circle})} \quad (7)$$

$$
H_{r(\text{circle})} = \frac{NI}{10}\frac{\sqrt{d}}{D\sqrt{D}}\bigg[\frac{2xD}{u^2} + \frac{x}{d}\bigg(\frac{5}{2} - \frac{77}{32}\frac{u^2}{Dd} \\
+ \frac{141}{64}\frac{u^4}{D^2 d^2} - \frac{17,165}{8,192}\frac{u^6}{D^3 d^3}\cdots\bigg)
$$

$$- \left\{ \log n \, \frac{16Dd}{u^2} \right\} \left\{ \frac{3}{2} \frac{x}{d} \left(1 - \frac{5}{8} \frac{u^2}{Dd} + \frac{35}{64} \frac{u^4}{D^2 d^2} \right. \right.$$

$$\left. \left. - \frac{525}{1,024} \frac{u^6}{D^3 d^3} + \cdots \right) \right\} \right] \quad \text{lines/sq cm} \quad (8)$$

where $u^2 = x^2 + c^2$.

In equation (8), the dimension D, which is twice the radial distance to the point P (Fig. 1) may be either larger or smaller than d, the diameter of the circle. Only even powers of the quantity c are involved.

The minus sign occurs in equation (7) since the mutual inductance of the two circles in Fig. 1 decreases as x increases.

For the radial field at a point P in the end plane of an infinitely thin solenoid of diameter d, multiply (8) by $n \, dx/N$ and integrate from 0 to x, where n is the number of turns per centimeter of axial length.

$$H_{r(s)} = \frac{nI \sqrt{d}}{10 \sqrt{D}} \left[\left\{ \log n \, \frac{16Dd}{c^2} \right\} \left\{ 1 + \frac{3}{4} \frac{c^2}{Dd} - \frac{15}{64} \frac{c^4}{D^2 d^2} \right. \right.$$

$$\left. + \frac{35}{256} \frac{c^6}{D^3 d^3} - \frac{1,575}{128^2} \frac{c^8}{D^4 d^4} \cdots \right\}$$

$$- \left\{ \log n \, \frac{16Dd}{u^2} \right\} \left\{ 1 + \frac{3}{4} \frac{u^2}{Dd} - \frac{15}{64} \frac{u^4}{D^2 d^2} + \frac{35}{256} \frac{u^6}{D^3 d^3} \right.$$

$$\left. - \frac{1,575}{128^2} \frac{u^8}{D^4 d^4} \cdots \right\} + \frac{u^2 - c^2}{2Dd} - \frac{31}{64} \frac{u^4 - c^4}{D^2 d^2}$$

$$\left. + \frac{247}{768} \frac{u^6 - c^6}{D^3 d^3} - \frac{7,795}{128 \times 256} \frac{u^8 - c^8}{D^4 d^4} \cdots \right] \quad (9)$$

where $u^2 = x^2 + c^2$. Here also, $D = 2y$ may be greater or less than d.

The first few terms of (9) were checked by Mason F. Miller by expansion of (13) in series.

Note that the radial field close to the end of an infinitely thin solenoid becomes infinitely great, because c approaches 0 and $\log n \, c$ is involved.

By equation (4), $\quad H_{r(\text{coil})} = H_{r(s)} + \Delta H_r$

where $\Delta H_r = \dfrac{nI}{10} \left[\dfrac{t^2}{D^2} \left\{ \log n \, \dfrac{x^2 + c^2}{c^2} \right\} \left\{ \dfrac{1}{12} + \dfrac{1}{4} \dfrac{c}{D} \right. \right.$

$$\left. + \frac{17}{32} \frac{c^2}{D^2} + \frac{95}{96} \frac{c^3}{D^3} \cdots \right\}$$

$$- \frac{t^2}{D^2} \left\{ \operatorname{logn} \frac{16D^2}{x^2 + c^2} \right\} \left\{ \frac{x^2}{D^2} \left(\frac{7}{32} + \frac{15}{32} \frac{c}{D} \cdots \right) \right\}$$

$$+ \frac{t^2}{x^2 + c^2} \left\{ \frac{1}{3} - \frac{c}{D} + \frac{5}{12} \frac{c^2}{D^2} + \frac{7}{12} \frac{c^3}{D^3} + \frac{51}{64} \frac{c^4}{D^4} \right.$$

$$+ \frac{247}{96} \frac{c^5}{D^5} \cdots + \frac{x^2}{D^2} \left(\frac{1}{4} + \frac{3}{4} \frac{c}{D} + \frac{35}{32} \frac{c^2}{D^2} \right.$$

$$\left. + \frac{35}{32} \frac{c^3}{D^3} \cdots \right) - \frac{x^4}{D^4} \left(\frac{5}{64} + \frac{45}{64} \frac{c}{D} \cdots \right) \right\}$$

$$- \frac{t^2 c^2}{(x^2 + c^2)^2} \left\{ \frac{2}{3} - \frac{2}{3} \frac{c}{D} + \frac{1}{6} \frac{c^2}{D^2} + \frac{1}{6} \frac{c^3}{D^3} + \frac{17}{96} \frac{c^4}{D^4} \right.$$

$$+ \frac{19}{96} \frac{c^5}{D^5} \cdots + \frac{x^2}{D^2} \left(\frac{1}{2} + \frac{1}{2} \frac{c}{D} + \frac{7}{16} \frac{c^2}{D^2} \right.$$

$$\left. + \frac{5}{16} \frac{c^3}{D^3} \cdots \right) - \frac{x^4}{D^4} \left(\frac{5}{32} + \frac{15}{32} \frac{c}{D} \cdots \right) \right\}$$

$$+ \frac{t^2}{c^2} \left\{ \frac{1}{3} + \frac{1}{3} \frac{c}{D} - \frac{1}{4} \frac{c^2}{D^2} - \frac{5}{12} \frac{c^3}{D^3} - \frac{119}{192} \frac{c^4}{D^4} \right.$$

$$\left. \left. - \frac{57}{64} \frac{c^5}{D^5} \cdots + \frac{x^2}{D^2} \left(\frac{89}{96} \frac{c^2}{D^2} + \frac{101}{32} \frac{c^3}{D^3} \cdots \right) \right\} \right] \quad (10)$$

Since equation (10) is applicable only to thin solenoids with a small value of t^2/c^2, because terms in t^4 and higher powers of t have been omitted, the following formula, obtained by integration of (9) after it was expressed in terms of D, is given for use with thicker coils:

$$H_{r(\text{coil})} = \frac{nI}{10} \left[\frac{x^2}{Dt} \left\{ \operatorname{logn} \frac{16D^2}{x^2 + c^2} \right\} \left\{ \frac{1}{2} - \frac{3}{4} \frac{c}{D} - \frac{3}{8} \frac{c^2}{D^2} \right. \right.$$

$$- \frac{7}{32} \frac{c^3}{D^3} - \frac{15}{128} \frac{c^4}{D^4} \cdots$$

$$\left. - \frac{x^2}{D^2} \left(\frac{5}{16} - \frac{15}{64} \frac{c}{D} - \frac{45}{128} \frac{c^2}{D^2} \cdots \right) + \frac{161}{384} \frac{x^4}{D^4} \cdots \right\}$$

$$+ \frac{c}{t} \left\{ \operatorname{logn} \frac{x^2 + c^2}{c^2} \right\} \left\{ 1 - \frac{1}{2} \frac{c}{D} + \frac{1}{12} \frac{c^2}{D^2} + \frac{1}{16} \frac{c^3}{D^3} \right.$$

$$\left. + \frac{17}{320} \frac{c^4}{D^4} + \frac{19}{384} \frac{c^5}{D^5} \cdots \right\}$$

$$+ \frac{2x}{t} \left(\tan^{-1} \frac{c}{x} \right) \left(1 + \frac{2}{3} \frac{x^2}{D^2} - \frac{2}{5} \frac{x^4}{D^4} \cdots \right)$$

$$- \frac{c}{t} \frac{x^2}{D^2} \left(\frac{5}{6} - \frac{11}{16} \frac{c}{D} - \frac{49}{60} \frac{c^2}{D^2} - \frac{145}{192} \frac{c^3}{D^3} \cdots \right)$$

$$\left. + \frac{c}{t} \frac{x^4}{D^4} \left(\frac{101}{320} - \frac{13}{24} \frac{c}{D} \cdots \right) \right]_{c=c_1}^{c_2} \quad \text{lines/sq cm} \quad (11)$$

If y is less than a_1, then c_1 and c_2 are negative.   If y lies in value between a_1 and a_2, then c_1 is negative and c_2 is positive.

Note that, if the current is assumed to flow in a mathematically exact rectangular cross section, the radial field is not infinite at the corners or elsewhere.   The limit of $c \log n \, c$ is 0 when c approaches 0.   See Nos. 72 and 605 of footnote 2.

The following general formulas for the flux density, in any position whatever relative to a circle which carries a current, have been published by Alexander Russell[3] and give the same results as equations (2) and (8):

$$H_{x \text{(circle)}} = \frac{2NI}{10r_1} \left\{ \frac{2a(a-y)}{r_2{}^2} E + (K - E) \right\} \tag{12}$$

$$H_{r \text{(circle)}} = \frac{2NI}{10r_1} \left\{ \frac{2ax}{r_2{}^2} E - \frac{x}{y}(K - E) \right\} \tag{13}$$

where the dimensions are as in Fig. 1 and where

$$r_1{}^2 = (a + y)^2 + x^2 \tag{14}$$
$$r_2{}^2 = (a - y)^2 + x^2 = c^2 + x^2 \tag{15}$$

K and E are complete elliptic integrals of the first and second kinds of modulus k, where

$$k^2 = 1 - \frac{r_2{}^2}{r_1{}^2} \tag{16}$$

Values of K and E may be taken from tables, as for instance, pp. 199 and 204, of footnote 4.

It is seen from Fig. 1 that r_2 is the distance from P to the nearest part of the circumference of the circle carrying current.   If this distance is very small, k^2 approaches 1 and the value of the elliptic integral K approaches infinity.   When this occurs, the values in any table become far apart so that interpolated values cannot be obtained with precision, and it becomes better to use a series involving logarithms than to use a table of values.   That, however, is equivalent to using formulas (2) and (8), which involve logarithms.   It is always possible to find the precise

[2] "Tables of Integrals and Other Mathematical Data," by H. B. Dwight, The Macmillan Company, New York, 1934.

[3] "Alternating Currents," by A. Russell, Cambridge University Press, London, 1914, Vol. I, equations 21 and 22, p. 98.

[4] "Mathematical Tables," by H. B. Dwight, McGraw-Hill Book Company, Inc., New York, 1941.

value of the logarithm of any given number, however large or small, one way being to find first the logarithm to base 10.

Since equations (2) and (8) are power series in $r_2{}^2/(ay)$, they have greater precision, the closer the point P approaches to the circumference of the circle and the greater becomes the difficulty of obtaining the value of K from a table.

Other formulas will now be listed. The formulas for solenoids are put in the more useful and usually more concise form giving the flux density at a point in the end plane of the solenoid.

For points near the center of the circle,

$$H_{x(\text{circle})} = \frac{2\pi NI}{10a} \left[1 - \frac{3}{2} \frac{r^2}{a^2} P_2 \left(\frac{x}{r} \right) + \frac{3 \cdot 5}{2 \cdot 4} \frac{r^4}{a^4} P_4 \left(\frac{x}{r} \right) - \cdots \right]$$
(17)

where $$r^2 = x^2 + y^2$$ (18)

and where the single dots represent multiplication. $P_2 \left(\dfrac{x}{r} \right)$, $P_4 \left(\dfrac{x}{r} \right)$, etc., are surface zonal harmonics which may be defined by

$$P_n(\mu) = \frac{1}{2^n n!} \frac{\partial^n}{\partial \mu^n} (\mu^2 - 1)^n$$

Values are tabulated in page 188 of footnote 4 and elsewhere, or they may be calculated from series [see p. 169 of footnote 2 and equation (55) of this chapter].

$$H_{r(\text{circle})} = \frac{\pi NI}{10} \frac{yr}{a^3} \left[P_2' \left(\frac{x}{r} \right) - \frac{3}{4} \frac{r^2}{a^2} P_4' \left(\frac{x}{r} \right) \right.$$
$$\left. + \frac{3 \cdot 5}{4 \cdot 6} \frac{r^4}{a^4} P_6' \left(\frac{x}{r} \right) - \cdots \right]$$
(19)

where $P_n'(\mu) = \dfrac{\partial}{\partial \mu} P_n(\mu)$.

Values are tabulated in footnote 5 or 4, 1st ed., 3d impression, p. 195A, or they may be calculated from series, as above.

[5] (a) Tables of the Spherical Function $P_n(x)$ and Its Derived Functions, by H. Tallquist, *Acta Soc. Sci. Fennicae*, Helsingfors, Finland, Vol. 32, 1906, pp. 5–27 and Vol. 33, No. 9, 1908.

(b) Six-place Tables of the 16 First Surface Zonal Harmonics $P_n(x)$, by H. Tallquist, *Acta Soc. Sci. Fennicae*, Helsingfors, Finland, 1937.

(c) Six-place Tables of the 32 First Surface Zonal Harmonics $P_n(\cos \theta)$, by H. Tallquist, *Acta Soc. Sci. Fennicae*, Helsingfors, Finland, 1938.

For points at a considerable distance from the center of the circle,

$$H_{x(\text{circle})} = \frac{2\pi NI}{10r} \left[\frac{a^2}{r^2} P_2\left(\frac{x}{r}\right) - \frac{3}{2} \frac{a^4}{r^4} P_4\left(\frac{x}{r}\right) \right. $$
$$\left. + \frac{3 \cdot 5}{2 \cdot 4} \frac{a^6}{r^6} P_6\left(\frac{x}{r}\right) - \cdots \right] \quad (20)$$

$$H_{r(\text{circle})} = \frac{\pi NIy}{10r^2} \left[\frac{a^2}{r^2} P_2' \frac{x}{r} - \frac{3}{4} \frac{a^4}{r^4} P_4'\left(\frac{x}{r}\right) \right. $$
$$\left. + \frac{3 \cdot 5}{4 \cdot 6} \frac{a^6}{r^6} P_6'\left(\frac{x}{r}\right) - \cdots \right] \quad (21)$$

See equations (3) and (4) of footnote 6.

For points not far from the axis of the circle,

$$H_{x(\text{circle})} = \frac{2\pi NIa^2}{10\rho^3} \left[P_1'\left(\frac{x}{\rho}\right) - \frac{1}{2} \frac{y^2}{\rho^2} P_3'\left(\frac{x}{\rho}\right) \right. $$
$$\left. + \frac{1 \cdot 3}{2 \cdot 4} \frac{y^4}{\rho^4} P_5'\left(\frac{x}{\rho}\right) - \cdots \right] \quad (22)$$

$$H_{r(\text{circle})} = \frac{2\pi NIa^2 y}{10\rho^4} \left[\frac{1}{2} P_2'\left(\frac{x}{\rho}\right) - \frac{1 \cdot 3}{2 \cdot 4} \frac{y^2}{\rho^2} P_4'\left(\frac{x}{\rho}\right) \right. $$
$$\left. + \frac{1 \cdot 3 \cdot 5}{2 \cdot 4 \cdot 6} \frac{y^4}{\rho^4} P_6'\left(\frac{x}{\rho}\right) - \cdots \right] \quad (23)$$

where
$$\rho^2 = x^2 + a^2 \quad (24)$$

Equations (22) and (23) are equivalent to equations (9) and (10) of "Absolute Measurements in Electricity and Magnetism," by Andrew Gray, p. 248 of Vol. 2, ed. of 1893 and p. 212, ed. of 1921, changing $1,680x^4$ to $1,680a^2x^4$.

All these formulas for circles can be integrated, though not always by one direct step, to give expressions for the flux density at a point in the end plane of a solenoid, each applicable to a certain range, as approximately indicated in Fig. 5. Each formula may be used in an area in Fig. 5 in which its number, such as (25), occurs, and up to the boundary marked by an arrow leading from that number. The areas are seen to overlap. Satisfactory convergence may be found beyond the boundaries marked. On the other hand the rapidity of convergence may be

---

6 Some Formulas for the Strength of the Magnetic Field of a Cylindrical Coil, by Robert F. H. Chao, *Jour. Math. Phys.*, Vol. 10, pp. 13–18, 1931.

very poor for the thickness correction formulas near the boundaries. Figure 5 is a preliminary guide, and the criterion for use of a certain formula in any given case is the rapidity of convergence of the series. If the convergence is not suitably rapid, the formula should not be used in that particular case.

By integrating (17) and (19) from 0 to x, for values of

$$r = \sqrt{x^2 + y^2}$$

less than approximately $0.7a$, (see Figs. 3 and 5),

$$H_{x\text{(coil)}} = \frac{2\pi n I}{10} \left[\frac{r}{a} P_1 \left(\frac{x}{r}\right) \left\{ 1 + \frac{t^2}{12a^2} + \frac{t^4}{80a^4} + \frac{t^6}{448a^6} + \cdots \right\} \right.$$
$$- \frac{1}{2} \frac{r^3}{a^3} P_3 \left(\frac{x}{r}\right) \left\{ 1 + \frac{t^2}{2a^2} + \frac{3}{16} \frac{t^4}{a^4} + \frac{1}{16} \frac{t^6}{a^6} + \cdots \right\}$$
$$+ \frac{1 \cdot 3}{2 \cdot 4} \frac{r^5}{a^5} P_5 \left(\frac{x}{r}\right) \left\{ 1 + \frac{5}{4} \frac{t^2}{a^2} + \frac{7}{8} \frac{t^4}{a^4} + \frac{15}{32} \frac{t^6}{a^6} + \cdots \right\}$$
$$- \frac{1 \cdot 3 \cdot 5}{2 \cdot 4 \cdot 6} \frac{r^7}{a^7} P_7 \left(\frac{x}{r}\right) \left\{ 1 + \frac{7}{3} \frac{t^2}{a^2} + \frac{21}{8} \frac{t^4}{a^4} \right.$$
$$\left. \left. + \frac{33}{16} \frac{t^6}{a^6} + \cdots \right\} \cdots \right] \text{ lines/sq cm} \quad (25)$$

where n = turns per centimeter of axial length of the coil. For dimensions see Fig. 3.

$$H_{r\text{(coil)}} = \frac{3\pi n I y}{20a} \left[\frac{x^2}{a^2} \left\{ 1 + \frac{t^2}{2a^2} + \frac{3}{16} \frac{t^4}{a^4} + \frac{1}{16} \frac{t^6}{a^6} + \cdots \right\} \right.$$
$$- \frac{5}{4} \left(\frac{x^4}{a^4} - \frac{3x^2 y^2}{2a^4} \right) \left\{ 1 + \frac{5}{4} \frac{t^2}{a^2} + \frac{7}{8} \frac{t^4}{a^4} + \frac{15}{32} \frac{t^6}{a^6} + \cdots \right\}$$
$$+ \frac{35}{24} \left(\frac{x^6}{a^6} - \frac{15}{4} \frac{x^4 y^2}{a^6} + \frac{15}{8} \frac{x^2 y^4}{a^6} \right) \left\{ 1 + \frac{7}{3} \frac{t^2}{a^2} + \frac{21}{8} \frac{t^4}{a^4} \right.$$
$$\left. \left. + \frac{33}{16} \frac{t^6}{a^6} + \cdots \right\} \right] \quad (26)$$

Formulas for $H_{x(s)}$ and $H_{r(s)}$ are obtained by putting $t = 0$. For thick coils, the brackets containing power series in t/a may be replaced by the complete expression

$$\frac{a}{mt} \left\{ \left(1 - \frac{t}{2a} \right)^{-m} - \left(1 + \frac{t}{2a} \right)^{-m} \right\} \quad (27)$$

where m is 0 or an even number. The values of m are 0, 2, 4, 6 in (25) and 2, 4, 6 in (26). For $m = 0$, the binomials may be expanded and m canceled out before m is put $= 0$, thus giving $\frac{a}{t} \log_n \frac{a_2}{a_1}$ which may be obtained also by integration of $1/a$. The complete expressions may be used also for extending the formulas.

It is not permissible to integrate expressions (20) or (21) from the limit $x = 0$, or past that point, for small values of y, because a/r would be greater than 1 and the series would be divergent. But the series and their integrals become 0 when x becomes infinitely great, and so it is possible to integrate from x to ∞ and obtain the field density at P due to a coil extending from x to ∞. By subtracting this from the field at P due to a coil extending from 0 to ∞, which may be called $H_{x\infty}$ and $H_{r\infty}$, respectively, one obtains the field due to a coil from 0 to x, at a point in the end plane, the same as for all the other formulas for solenoids listed in this chapter.

The axial component of field at a point P outside a solenoid which extends to an infinite distance in both directions from P is 0, as is well known. Such a coil is the limiting condition of a toroidal coil of very large coil diameter compared to the section diameter. The parts of the solenoid to the right and left of the radial plane through P give equal axial fields, which are therefore 0. Thus,

$$H_{x\infty} = 0 \tag{28}$$

for points outside the solenoid.

The axial field inside a coil extending to infinity in both directions is also well known to be $4\pi nI/10$, a constant. By taking a radial plane through P, the axial field due to the half coil to the left of P is by symmetry equal to

$$H_{x\infty} = \frac{2\pi nI}{10} \tag{29}$$

For values of y that lie between a_1 and a_2 (Fig. 3), the value of $H_{x\infty}$ is that due to the turns lying outside of y. In such a case,

$$H_{x\infty} = \frac{a_2 - y}{a_2 - a_1} \times \frac{2\pi nI}{10} \tag{30}$$

The value of $H_{r\infty}$ requires more computation, for various values of y. First, for large values of y, the integration of (21) from $x = 0$ to ∞ is permissible and gives

$$H_{r\infty} = \frac{\pi n I}{10} \left[\frac{a^2}{y^2}\left(1 + \frac{t^2}{12a^2}\right) + \frac{1 \cdot 3}{4 \cdot 2}\frac{a^4}{y^4}\left(1 + \frac{t^2}{2a^2} + \frac{t^4}{80a^4}\right) \right.$$
$$+ \frac{1 \cdot 3}{4 \cdot 6} \times \frac{3 \cdot 5}{2 \cdot 4}\frac{a^6}{y^6}\left(1 + \frac{5}{4}\frac{t^2}{a^2} + \frac{3}{16}\frac{t^4}{a^4} + \frac{t^6}{448a^6}\right)$$
$$+ \frac{1 \cdot 3 \cdot 5}{4 \cdot 6 \cdot 8} \times \frac{3 \cdot 5 \cdot 7}{2 \cdot 4 \cdot 6}\frac{a^8}{y^8}\left(1 + \frac{7}{3}\frac{t^2}{a^2} + \frac{7}{8}\frac{t^4}{a^4} + \frac{t^6}{16a^6}\right.$$
$$\left. \left. + \frac{t^8}{2{,}304a^8}\right) + \cdots \right] \quad (31)$$

See equation (40). The series in t/a are not infinite but are complete. The general expression is given in (41).

For convenience in computation, the numerical coefficients of powers of a/y in (31) are 1, $\frac{3}{8}$, $\frac{15}{64}$, and $175/1{,}024$.

For small values of y, integration of (23) from $x = 0$ to ∞ gives

$$H_{r\infty} = \frac{\pi n I y}{10a}\left[1 + \frac{3}{8}\frac{y^2}{a^2} + \frac{15}{64}\frac{y^4}{a^4} + \frac{175}{1{,}024}\frac{y^6}{a^6} + \cdots\right.$$
$$+ \frac{t^2}{a^2}\left(\frac{1}{12} + \frac{3}{16}\frac{y^2}{a^2} + \frac{75}{256}\frac{y^4}{a^4} + \frac{1{,}225}{3{,}072}\frac{y^6}{a^6} + \cdots\right)$$
$$+ \frac{t^4}{a^4}\left(\frac{1}{80} + \frac{9}{128}\frac{y^2}{a^2} + \frac{105}{512}\frac{y^4}{a^4} + \frac{3{,}675}{8{,}192}\frac{y^6}{a^6} + \cdots\right)$$
$$\left. + \text{terms in } \frac{t^6}{a^6} \text{ etc.}\right] \quad (32)$$

For thicker coils,

$$H_{r\infty} = \frac{\pi n I y}{10t}\left[\log n \frac{a_2}{a_1} + \frac{3}{16}y^2\left(\frac{1}{a_1{}^2} - \frac{1}{a_2{}^2}\right) + \frac{15}{256}y^4\left(\frac{1}{a_1{}^4} - \frac{1}{a_2{}^4}\right)\right.$$
$$\left. + \frac{175}{6{,}144}y^6\left(\frac{1}{a_1{}^6} - \frac{1}{a_2{}^6}\right) + \cdots\right] \quad (33)$$

For values of y not very different from a, consider the mutual inductance of two infinitely thin coaxial solenoids of lengths b_1 and b_2 and with a distance between their adjacent end planes equal to w, as in Fig. 4. The mutual inductance is given by equation (1) of Chap. 27, as follows:

$$\frac{M}{nn'} = \frac{1}{2}\left[M'_{(x1)} - M'_{(x2)} - M'_{(x3)} + M'_{(x4)}\right] \quad (34)$$

where, in the notation used in Fig. 4,

$$x_1 = b_1 + b_2 + w$$
$$x_2 = b_1 + w$$
$$x_3 = b_2 + w$$
$$x_4 = w$$

and where n and n' are the turns per centimeter of the two coils.

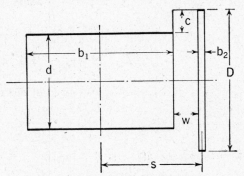

FIG. 4.—Two coils of unequal lengths.

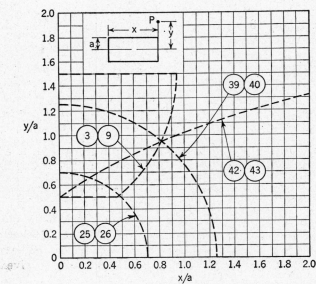

FIG. 5.—Approximate ranges of application of formulas for magnetic field in end plane of a solenoid.

Assume that w is a small quantity, and that b_2 is smaller still, so that the right-hand coil is equivalent to a turn of very fine wire. Then $M'_{(x1)}$ and $M'_{(x2)}$ are to be computed by equation (7) and $M'_{(x3)}$ and $M'_{(x4)}$ by equation (6), of Chap. 27. Allow w to increase a small amount. Then, as in equation (7) of this chapter, the radial flux density at the circumference of the right-hand coil is

$$- \frac{1}{\pi Dn'b_2} \frac{\partial M}{\partial w} \tag{35}$$

Differentiating $M'_{(x1)} - M'_{(x2)}$ with respect to w or x and expanding the first few terms in powers of $1/b_1$, it is found that the result is 0 when b_1 becomes infinite. Differentiating $\dfrac{M'_{(x3)} - M'_{(x4)}}{\pi Dn'b_2}$ and discarding higher powers of b_2 and w, the result, excepting the terms in c^8, is

$$
\begin{aligned}
H_{r(s)\infty} = \frac{nI}{10} \frac{\sqrt{d}}{\sqrt{D}} &\left[\left(\operatorname{logn} \frac{16Dd}{c^2} \right) \left(1 + \frac{3}{4} \frac{c^2}{Dd} - \frac{15}{64} \frac{c^4}{D^2 d^2} \right. \right. \\
&\left. + \frac{35}{256} \frac{c^6}{D^3 d^3} - \frac{1,575}{128^2} \frac{c^8}{D^4 d^4} \cdots \right) - 4 - \frac{1}{2} \frac{c^2}{Dd} + \frac{31}{64} \frac{c^4}{D^2 d^2} \\
&\left. - \frac{247}{768} \frac{c^6}{D^3 d^3} + \frac{7,795}{128 \times 256} \frac{c^8}{D^4 d^4} \cdots \right]
\end{aligned} \tag{36}
$$

The process of taking the same function of w and $w + b_2$, subtracting, and dividing by the small quantity b_2 is equivalent to differentiating with respect to w. Expression (36) is therefore the result of differentiating $M'_{(x)}$ twice. But $M'_{(x)}$ was the result of integrating equation (5), Chap. 26, twice. Equation (36) should therefore correspond to equation (5), Chap. 26, which it does, and so the two terms in c^8 can be added from the earlier formula.

The following correction for thickness may be added to (36):

$$
\begin{aligned}
\Delta H_{r\infty} = \frac{nI}{10} &\left[\left(\operatorname{logn} \frac{16D^2}{c^2} \right) \frac{t^2}{D^2} \left(\frac{1}{12} + \frac{1}{4} \frac{c}{D} + \frac{17}{32} \frac{c^2}{D^2} \right. \right. \\
&\left. + \frac{95}{96} \frac{c^3}{D^3} \cdots \right) + \frac{t^2}{c^2} \left(\frac{1}{3} + \frac{1}{3} \frac{c}{D} + \frac{1}{4} \frac{c^2}{D^2} - \frac{1}{12} \frac{c^3}{D^3} \right. \\
&\left. \left. - \frac{157}{192} \frac{c^4}{D^4} - \frac{1,271}{576} \frac{c^5}{D^5} \cdots \right) \right]
\end{aligned} \tag{37}
$$

Since terms in t^4 and higher powers of t are omitted in (37), the following formula for thick coils may be used instead of (36) and (37):

$$H_{r\infty} = \frac{nI}{10}\left[\frac{c}{t}\left(\text{logn}\,\frac{16D^2}{c^2}\right)\left(1 - \frac{1}{2}\frac{c}{D} + \frac{1}{12}\frac{c^2}{D^2} + \frac{1}{16}\frac{c^3}{D^3}\right.\right.$$
$$\left.+ \frac{17}{320}\frac{c^4}{D^4} + \frac{19}{384}\frac{c^5}{D^5}\cdots\right) + \frac{c}{t}\left(-2 + \frac{1}{2}\frac{c}{D}\right.$$
$$\left.\left.+ \frac{5}{9}\frac{c^2}{D^2} + \frac{11}{96}\frac{c^3}{D^3} + \frac{7}{4{,}800}\frac{c^4}{D^4} - \frac{71}{1{,}440}\frac{c^5}{D^5}\cdots\right)\right]_{c=c_1}^{c_2} \quad (38)$$

If y is less than a_1 (Fig. 3) then c_1 and c_2 are negative. If y has a value between that of a_1 and a_2, then c_1 is negative and c_2 is positive.

By an integration of (20) from $x = x$ to ∞, there is obtained the following formula for the axial flux density at a point P in the end plane of a solenoid of length x, for cases in which

$$r = \sqrt{x^2 + y^2}$$

is greater than about $1.25a$ (see Figs. 3 and 5):

$$H_{x(\text{coil})} = H_{x\infty} - \frac{\pi nI}{10}\left[\frac{a^2}{r^2}P_1\left(\frac{x}{r}\right)\left\{1 + \frac{t^2}{12a^2}\right\}\right.$$
$$- \frac{3}{4}\frac{a^4}{r^4}P_3\left(\frac{x}{r}\right)\left\{1 + \frac{t^2}{2a^2} + \frac{t^4}{80a^4}\right\}$$
$$+ \frac{3\cdot5}{4\cdot6}\frac{a^6}{r^6}P_5\left(\frac{x}{r}\right)\left\{1 + \frac{5}{4}\frac{t^2}{a^2} + \frac{3}{16}\frac{t^4}{a^4} + \frac{t^6}{448a^6}\right\}$$
$$- \frac{3\cdot5\cdot7}{4\cdot6\cdot8}\frac{a^8}{r^8}P_7\left(\frac{x}{r}\right)\left\{1 + \frac{7}{3}\frac{t^2}{a^2} + \frac{7}{8}\frac{t^4}{a^4}\right.$$
$$\left.\left.+ \frac{t^6}{16a^6} + \frac{t^8}{2{,}304a^8}\right\}\cdots\right] \quad (39)$$

See footnote 7. The value of $H_{x\infty}$ is given by (28), (29), or (30), depending on the value of y.

By integrating (21) from $x = x$ to ∞, the corresponding formula for radial flux density is obtained:

$$H_{r(\text{coil})} = H_{r\infty} - \frac{\pi nIy}{10a}\left[\frac{a^3}{r^3}P_1'\left(\frac{x}{r}\right)\left\{1 + \frac{t^2}{12a^2}\right\}\right.$$
$$- \frac{1}{4}\frac{a^5}{r^5}P_3'\left(\frac{x}{r}\right)\left\{1 + \frac{t^2}{2a^2} + \frac{t^4}{80a^4}\right\}$$

---

[7] The Force between Unequal Reactance Coils with Parallel Axes, by H. B. Dwight and R. W. Purssell, *Gen. Elec. Rev.*, July, 1930, p. 401, equation (4).

$$+ \frac{1 \cdot 3}{4 \cdot 6} \frac{a^7}{r^7} P'_5 \left(\frac{x}{r}\right) \left\{ 1 + \frac{5}{4} \frac{t^2}{a^2} + \frac{3}{16} \frac{t^4}{a^4} + \frac{t^6}{448 a^6} \right\}$$

$$- \frac{1 \cdot 3 \cdot 5}{4 \cdot 6 \cdot 8} \frac{a^9}{r^9} P'_7 \left(\frac{x}{r}\right) \left\{ 1 + \frac{7}{3} \frac{t^2}{a^2} + \frac{7}{8} \frac{t^4}{a^4} \right.$$

$$\left. \left. + \frac{t^6}{16 a^6} + \frac{t^8}{2{,}304 a^8} \right\} \cdots \right] \quad (40)$$

where $r^2 = x^2 + y^2$. See equation (5) of footnote 6.

The value of $H_{r\infty}$ is given by (31) to (33), (36) to (38) and sometimes two of these formulas can be used to check each other. If in Fig. 3, $x_1^2 + y^2$ and $x_2^2 + y^2$ are so large that equation (40) is used for both, then it is evident that in the subtraction of the two results $H_{r\infty}$ cancels out and so does not need to be computed.

The general expression for the brackets in t is

$$\frac{a}{mt} \left\{ \left(1 + \frac{t}{2a}\right)^m - \left(1 - \frac{t}{2a}\right)^m \right\} \quad (41)$$

where $m = 3, 5, 7$, and 9 for (39) and (40) as far as shown. They are not infinite series but are complete.

From (22) and (23),

$$H_{x(\text{coil})} = H_{x\infty} - \frac{2\pi nI}{10} \left[1 - \frac{x}{\rho} - \frac{a^2}{\rho^2} \left\{ \frac{1}{2 \cdot 2} \frac{y^2}{\rho^2} P'_2 \left(\frac{x}{\rho}\right) \right.\right.$$

$$\left. - \frac{1 \cdot 3}{2 \cdot 4 \cdot 4} \frac{y^4}{\rho^4} P'_4 \left(\frac{x}{\rho}\right) + \frac{1 \cdot 3 \cdot 5}{2 \cdot 4 \cdot 6 \cdot 6} \frac{y^6}{\rho^6} P'_6 \left(\frac{x}{\rho}\right) \cdots \right\}$$

$$+ \frac{t^2 x}{\rho^3} \left\{ \frac{1}{24} \frac{x^2}{\rho^2} - \frac{1}{12} \frac{a^2}{\rho^2} - \frac{y^2}{\rho^2} \left(\frac{1}{16} \frac{x^4}{\rho^4} - \frac{21}{32} \frac{x^2 a^2}{\rho^4} \right.\right.$$

$$\left.\left.\left. + \frac{3}{8} \frac{a^4}{\rho^4} \right) \cdots \right\} \right] \quad (42)$$

$$H_{r(\text{coil})} = H_{r\infty} - \frac{\pi nIa^2}{10\rho^2} \left[\frac{y}{\rho} P'_1 \left(\frac{x}{\rho}\right) - \frac{1}{4} \frac{y^3}{\rho^3} P'_3 \left(\frac{x}{\rho}\right) \right.$$

$$+ \frac{1 \cdot 3}{4 \cdot 6} \frac{y^5}{\rho^5} P'_5 \left(\frac{x}{\rho}\right) - \frac{1 \cdot 3 \cdot 5}{4 \cdot 6 \cdot 8} \frac{y^7}{\rho^7} P'_7 \left(\frac{x}{\rho}\right) + \cdots$$

$$+ \frac{t^2 y}{a^2 \rho} \left(\frac{1}{12} \frac{x^4}{\rho^4} - \frac{11}{24} \frac{x^2 a^2}{\rho^4} + \frac{1}{12} \frac{a^4}{\rho^4}\right) - \frac{t^2 y^3}{a^2 \rho^3} \left(\frac{1}{8} \frac{x^6}{\rho^6}\right.$$

$$\left.\left. - \frac{17}{8} \frac{x^4 a^2}{\rho^6} + \frac{159}{64} \frac{x^2 a^4}{\rho^6} - \frac{3}{16} \frac{a^6}{\rho^6}\right) \cdots \right] \quad (43)$$

where $\rho^2 = x^2 + a^2$.

Since terms in t^4 and higher powers of t have been omitted from (42) and (43), the following equations may be used for thick coils:

$$H_{x(\text{coil})} = H_{x\infty} - \frac{2\pi nI}{10}\left[1 - \frac{x}{t}\left\{\log n\,\frac{a_2 + \rho_2}{a_1 + \rho_1} + \left(\frac{1}{4}\frac{y^2}{x^2}\right.\right.\right.$$

$$-\frac{5}{16}\frac{y^4}{x^4}\right)\left(\frac{a_2{}^3}{\rho_2{}^3} - \frac{a_1{}^3}{\rho_1{}^3}\right) + \frac{33}{64}\frac{y^4}{x^4}\left(\frac{a_2{}^5}{\rho_2{}^5} - \frac{a_1{}^5}{\rho_1{}^5}\right)$$

$$\left.\left.-\frac{15}{64}\frac{y^4}{x^4}\left(\frac{a_2{}^7}{\rho_2{}^7} - \frac{a_1{}^7}{\rho_1{}^7}\right) + \text{terms in higher powers of } y\right\}\right] \quad (44)$$

$$H_{r(\text{coil})} = H_{r\infty} - \frac{\pi nIy}{10t}\left[\log n\,\frac{a_2 + \rho_2}{a_1 + \rho_1} - \frac{a_2}{\rho_2} + \frac{a_1}{\rho_1} - \left(\frac{1}{2}\frac{y^2}{x^2}\right.\right.$$

$$-\frac{5}{8}\frac{y^4}{x^4}\right)\left(\frac{a_2{}^3}{\rho_2{}^3} - \frac{a_1{}^3}{\rho_1{}^3}\right) + \left(\frac{3}{8}\frac{y^2}{x^2} - \frac{27}{16}\frac{y^4}{x^4}\right)\left(\frac{a_2{}^5}{\rho_2{}^5} - \frac{a_1{}^5}{\rho_1{}^5}\right)$$

$$\left.+\frac{105}{64}\frac{y^4}{x^4}\left(\frac{a_2{}^7}{\rho_2{}^7} - \frac{a_1{}^7}{\rho_1{}^7}\right) - \frac{35}{64}\frac{y^4}{x^4}\left(\frac{a_2{}^9}{\rho_2{}^9} - \frac{a_1{}^9}{\rho_1{}^9}\right)\right.$$

$$\left.+ \text{terms in higher powers of } y\right] \quad (45)$$

where $\rho_1{}^2 = x^2 + a_1{}^2$ and $\rho_2{}^2 = x^2 + a_2{}^2$.

See also "Absolute Measurements," by A. Gray, ed. of 1921, equation 28, p. 222 (change $5a$ to $5a^2$) and equation (31), p. 225.

Note that $r_1{}^2 = a^2 + \left(x + \dfrac{b}{2}\right)^2$ and $r_2{}^2 = a^2 + \left(x - \dfrac{b}{2}\right)^2$ where b is the length of the solenoid.

It is to be noticed that, in the formulas, ratios of dimensions occur almost entirely and, in such ratios, dimensions in inches may be used throughout instead of dimensions in centimeters, since powers of 2.54, the conversion factor, would occur equally in the numerator and denominator of a ratio and would cancel out. However, the letter n means turns per centimeter and not turns per inch. The letter N means turns per coil.

Laboratory measurements were made which agreed with calculated values within a very few per cent.

Example 1. The following case, near to the meeting point of three boundaries, enables one formula to be checked by two others. Find the radial component of field in the end plane of a solenoid where $x/a = 0.9$, $y/a = 0.95$, $t/a = 0$, $c/a = -0.05$

By equation (9), $\qquad\qquad H_{r(s)} = 5.36\,\dfrac{nI}{10}$

By equation (36), $\qquad\qquad H_{r(s)\infty} = 6.26\,\dfrac{nI}{10}$

By equation (40), $H_{r(s)} = 6.26 - \pi \times 0.95(0.446 - 0.133 - 0.033$
$$+ 0.020 + 0.007 \cdots) \frac{nI}{10}$$

$$= 5.35 \frac{nI}{10}$$

By equation (43), $H_{r(s)} = 6.26 - \dfrac{\pi}{1.81} (0.706 - 0.164 - 0.044 + 0.020$
$$+ 0.007 \cdots) \frac{nI}{10}$$

$$= 5.35 \frac{nI}{10}$$

Example 2. The following problem also can be computed by three different formulas. Find the horizontal component of the field in the end plane of the following solenoid: $x/a = 0.4$, $y/a = 0.6$, $t/a = 0$, $c/a = -0.4$

By equation (3), $\qquad\qquad H_{x(s)} = 2.90 \dfrac{nI}{10}$

By equation (25),

$$H_{x(s)} = 2\pi \frac{nI}{10} 0.721(0.555 + 0.105 - 0.004 - 0.013 - 0.004) = 2.90 \frac{nI}{10}$$

By equation (29), $\qquad\qquad H_{x(s)\infty} = 2\pi \dfrac{nI}{10}$

By equation (42),

$$H_{x(s)} = \left[2\pi - 2\pi \left\{ 1 - 0.3712 - \frac{1}{1.16} (0.0864 + 0.0171 + 0.0023 \right. \right.$$
$$\left. \left. - 0.0001) \right\} \right] \frac{nI}{10}$$

$$= 2.90 \frac{nI}{10}$$

Example 3. A solenoid consists of a single layer of fine wire, $a = 0.971$ in.; $x = 18.25$ in.; $y = 0$. The search coil is in the calibrating position, at the center of the solenoid.
By (29) and (42),

$$H_{x(s)} = \frac{2\pi nI}{10} \left[1 - 1 + \left(1 + \frac{a^2}{x^2} \right)^{-\frac{1}{2}} \right] = \frac{2\pi nI}{10} \left[1 - \frac{a^2}{2x^2} \cdots \right]$$
$$= \frac{2\pi nI}{10} [1 - 0.0014]$$

due to the half coil, which is 0.14 % less than the nominal value for a very long solenoid.

It is evident that, for accurate work, the calibration of search coils, or other measurements depending on the magnetic field in the middle of a long solenoid, should include a correction according to the formulas in this chapter of the nominal field $4\pi NI/10$ in the middle of the solenoid.

Example 4.   Find the radial component of the field in the end plane of the solenoid of Example 3, at 8 in. from the axis.   In this problem, x is equal to the full length of the solenoid, 36.5 in.

By (31),
$$H_{r(s)_\infty} = \frac{\pi n I}{10} \times 0.014\ 82$$

By (43),
$$H_{r(s)} = \frac{\pi n I}{10} (0.014\ 82 - 0.000\ 14)$$

Only a very few terms in each series are needed.   The turns per centimeter are 7.57 and the current in the test was 1.70 amp, giving $H_{r(s)}$, by (43) = 0.0593 lines per sq cm.   Test value = 0.0589 (measurement by M. F. Miller).

ROUND COILS OF SMALL CROSS SECTION

The formulas given so far in this chapter take account of the length and thickness of the coil by algebraic terms which have been obtained by an integration over the cross section of the coil. This requires a calculation to be made twice, once for the end of the coil nearer the point for which the magnetic field is being computed, and once for the farther end.   When the distance to this point is large compared with the dimensions of the coil section, the final computed result is a small difference of two larger quantities, resulting in a loss of accuracy.   In this section, formulas for the magnetic field strength are given[8] which not only preserve the accuracy of computation, in such cases where they are applicable, but also save a considerable amount of work.

When the length and thickness of the solenoid or coil are so small compared with the radius that they may be neglected, formulas are available which give the field strength directly in terms of elliptic integrals or of a series of zonal harmonics [see equations (12) to (24)].   These formulas can be used with actual coils by taking the position and diameter of the coil to be those of the circle at the middle of the coil section.

In this section, correction formulas are given which can be used along with those of the preceding paragraph and which will give the effect of the dimensions of the cross section.   These formulas are in the form of convergent series and, as is usual in such cases, their applicability is determined by the rapidity with which the terms become smaller and smaller, for any given

[8] Computation of Magnetic Field Strength of Round Coils of Small Cross Section, by H. B. Dwight and G. O. Peters, *Trans. A.I.E.E.*, 1944, p. 684.

problem. If in any case they are found inapplicable for this reason, recourse may be had to the more general set of formulas indicated by numbers in Fig. 5.

The general method by which correction terms for the section of a cylindrical coil may be derived is given in "Electricity and Magnetism," by J. C. Maxwell, V. 2, Par. 700. If the coil section, which is a rectangle of length b and radial dimension t, be plotted with the middle point of the section as origin, then the magnetic field due to any small circular wire through the point (u,v) may be called H_{uv}. Expressing this as H_o and a series of its derivatives, and integrating from $-t/2$ to $t/2$ and from $-b/2$ to $b/2$, there results,

$$H_{\text{coil}} = H_o + \Delta H_o$$

H_o is the magnetic field strength due to the single turn at the center of the cross section, the entire current of the cross section

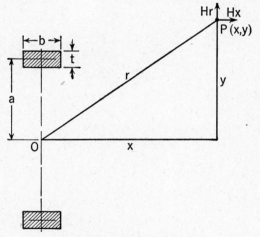

Fig. 6.—Circular coil.

being taken to be concentrated in this turn. H_o may be computed by any of the formulas for single circular turns described in the preceding paragraphs.

$$\Delta H_o = \frac{1}{1!3!2^2}\left(t^2\frac{\partial^2 H_o}{\partial a^2} + b^2\frac{\partial^2 H_o}{\partial x^2}\right) + \frac{1}{1!5!2^4}\left(t^4\frac{\partial^4 H_o}{\partial a^4}\right.$$
$$\left. + b^4\frac{\partial^4 H_o}{\partial x^4}\right) + \frac{1}{3!3!2^4}t^2b^2\frac{\partial^4 H_o}{\partial a^2\partial x^2} + \cdots \quad (46)$$

A case in which the method of this section is very applicable is where the point $P(x,y)$ (see Fig. 6), at which the value of the magnetic field strength is desired, is at a large distance from the coil.

A formula for the axial component of the magnetic field for this case is equation (20), as follows:

$$H_{xo} = \frac{2\pi NI}{10r} \left[\frac{a^2}{r^2} P_2\left(\frac{x}{r}\right) - \frac{3}{2}\frac{a^4}{r^4} P_4\left(\frac{x}{r}\right) + \frac{3\cdot 5}{2\cdot 4}\frac{a^6}{r^6} P_6\left(\frac{x}{r}\right) \right.$$
$$\left. - \frac{3\cdot 5\cdot 7}{2\cdot 4\cdot 6}\frac{a^8}{r^8} P_8\left(\frac{x}{r}\right) + \cdots \right] \quad (47)$$

By applying equation (46), there is obtained

$$\Delta H_{xo} = \frac{2\pi NI}{10r} \left[C_{(2)}\frac{a^2}{r^2} P_2\left(\frac{x}{r}\right) - C_{(4)}\frac{3}{2}\frac{a^4}{r^4} P_4\left(\frac{x}{r}\right) \right.$$
$$\left. + C_{(6)}\frac{3\cdot 5}{2\cdot 4}\frac{a^6}{r^6} P_6\left(\frac{x}{r}\right) - C_{(8)}\frac{3\cdot 5\cdot 7}{2\cdot 4\cdot 6}\frac{a^8}{r^8} P_8\left(\frac{x}{r}\right) + \cdots \right] \quad (48)$$

where $C_{(2)} = \dfrac{t^2}{12a^2}$.

$$C_{(4)} = \left(\frac{t^2}{2a^2} - \frac{b^2}{3a^2} + \frac{t^4}{80a^4} - \frac{t^2 b^2}{36a^4} \right).$$
$$C_{(6)} = \left(\frac{5}{4}\frac{t^2}{a^2} - \frac{b^2}{a^2} + \frac{3}{16}\frac{t^4}{a^4} - \frac{t^2 b^2}{2a^4} + \frac{b^4}{10a^4} + \cdots \right).$$
$$C_{(8)} = \left(\frac{7}{3}\frac{t^2}{a^2} - \frac{2b^2}{a^2} + \frac{7}{8}\frac{t^4}{a^4} - \frac{5}{2}\frac{t^2 b^2}{a^4} + \frac{3}{5}\frac{b^4}{a^4} + \cdots \right).$$

Similarly, the radial component at the point $P(x,y)$ is, by (21),

$$H_{ro} = \frac{\pi NI y}{10r^2} \left[\frac{a^2}{r^2} P_2'\left(\frac{x}{r}\right) - \frac{3}{4}\frac{a^4}{r^4} P_4'\left(\frac{x}{r}\right) + \frac{3\cdot 5}{4\cdot 6}\frac{a^6}{r^6} P_6'\left(\frac{x}{r}\right) \right.$$
$$\left. - \frac{3\cdot 5\cdot 7}{4\cdot 6\cdot 8}\frac{a^8}{r^8} P_8'\left(\frac{x}{r}\right) + \cdots \right] \quad (49)$$

The same coefficients are used for each term as in equation (48); thus, by equation (46),

$$\Delta H_{ro} = \frac{\pi NI y}{10r^2} \left[C_{(2)}\frac{a^2}{r^2} P_2'\left(\frac{x}{r}\right) - C_{(4)}\frac{3}{4}\frac{a^4}{r^4} P_4'\left(\frac{x}{r}\right) \right.$$
$$\left. + C_{(6)}\frac{3\cdot 5}{4\cdot 6}\frac{a^6}{r^6} P_6'\left(\frac{x}{r}\right) - C_{(8)}\frac{3\cdot 5\cdot 7}{4\cdot 6\cdot 8}\frac{a^8}{r^8} P_8'\left(\frac{x}{r}\right) + \cdots \right] \quad (50)$$

In the foregoing formulas, the magnetic field is given at the point (x,y), the center of the round coil being the origin of coordinates and the axis of the coil being the axis of x (see Fig. 6). The quantity $r^2 = x^2 + y^2$. The coil has a mean radius of a cm. Its cross section is rectangular, the radial thickness being t and the axial length, b. It is evident from the form of (48) and (50) that t and b should be small compared with the radius a for these formulas to be applicable. Dimensions are in centimeters.

$P_n(\mu)$ is a surface zonal harmonic [see equation (17) and following].

Since these formulas are to be used when there is no iron or magnetic material near the coil, the flux density at the point $P(x,y)$, in lines per square centimeter, is numerically equal to the value of H given by the formulas.

Example 5. For a numerical example, take $a = 10$ cm, $t = 0$, $b = 5$ cm, $x = 24$ cm, and $y = 32$ cm (see Fig. 6). Then $r^2 = 1,600$, $r = 40$, and $x/r = 0.6$. By (47),

$$H_{xo} = \frac{2\pi NI}{10^4 a} \times \frac{10}{40} (2.500 + 2.391 + 0.079 - 0.007 \cdots) = \frac{2\pi NI}{10^4 a} \times 1.241$$

$$\Delta H_{xo} = \frac{2\pi NI}{10^4 a} \times \frac{10}{40} \left(-2.391 \times \frac{1}{12} - 0.079 \times \frac{39}{160} + 0.007 \times \frac{37}{80} \cdots \right)$$

$$= \frac{-2\pi NI}{10^4 a} \times 0.054$$

$$H_x = H_{xo} + \Delta H_{xo} = \frac{2\pi NI}{10^4 a} \times 1.187$$

An alternative way of computing this result is by two applications of (39). First, with $t = 0$, by (39),

$$H_{x_1} = H_{x\infty} - \frac{\pi nI}{10} \left[\frac{a^2}{r_1^2} P_1 \left(\frac{x_1}{r_1} \right) - \frac{3}{4} \frac{a^4}{r_1^4} P_3 \left(\frac{x_1}{r_1} \right) + \frac{3 \cdot 5}{4 \cdot 6} \frac{a^6}{r_1^6} P_5 \left(\frac{x_1}{r_1} \right) \right.$$
$$\left. - \frac{3 \cdot 5 \cdot 7}{4 \cdot 6 \cdot 8} \frac{a^8}{r_1^8} P_7 \left(\frac{x_1}{r_1} \right) + \cdots \right]$$

where $H_{x\infty} = \dfrac{2\pi nI}{10}$.

$n = \dfrac{N}{b}$ = turns per cm.

$r_1^2 = x_1^2 + y^2$.

$x_1 = x - \dfrac{b}{2} = 24 - 2.5 = 21.5$ cm.

$$H_{x_1} = \frac{\pi NI}{10a} \times \frac{a}{b} [2 - 0.037\,523 - 0.001\,368 + 0.000\,009\,0$$
$$+ 0.000\,003\,4 + 0.000\,000\,1 \cdots]$$

$$= \frac{\pi NI}{10a} \times \frac{10}{5} \times 1.961\,121$$

For $\quad x_2 = x + \dfrac{b}{2} = 24 + 2.5 = 26.5$

$$H_{x_2} = \frac{\pi NI}{10a} \times \frac{10}{5} \times 1.962\ 307$$

$$H_x = H_{x_2} - H_{x_1} = \frac{2\pi NI}{10a}(1.962\ 307 - 1.961\ 121) = \frac{2\pi NI}{10^4 a} \times 1.186$$

This agrees very well with the result by means of ΔH_o. The method by (39) takes about twice as long as (47) and (48), for this example. It has the advantage that further terms can be computed indefinitely if desired.

For the same shape of coil as has been taken up, namely, with t and b small compared to the radius a, the magnetic field strength near the center of the coil can be computed by means of (46), by applying it to (17) and (19).

By equation (17), $H_{xo} = \dfrac{2\pi NI}{10a}\left[1 - \dfrac{3}{2}\dfrac{r^2}{a^2}P_2\left(\dfrac{x}{r}\right)\right.$

$$+ \frac{3 \cdot 5}{2 \cdot 4}\frac{r^4}{a^4}P_4\left(\frac{x}{r}\right) - \frac{3 \cdot 5 \cdot 7}{2 \cdot 4 \cdot 6}\frac{r^6}{a^6}P_6\left(\frac{x}{-}\right) + \cdots \left.\vphantom{\frac{3}{2}}\right] \quad (51)$$

By equation (46), $\Delta H_{xo} = \dfrac{2\pi NI}{10a}\left[D_{(0)} - D_{(2)}\dfrac{3}{2}\dfrac{r^2}{a^2}P_2\left(\dfrac{x}{r}\right)\right.$

$$+ D_{(4)}\frac{3 \cdot 5}{2 \cdot 4}\frac{r^4}{a^4}P_4\left(\frac{x}{r}\right) - D_{(6)}\frac{3 \cdot 5 \cdot 7}{2 \cdot 4 \cdot 6}\frac{r^6}{a^6}P_6\left(\frac{x}{r}\right) + \cdots \left.\vphantom{\frac{3}{2}}\right] \quad (52)$$

where $D_{(0)} = \left(\dfrac{t^2}{12a^2} - \dfrac{b^2}{8a^2} + \dfrac{t^4}{80a^4} - \dfrac{t^2 b^2}{16a^4} + \dfrac{3}{128}\dfrac{b^4}{a^4} \cdots\right).$

$$D_{(2)} = \left(\frac{t^2}{2a^2} - \frac{5}{8}\frac{b^2}{a^2} + \frac{3}{16}\frac{t^4}{a^4} - \frac{25}{32}\frac{t^2 b^2}{a^4} + \frac{35}{128}\frac{b^4}{a^4} \cdots\right).$$

$$D_{(4)} = \left(\frac{5}{4}\frac{t^2}{a^2} - \frac{35}{24}\frac{b^2}{a^2} + \frac{7}{8}\frac{t^4}{a^4} - \frac{245}{72}\frac{t^2 b^2}{a^4} + \frac{147}{128}\frac{b^4}{a^4} \cdots\right).$$

$$D_{(6)} = \left(\frac{7}{3}\frac{t^2}{a^2} - \frac{21}{8}\frac{b^2}{a^2} + \frac{21}{8}\frac{t^4}{a^4} - \frac{315}{32}\frac{t^2 b^2}{a^4} + \frac{2{,}079}{640}\frac{b^4}{a^4} \cdots\right)$$

For the radial component of the field near the coil center, by (19),

$$H_{ro} = \frac{\pi NIyr}{10a^3}\left[P_2'\left(\frac{x}{r}\right) - \frac{3}{4}\frac{r^2}{a^2}P_4'\left(\frac{x}{r}\right)\right.$$

$$\left. + \frac{3 \cdot 5}{4 \cdot 6}\frac{r^4}{a^4}P_6'\left(\frac{x}{r}\right) - \cdots \right] \quad (53)$$

and by equation (46), $\Delta H_{ro} = \dfrac{\pi NIyr}{10a^3}\left[D_{(2)}P_2'\left(\dfrac{x}{r}\right)\right.$

$$\left. - D_{(4)}\frac{3}{4}\frac{r^2}{a^2}P_4'\left(\frac{x}{r}\right) + D_{(6)}\frac{3 \cdot 5}{4 \cdot 6}\frac{r^4}{a^4}P_6'\left(\frac{x}{r}\right) - \cdots \right] \quad (54)$$

where $r^2 = x^2 + y^2$ and where the coefficients $D_{(2)}$, $D_{(4)}$, and $D_{(6)}$ are given after equation (52).

Formulas for the first few surface zonal harmonics are

$$P_1(\mu) = \mu$$
$$P_2(\mu) = \tfrac{1}{2}(3\mu^2 - 1)$$
$$P_3(\mu) = \tfrac{1}{2}(5\mu^3 - 3\mu)$$
$$P_4(\mu) = \frac{1}{2 \cdot 4}\,(5 \cdot 7\mu^4 - 2 \cdot 3 \cdot 5\mu^2 + 1 \cdot 3)$$
$$P_5(\mu) = \frac{1}{2 \cdot 4}\,(7 \cdot 9\mu^5 - 2 \cdot 5 \cdot 7\mu^3 + 3 \cdot 5\mu)$$
$$P_6(\mu) = \frac{1}{2 \cdot 4 \cdot 6}\,(7 \cdot 9 \cdot 11\mu^6 - 3 \cdot 5 \cdot 7 \cdot 9\mu^4 + 3 \cdot 3 \cdot 5 \cdot 7\mu^2 - 1 \cdot 3 \cdot 5)$$
$$P_7(\mu) = \frac{1}{2 \cdot 4 \cdot 6}\,(9 \cdot 11 \cdot 13\mu^7 - 3 \cdot 7 \cdot 9 \cdot 11\mu^5 + 3 \cdot 5 \cdot 7 \cdot 9\mu^3 - 3 \cdot 5 \cdot 7\mu)$$
$$P_8(\mu) = \frac{1}{2 \cdot 4 \cdot 6 \cdot 8}\,(9 \cdot 11 \cdot 13 \cdot 15\mu^8 - 4 \cdot 7 \cdot 9 \cdot 11 \cdot 13\mu^6 + 6 \cdot 5 \cdot 7 \cdot 9 \cdot 11\mu^4 - 4 \cdot 3 \cdot 5 \cdot 7 \cdot 9\mu^2 + 1 \cdot 3 \cdot 5 \cdot 7)$$
$$P_1'(\mu) = 1$$
$$P_2'(\mu) = 3\mu$$
$$P_3'(\mu) = \tfrac{1}{2}(3 \cdot 5\mu^2 - 1 \cdot 3)$$
$$P_4'(\mu) = \tfrac{1}{2}(5 \cdot 7\mu^3 - 3 \cdot 5\mu) \tag{55}$$

and so on, by simple differentiation of the formulas given above.

CHAPTER 33

FORCE BETWEEN COAXIAL COILS WITHOUT IRON

Relation between Force and Inductance. Find the work done in building up a current I in a circuit of self-inductance L. When the current has a value i, the voltage due to its increase is $L \, di/dt$ using absolute electromagnetic units. This acts in a direction so as to oppose the increase of the current. The rate of supply of energy for this is $P = Li \, di/dt$.

The total energy supplied in building the current up from 0 to I is

$$W = \int P \, dt = \int_{i=0}^{I} Li \, di$$
$$W = \tfrac{1}{2}LI^2 \tag{1}$$

Similarly, it is shown that this amount of energy is returned to the source of the electric current when the current dies down to zero. The energy is said to be stored in the magnetic field.

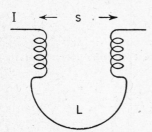

FIG. 1.—Two coils in series.

The energy to overcome resistance need not be considered in this connection. It is changed to heat as fast as it is supplied and is not returned to the electric circuit.

Let two coils be connected in series by a flexible connector so that one is free to move. Let the self-inductance of the circuit be L, which will change in value when there is motion of the coils. Assume that I is kept constant. See Fig. 1.

The voltage in the circuit because of the motion is $I \, dL/dt$ since LI is the number of magnetic lines of force linking the circuit. The rate of supplying energy, due to this voltage, is $I^2 \, dL/dt$.

This energy goes to supply the mechanical work of moving the movable coil and to increase the stored energy of the magnetic field. If the velocity of the movable coil is ds/dt and if the force in this direction is F, the rate of doing mechanical work is $F\, ds/dt$. The rate of changing the stored energy is $\frac{1}{2}I^2\, dL/dt$ from (1).

Then
$$I^2 \frac{dL}{dt} = F \frac{ds}{dt} + \frac{1}{2} I^2 \frac{dL}{dt} \qquad\qquad (2)$$

$$F\, ds = \tfrac{1}{2}I^2\, dL$$

$$F = \frac{1}{2} I^2 \frac{dL}{ds} \qquad\qquad\qquad \text{dynes} \quad (3)$$

where I is in abamperes, L in abhenries, and s in centimeters.

Now
$$L = L_1 + L_2 + 2M$$

$$\frac{dL}{ds} = 2 \frac{dM}{ds} \qquad \text{since } L_1 \text{ and } L_2 \text{ are constant}$$

$$F = I^2 \frac{dM}{ds} \qquad\qquad\qquad \text{dynes} \quad (4)$$

When the two coils are in separate circuits and have equal currents I_1 abamp, the mechanical force between them is given by (4).   If the current in the second coil becomes I_2, the force on it is changed in the ratio I_2/I_1 and is

$$F = I_1 I_2 \frac{dM}{ds} \qquad\qquad\qquad \text{dynes} \quad (5)$$

If I_1 and I_2 are in amperes, the component of mechanical force in the direction of s is

$$F = \frac{I_1 I_2}{4.45 \times 10^7} \frac{dM}{ds} \qquad\qquad \text{pounds} \quad (6)$$

since 1 gram = 981 dynes and 1 lb = 454 grams.

Force between Circular Filaments in Air.   A mechanical force in the direction of the axis is exerted on a circular filament carrying current, by another coaxial circular filament not in the same plane.   Since the force in dynes on 1 cm of wire is equal to its current in abamperes multiplied by the component of magnetic field in the direction across the wire, the force on the circular filament is obtained by multiplying its current and its circumference by the radial component of the magnetic field of the other circular filament, using absolute electromagnetic units.   This is in agreement with equation (5) of this chapter and with the derivation of expressions for radial component of magnetic field given in Chap. 32.

The computed value of force is useful, especially with large current-limiting reactance coils, for designing the supports of the coils and for determining how close together the coils may be mounted without danger of damage at times of short circuit.

For two circular filaments or for two coils of relatively small cross section of winding with I_1 and I_2 amp and N_1 and N_2 turns, the mechanical force is obtained by multiplying (13), Chap. 32, by $2\pi y I_2 N_2/10$ and dividing by 981×454 to change from dynes to pounds.   The force is

$$F = \frac{4\pi y N_1 N_2 I_1 I_2}{4.45 \times 10^7 r_1} \left\{ \frac{2ax}{r_2{}^2} E - \frac{x}{y}(K - E) \right\} \quad \text{pounds} \quad (7)$$

where the dimensions are as in Fig. 1, Chap. 32, and where

$$r_1{}^2 = (a + y)^2 + x^2$$
$$r_2{}^2 = (a - y)^2 + x^2 = c^2 + x^2$$

K and E are complete elliptic integrals of the first and second kinds of modulus k, where

$$k^2 = 1 - \frac{r_2{}^2}{r_1{}^2}$$

Values of K and E may be taken from tables ⌊see following equation (3), Chap. 26].   The second coil has a mean radius of y and passes through P.

For circular coils near together, with small cross section of winding, or for circular filaments,

$$F = \frac{I_1 I_2 N_1 N_2}{4.45 \times 10^7} \frac{\pi}{\sqrt{D}} \sqrt{d} \left[\frac{2xD}{u^2} + \frac{x}{d}\left(\frac{5}{2} - \frac{77}{32}\frac{u^2}{Dd}\right.\right.$$
$$+ \frac{141}{64}\frac{u^4}{D^2d^2} - \frac{17,165}{8,192}\frac{u^6}{D^3d^3} \cdots \left.\right)$$
$$- \left\{\operatorname{logn} \frac{16Dd}{u^2}\right\}\left\{\frac{3}{2}\frac{x}{d}\left(1 - \frac{5}{8}\frac{u^2}{Dd} + \frac{35}{64}\frac{u^4}{D^2d^2}\right.\right.$$
$$\left.\left.\left. - \frac{525}{1,024}\frac{u^6}{D^3d^3} \cdots \right)\right\}\right] \quad \text{pounds} \quad (8)$$

where $u^2 = x^2 + c^2$ and where dimensions are either all in inches or all in centimeters, and are as in Fig. 1, Chap. 32, the second coil passing through P,

x = mean axial separation between the coils.

D and d = mean diameters of the coils.

$$c = \frac{D - d}{2} = \text{difference of the radii.}$$

The dimension D may be either larger or smaller than d. Only even powers of the quantity c are involved. Formula (8) is obtained directly from (8), Chap. 32.

For a circular coil lying near the center of a larger coaxial circular coil, from (19), Chap. 32,

$$F = \frac{I_1 I_2 N_1 N_2}{4.45 \times 10^7} \frac{2\pi^2 y^2 r}{3a^3} \left[P_2'\left(\frac{x}{r}\right) - \frac{3}{4}\frac{r^2}{a^2} P_4'\left(\frac{x}{r}\right) \right.$$
$$\left. + \frac{3 \times 5}{4 \times 6}\frac{r^4}{a^4} P_6'\left(\frac{x}{r}\right) - \cdots \right] \quad \text{pounds} \quad (9)$$

where $r^2 = x^2 + y^2$.

For coaxial coils far apart, from (21), Chap. 32,

$$F = \frac{I_1 I_2 N_1 N_2}{4.45 \times 10^7} \frac{2\pi^2 y^2}{r^2} \left[\frac{a^2}{r^2} P_2'\left(\frac{x}{r}\right) - \frac{3}{4}\frac{a^4}{r^4} P_4'\left(\frac{x}{r}\right) \right.$$
$$\left. + \frac{3 \times 5}{4 \times 6}\frac{a^6}{r^6} P_6'\left(\frac{x}{r}\right) - \cdots \right] \quad \text{pounds} \quad (10)$$

From (23), Chap. 32,

$$F = \frac{I_1 I_2 N_1 N_2}{4.45 \times 10^7} \frac{4\pi^2 a^2 y^2}{\rho^4} \left[\frac{1}{2} P_2'\left(\frac{x}{\rho}\right) - \frac{1 \times 3}{2 \times 4}\frac{y^2}{\rho^2} P_4'\left(\frac{x}{\rho}\right) \right.$$
$$\left. + \frac{1 \times 3 \times 5}{2 \times 4 \times 6}\frac{y^4}{\rho^4} P_6'\left(\frac{x}{\rho}\right) - \cdots \right] \quad \text{pounds} \quad (11)$$

where $\qquad \rho^2 = x^2 + a^2$

Formulas (7) to (11) apply where the cross sections are relatively small, especially to single circular filaments. For a description of the zonal harmonics see (18), (19), and (55), Chap. 32.

Corrections for the dimensions of the cross sections in the cases of (8) to (11) may be computed by means of (8), Chap. 26, changing M to F.

Force between Coaxial Solenoids in Air. When two coaxial solenoids are not concentric, a mechanical force is exerted by one on the other in the direction of the axis, whose magnitude may be found by means of equation (5) or (6).

Differentiating equation (1), Chap. 27, with respect to s, the mechanical force is

$$F = \frac{I_1 I_2 N_1 N_2}{4.45 \times 10^7} \left[G_{(x1)} - G_{(x2)} - G_{(x3)} + G_{(x4)} \right] \quad \text{pounds} \quad (12)$$

where I_1 and I_2 are in amperes and N_1 and N_2 are the numbers of turns in the coils, and where

$$x_1 = s + m_1 + m_2.$$
$$x_2 = s + m_1 - m_2.$$
$$x_3 = s - m_1 + m_2. \quad .$$
$$x_4 = s - m_1 - m_2.$$

The distance between centers of the coils is s and the lengths of the two coils are $2m_1$ and $2m_2$. See equations (2) to (5) in Chap. 27.

For small values of x, the derivative of (6), Chap. 27, may be taken from the first step of the integration by which (6) was obtained. This gives

$$\begin{aligned}
G_{(x)} = \frac{\pi x \sqrt{Dd}}{4 m_1 m_2} & \left[\left\{ \operatorname{logn} \frac{16 Dd}{x^2 + c^2} \right\} \left\{ 1 + \frac{3}{4} \frac{c^2}{Dd} - \frac{15}{64} \frac{c^4}{D^2 d^2} \right. \right. \\
& + \frac{35}{256} \frac{c^6}{D^3 d^3} + \frac{x^2}{4 Dd} \left(1 - \frac{5}{8} \frac{c^2}{Dd} + \frac{35}{64} \frac{c^4}{D^2 d^2} \right) \\
& \left. - \frac{3}{64} \frac{x^4}{D^2 d^2} \left(1 - \frac{7}{4} \frac{c^2}{Dd} \right) + \frac{5}{256} \frac{x^6}{D^3 d^3} \cdots \right\} \\
& - \left\{ \frac{2c}{x} \tan^{-1} \frac{x}{c} \right\} \left\{ 1 + \frac{c^2}{2 Dd} - \frac{c^4}{8 D^2 d^2} + \frac{c^6}{16 D^3 d^3} \right\} \\
& + \left(-2 + \frac{c^2}{2 Dd} + \frac{15}{64} \frac{c^4}{D^2 d^2} - \frac{151}{768} \frac{c^6}{D^3 d^3} \right) \\
& + \frac{x^2}{Dd} \left(\frac{c^2}{4 Dd} - \frac{209}{768} \frac{c^4}{D^2 d^2} \right) + \frac{x^4}{D^2 d^2} \left(\frac{5}{64} - \frac{43}{256} \frac{c^2}{Dd} \right) \\
& \left. - \frac{31}{768} \frac{x^6}{D^3 d^3} \cdots \right] \quad (13)
\end{aligned}$$

where D and d = diameters of the solenoids.

$$c = (D - d)/2 = \text{difference of the radii.}$$

The dimension D may be larger or smaller than d.

In formulas for force, as well as for inductance, each dimension of the coil should be taken equal to the number of wires or cables in that dimension times the pitch, the values of the dimensions thus being slightly greater than the actual lengths measured over the copper.

For larger values of x the following expression for $G_{(x)}$ may be obtained by differentiating (7), Chap. 26.

$$
\begin{aligned}
G_{(x)} = \frac{\pi^2 a^2 x}{2 m_1 m_2 r} \Bigg[& 1 + \frac{3}{8} \frac{a^2 A^2}{r^4} - \frac{5}{16} \frac{a^4 A^2}{r^6} + \frac{35}{64} \frac{a^4 A^4}{r^8} \\
& + \frac{35}{128} \frac{a^6 A^2}{r^8} - \frac{315}{256} \frac{a^6 A^4}{r^{10}} - \frac{63}{256} \frac{a^8 A^2}{r^{10}} + \frac{1{,}155}{1{,}024} \frac{a^6 A^6}{r^{12}} \\
& + \frac{2{,}079}{1{,}024} \frac{a^8 A^4}{r^{12}} + \frac{231}{1{,}024} \frac{a^{10} A^2}{r^{12}} - \frac{9{,}009}{2{,}048} \frac{a^8 A^6}{r^{14}} - \frac{3{,}003}{1{,}024} \frac{a^{10} A^4}{r^{14}} \\
& - \frac{429}{2{,}048} \frac{a^{12} A^2}{r^{14}} + \cdots \Bigg] \quad (14)
\end{aligned}
$$

where $r^2 = x^2 + A^2$ and where A and a are the radii of the coils. This algebraic series is the same as in (22), Chap. 28, and as in equation (1) of Mechanical Forces in Transformers, by J. E. Clem, *Trans. A.I.E.E.*, 1927, p. 577. For formulas corresponding to (13) and (14) see also footnote 1, Chap. 27.

Since in (13) and (14) only ratios of dimensions appear, it does not matter what unit is used so long as the same unit is used for all the dimensions. Thus the dimensions may be all in inches, or all in centimeters.

Force between Coaxial Solenoids of the Same Radius. When the two coaxial solenoids have the same radius, equation (14), Chap. 27, may be used for their mutual inductance and then (5) or (6) of this chapter may be applied. If the radial thickness of the coils is the same, it may be taken into account since formulas for self-inductance commonly have terms involving the thickness. The axial length of the coils need not necessarily be the same. In the following paragraphs three formulas for self-inductance have been differentiated so as to obtain formulas for $G_{(x)}$, any one of which may be used for a given case, as found suitable. These formulas are equivalent to (13) and (14) but are more special, since they refer to coils of equal mean radius ($c = 0$) and since terms involving the radial thickness t are included. The three formulas are as follows:

When x is greater than about d, the following may be used:[1]

[1] A New Formula for Use in Calculating Repulsion of Coaxial Coils, by H. B. Dwight, *Proc. Intern. Math. Congr.*, Toronto, Can., August, 1924 and *Elec. Jour.*, August, 1925, p. 389.

$$G_{(x)} = \frac{\pi^2 dx}{8m_1m_2}\left[2q + \frac{3}{4}q^5 - \frac{5}{8}q^7 + \frac{105}{64}q^9 - \frac{189}{64}q^{11} \right.$$

$$+ \frac{3,465}{512}q^{13} - \frac{13 \times 297}{256}q^{15} + \frac{45 \times 13,013}{16,384}q^{17} - \cdots$$

$$- \frac{2}{3}\frac{t}{x} + \frac{1}{3}\frac{t^2}{dx} + \frac{t^2}{d^2}\left(-\frac{2}{3}q^3 + \frac{5}{2}q^5 - \frac{20}{3}q^7 + \frac{665}{32}q^9 \right.$$

$$- \frac{1,953}{32}q^{11} + \frac{11 \times 2,135}{128}q^{13} - \frac{143 \times 1,961}{512}q^{15}$$

$$\left. + \frac{195 \times 68,915}{8,192}q^{17} - \cdots \right) + \frac{t^4}{d^4}\left(-\frac{q^3}{9} + \frac{17}{15}q^5 \right.$$

$$- \frac{265}{24}q^7 + \frac{8,855}{144}q^9 - \frac{38,857}{128}q^{11} + \frac{11 \times 3,913}{32}q^{13}$$

$$\left. - \frac{3,003 \times 9,551}{5,120}q^{15} + \frac{2,145 \times 10,625}{1,024}q^{17} - \cdots \right)$$

$$+ \frac{t^6}{d^6}\left(\frac{q^5}{10} - \frac{75}{28}q^7 + \frac{1,117}{24}q^9 - \frac{3,549}{8}q^{11} + \frac{231 \times 3,641}{256}q^{13} \right.$$

$$\left.\left. - \frac{143 \times 367,621}{2,560}q^{15} + \frac{2,145 \times 109,353}{2,048}q^{17} - \cdots \right) \right] \quad (15)$$

where $q^2 = \dfrac{d^2}{d^2 + 4x^2}$.

When x is less than d and greater than t, the following may be used:[2]

$$G_{(x)} = \frac{\pi dx}{4m_1m_2}\left[\left(\log n \frac{4d}{x} \right)\left(2 + \frac{x^2}{2d^2} + \frac{t^2}{12d^2} - \frac{3}{32}\frac{x^4}{d^4} \cdots \right) \right.$$

$$\left. - 2 - \frac{\pi}{3}\frac{t}{x} + \frac{5}{24}\frac{t^2}{d^2} + \frac{t^2}{6x^2} + \frac{5}{64}\frac{x^4}{d^4} \cdots \right] \quad (16)$$

When x is less than t,

$$G_{(x)} = \frac{\pi dx}{4m_1m_2}\left[\left(\log n \frac{4d}{t} \right)\left(2 + \frac{x^2}{2d^2} + \frac{t^2}{12d^2} \right) + \frac{2}{3}\frac{x^2}{t^2}\log n \frac{t}{x} \right.$$

$$- \frac{\pi x}{t}\left(1 + \frac{x^2}{3d^2} \right) - 1 + \frac{x^2}{2d^2} + \frac{11}{9}\frac{x^2}{t^2} + \frac{43}{144}\frac{t^2}{d^2}$$

$$\left. + \frac{7}{16}\frac{x^4}{t^2d^2} + \frac{x^4}{30t^4} \cdots \right] \quad (17)$$

In the foregoing formulas, the dimensions may be all in inches or all in centimeters, since only ratios of lengths are involved.

[2] Repulsion and Mutual Inductance of Reactance Coils with the Same Axis, by H. B. Dwight, *Elec. Jour.*, May, 1918, p. 166.

The values of $G_{(x)}$ should be calculated with some precision as the result of the subtraction is generally smaller than the separate values.   Note that logn $p = 2.3026 \log_{10} p$.

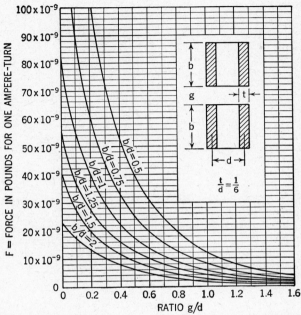

Fig. 2.—Mechanical force between reactance coils with the same axis.   Average force in pounds = F (from curves) $I_1 I_2 N^2 \cos \theta$ where θ is the phase angle between I_1 and I_2, which are in amperes.

In Fig. 2 are given curves for the force between two equal coils.   These curves may be used in practical cases.

Example 1.   Find the force between two duplicate reactance coils, without iron, in which a single-phase short-circuit current of 11,700 effective amperes is flowing.   The coils are on the same axis.
Mean diameter = d = 22.5 in.
Radial thickness = t = 13.5 in.
Axial length = $2m_1 = 2m_2$ = 8.5 in.
Axial spacing, center to center, = s = 40 in.
Turns per coil = 100.
Computed force by (12) and (15) = 9,110 lb.
Example 2.   Find the average mechanical force acting on each of two coils, without iron, placed end to end, as follows:
Mean diameter = d = 25.53 in.
Thickness of winding = t = 4.87 in.

Length $= 2m_1 = 2m_2 = 30.87$ in.
Axial spacing, center to center, $= s = 45.47$ in.
Current $= I_1 = I_2 = 500$ amp.
Number of turns per coil $= 114$.
Computed force, by (12, (15), and (16), $= 35.7$ lb.

Measured force (*Elec. Jour.*, April, 1914, p. 206, Fig. 8) $= 38.7$ lb.

Example 3. Find the total average force exerted on each of three coils placed end to end, without iron, the dimensions being the same as in Example 2, and three-phase current of 500 amp flowing in the coils.

The average, or steady, force between two of the coils is proportional to the average of the products of the instantaneous values of two alternating currents which are 120° out of phase. The force may therefore be computed the same as the watts which are due to an alternating voltage and current which are 120° out of phase. The value will be equal to that for in-phase currents, multiplied by cos 120°. Therefore, the average force between the middle coil and an end coil is $35.7 \times \frac{1}{2} = 17.8$ lb.

For the two end coils, the currents are 120° out of phase but the spacing is larger. The force is 0.8 lb.

This average force is to be added to the previous value, making the total average force on either end coil 18.6 lb.

The average force on the middle coil is zero, since it is subjected to an equal repulsion from each of the end coils. The middle coil is, however, subjected to a momentary force during each cycle, first in one direction and then in the other. Where the danger expected is the breaking of a porcelain insulator or a support of brittle metal, the value of the momentary force is of importance.

The forces described in this example become much larger under short-circuit conditions since they increase as the square of the current.

Force between Thin Disk Coils in Air.

Formulas (15) to (17) are not very suitable for coils that are shorter than the mean radius, owing to slow convergence. The following formula[3] for the force exerted by two duplicate, infinitely thin, disk coils on each other was obtained by differentiating equation (1), Chap. 29, with respect to s.

$$F = \frac{\pi I_1 I_2 N^2}{4.45 \times 10^7} \left[\left(\operatorname{logn} \frac{16d^2}{s^2 + t^2} \right) \left(\frac{3}{2} \frac{s}{d} - \frac{15}{16} \frac{s^3}{d^3} + \frac{7}{32} \frac{st^2}{d^3} \cdots \right) \right.$$
$$+ \left(\operatorname{logn} \frac{s^2 + t^2}{s^2} \right) \left(\frac{2sd}{t^2} + \frac{5}{2} \frac{s^3}{t^2 d} + \frac{5}{2} \frac{s^3}{d^3} - \frac{161}{96} \frac{s^5}{t^2 d^3} \cdots \right)$$
$$\left. - 4 \left(\tan^{-1} \frac{t}{s} \right) \left(\frac{d}{t} + \frac{2s^2}{td} + \frac{2}{3} \frac{s^2 t}{d^3} - \frac{2s^4}{td^3} \cdots \right) \right]$$

[3] Mutual Inductance and Repulsion of Two Adjacent Disk Coils, by H. B. Dwight and T. Y. Lu, *Jour. Math. Phys.*, Vol. 9, p. 319, equation (2), 1930.

$$+ \frac{2sd}{s^2 + t^2}\left(1 + \frac{s^2}{t^2} + \frac{7}{12}\frac{s^2}{d^2} - \frac{t^2}{24d^2} + \frac{5}{8}\frac{s^4}{t^2d^2} + \frac{19}{320}\frac{s^4}{d^4}\right.$$

$$+ \frac{193}{576}\frac{s^2t^2}{d^4} - \frac{11}{2,880}\frac{t^4}{d^4} - \frac{161}{576}\frac{s^6}{t^2d^4} \cdots \left.\right) - \frac{2sd}{t^2} + \frac{37}{12}\frac{s}{d}$$

$$\left. - \frac{5}{4}\frac{s^3}{t^2d} - \frac{827}{180}\frac{s^3}{d^3} - \frac{st^2}{360d^3} + \frac{161}{288}\frac{s^5}{t^2d^3} \cdots \right] \quad \text{pounds} \quad (18)$$

where I_1 and I_2 are in amperes.

  N = number of turns in each coil.

  d = mean diameter.

  t = radial breadth of the coil winding.

  s = axial spacing.

Any unit may be used for the dimensions since only ratios of dimensions are involved.

Formula (18) was checked by a laboratory measurement on two coils for which $d = 23.56$ cm, $t = 8.32$ cm, $s = 4.68$ cm, and $N = 516$. The measured force was 119 grams at 1.42 amp. The computed force is 107 grams, which is 10 % less than the measured value.

CHAPTER 34

FORCE BETWEEN COILS WITH PARALLEL AXES

Formulas for calculating the mechanical force exerted between two equal reactance coils, without iron, placed side by side with parallel axes, may be derived by differentiating, with respect to s, expressions for the mutual inductance of the coils in that position.[1] This gives, from equation (1), Chap. 30, for two coils as in Fig. 1,

$$
\begin{aligned}
F = \frac{2\pi^2 a^2}{4.45 \times 10^7 b^2} & \left[\frac{a^2}{r^2}\left(\frac{r^2}{s^2} - \frac{s}{r}\right)\left(1 + \frac{c^2}{6a^2} + \frac{c^4}{144a^4}\right) \right. \\
& + \frac{3}{4}\frac{a^4}{r^4}\left(\frac{4s}{r} - \frac{5s^3}{r^3} + \frac{r^4}{s^4}\right)\left(1 + \frac{7}{12}\frac{c^2}{a^2} + \frac{13}{240}\frac{c^4}{a^4} + \frac{c^6}{960a^6}\right) \\
& - \frac{75}{64}\frac{a^6}{r^6}\left(\frac{8s}{r} - \frac{28s^3}{r^3} + \frac{21s^5}{r^5} - \frac{r^6}{s^6}\right)\left(1 + \frac{17}{15}\frac{c^2}{a^2} + \frac{169}{600}\frac{c^4}{a^4}\right. \\
& + \frac{41}{2,800}\frac{c^6}{a^6} + \frac{113}{672,000}\frac{c^8}{a^8}\right) + \frac{245}{256}\frac{a^8}{r^8}\left(\frac{32s}{r} - \frac{216s^3}{r^3} + \frac{396s^5}{r^5}\right. \\
& - \frac{429}{2}\frac{s^7}{r^7} + \frac{5}{2}\frac{r^8}{s^8}\right)\left(1 + \frac{155}{84}\frac{c^2}{a^2} + \frac{2,167}{2,520}\frac{c^4}{a^4} + \frac{541}{4,704}\frac{c^6}{a^6}\right. \\
& + \frac{2,129}{3,136 \times 180}\frac{c^8}{a^8} + \frac{197}{1,960 \times 3,456}\frac{c^{10}}{a^{10}}\right) \\
& \left. + \cdots \right]
\end{aligned}
$$

pounds for 1 ampere-turn in each coil   (1)

where $r^2 = s^2 + b^2$ and $a = d/2 =$ the mean radius of the coil.

The meanings of the letters are shown in Fig. 1, which gives curves that may be used for practical problems. See the note under Fig. 1 for alternating currents that are out of phase.

The dimensions may be given either all in inches or all in centimeters, since only ratios of dimensions appear. As with

[1] Some New Formulas for Reactance Coils, *Trans. A.I.E.E.*, 1919, p. **1675.**

other cases of force between coils, if all the dimensions, including spacing, of a group of coils are increased by a certain ratio but the currents are left the same, the mechanical force in pounds is not changed at all.   However, large coils are generally subject to large forces, since they carry proportionately large currents.

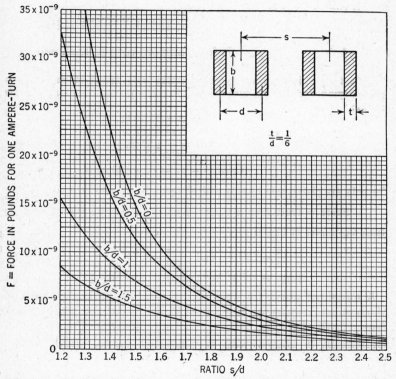

Fig. 1.—Mechanical force between reactance coils with parallel axes.   Average force in pounds = F (from curves) $I_1 I_2 N^2 \cos \theta$ where N is the number of turns in each coil and where θ is the phase angle between I_1 and I_2, which are in amperes.

As in the corresponding case for mutual inductance, expression (1) becomes indeterminate when $b = 0$ and, therefore, $r = s$. In such a case, which is that of two flat disks in the same plane, the following formula, obtained by differentiating (2), Chap. 30, with respect to s, may be used:

$$F = \frac{3\pi^2 a^4}{4.45 \times 10^7 s^4} \left[\left(1 + \frac{c^2}{6a^2} + \frac{c^4}{144a^4} \right) + \frac{15}{4} \frac{a^2}{s^2} \left(1 + \frac{7}{12} \frac{c^2}{a^2} \right. \right.$$

$$\left. + \frac{13}{240} \frac{c^4}{a^4} + \frac{c^6}{960a^6} \right) + \frac{875}{64} \frac{a^4}{s^4} \left(1 + \frac{17}{15} \frac{c^2}{a^2} + \frac{169}{600} \frac{c^4}{a^4} \right.$$

$$\left. + \frac{41}{2,800} \frac{c^6}{a^6} + \frac{113}{672,000} \frac{c^8}{a^8} \right) + \frac{25,725}{512} \frac{a^6}{s^6} \left(1 + \frac{155}{84} \frac{c^2}{a^2} \right.$$

$$\left. + \frac{2,167}{2,520} \frac{c^4}{a^4} + \frac{541}{4,704} \frac{c^6}{a^6} + \frac{2,129}{3,136 \times 180} \frac{c^8}{a^8} + \frac{197}{1,960 \times 3,456} \right.$$

$$\left. \left. \frac{c^{10}}{a^{10}} \right) + \cdots \right] \quad \text{pounds for 1 ampere-turn in each coil} \quad (2)$$

Example 1. Find the average mechanical force acting on each of two coils carrying single-phase currents which are in phase, the data being as follows:

Mean radius of coils $= a = 12.76$ in.
Length of coils $= b = 30.87$ in.
Thickness of winding $= c = 4.87$ in.
Number of turns $= N = 114$.
Current $= I_1 = I_2 = 400$ amp.

The coils are placed side by side with the parallel axes 45 in. apart.

Force $= 158(0.0362 + 0.0065 + 0.0010 + 0.0001) = 6.89$ pounds

Using the curves of Fig. 1,

$$\frac{b}{d} = 1.21 \quad \text{and} \quad \frac{s}{d} = 1.76$$

Force $= 3.3 \times 10^{-9} \times 400^2 \times 114^2 = 6.8$ pounds

A measured curve for coils of this size was published in The Mechanical Stresses in Reactance Coils, by W. M. Dann, *Elec. Jour.*, April, 1914, p. 206. It is reproduced in Fig. 2 and a comparison is shown with a computed curve, which agrees closely with it.

Example 2. Find the average mechanical force on each of three coils of the same size and spacing as those in Example 1, placed side by side in a row and carrying three-phase current, 400 amp per phase.

In determining the average or steady mechanical forces due to three-phase currents, the forces due to the products of the instantaneous values of two alternating currents which are 120° out of phase are computed in the same way as the watts due to the products of the instantaneous values of alternating current and voltage which are out of phase.

Let the three coils in a row be called A, B, and C. The currents in them are 120° apart, in phase. The average or steady force on A caused by I_B is

6.89 cos 120° $= 3.44$ pounds

the computation being similar to Example 1.

To find the force on A caused by I_C, formula (1) is used, the axial spacing being 90 in.   This is

$$0.50 \cos 120° = 0.25 \qquad \text{pounds}$$

This is to be added to the force caused by I_B, since it is in the same direction, namely, toward the center coil.

The force due to opposing currents acting on coils in the side by side position is an attraction while if the coils are in the end to end position the force is a repulsion.

The total average force on A is 3.69 lb.   An equal force acts on C.   Coil B is attracted by both A and C and, although there is an instantaneous force

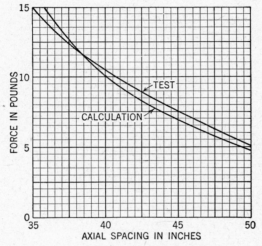

Fig. 2.—Comparison of calculation with test.

first in one direction and then in the other, the average force on B during a complete cycle is zero.

Since these forces increase as the square of the current, they attain large values at times of short circuit.

As in the case of mutual inductance [equation (4), Chap. 30], formulas for the force between unequal solenoids with parallel axes are of practical value.[2]   For this case the components of the mechanical force exerted on a coil when currents flow in the two coils may be computed by differentiating formula (4), Chap. 30, for M, the mutual inductance.

The component of force perpendicular to the parallel axes of the coils is obtained by taking the partial derivative of formula

[2] The Force between Unequal Reactance Coils Having Parallel Axes, by H. B. Dwight and R. W. Purssell, *Gen. Elec. Rev.*, July, 1930, p. 401.

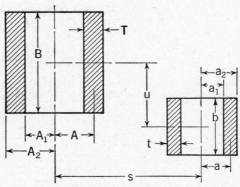

Fig. 3.—Unequal reactance coils with parallel axes.

(4), Chap. 30, with respect to s, the distance between the axes. It is as follows, in pounds for 1 amp in each coil (see Fig. 3):

$$
\begin{aligned}
F_s &= \frac{\pi^2 A^2 a^2 N_1 N_2}{4.45 \times 10^7 Bb} \left[s \left(\frac{1}{S_1{}^3} - \frac{1}{S_2{}^3} - \frac{1}{S_3{}^3} + \frac{1}{S_4{}^3} \right) \left(1 + \frac{T^2}{12A^2} \right) \right. \\
&\left(1 + \frac{t^2}{12a^2} \right) - \frac{3}{8} \left\{ 4s \left(\frac{1}{S_1{}^5} - \frac{1}{S_2{}^5} - \frac{1}{S_3{}^5} + \frac{1}{S_4{}^5} \right) \right. \\
&\left. - 5s^3 \left(\frac{1}{S_1{}^7} - \frac{1}{S_2{}^7} - \frac{1}{S_3{}^7} + \frac{1}{S_4{}^7} \right) \right\} \left\{ A^2 \left(1 + \frac{T^2}{2A^2} + \frac{T^4}{80A^4} \right) \right. \\
&\left. \left(1 + \frac{t^2}{12a^2} \right) + a^2 \left(1 + \frac{T^2}{12A^2} \right) \left(1 + \frac{t^2}{2a^2} + \frac{t^4}{80a^4} \right) \right\} \\
&+ \frac{15}{64} \left\{ 8s \left(\frac{1}{S_1{}^7} - \frac{1}{S_2{}^7} - \frac{1}{S_3{}^7} + \frac{1}{S_4{}^7} \right) - 28s^3 \left(\frac{1}{S_1{}^9} - \frac{1}{S_2{}^9} \right. \right. \\
&\left. \left. - \frac{1}{S_3{}^9} + \frac{1}{S_4{}^9} \right) + 21s^5 \left(\frac{1}{S_1{}^{11}} - \frac{1}{S_2{}^{11}} - \frac{1}{S_3{}^{11}} + \frac{1}{S_4{}^{11}} \right) \right\} \\
&\left\{ A^4 \left(1 + \frac{5}{4} \frac{T^2}{A^2} + \frac{3}{16} \frac{T^4}{A^4} + \frac{T^6}{448A^6} \right) \left(1 + \frac{t^2}{12a^2} \right) \right. \\
&+ 3A^2 a^2 \left(1 + \frac{T^2}{2A^2} + \frac{T^4}{80A^4} \right) \left(1 + \frac{t^2}{2a^2} + \frac{t^4}{80a^4} \right) \\
&\left. \left. + a^4 \left(1 + \frac{T^2}{12A^2} \right) \left(1 + \frac{5}{4} \frac{t^2}{a^2} + \frac{3}{16} \frac{t^4}{a^4} + \frac{t^6}{448a^6} \right) \right\} \right] \quad \text{pounds} \quad (3)
\end{aligned}
$$

If the two coils are alike and if $u = 0$, this equation becomes the same as equation (1).

The component of force parallel to the axes of the coils is obtained by taking the partial derivative of formula (4), Chap.

30, with respect to u, the axial distance between the coil centers. It is, in pounds for 1 amp in each coil:

$$F_u = \frac{\pi^2 A^2 a^2 N_1 N_2}{4.45 \times 10^7 Bb} \left[\left(\frac{u+m}{S_1^3} - \frac{u-n}{S_2^3} - \frac{u+n}{S_3^3} + \frac{u-m}{S_4^3} \right) \right.$$

$$\left(1 + \frac{T^2}{12A^2} \right) \left(1 + \frac{t^2}{12a^2} \right)$$

$$- \frac{3}{8} \left\{ 2 \left(\frac{u+m}{S_1^5} - \frac{u-n}{S_2^5} - \frac{u+n}{S_3^5} + \frac{u-m}{S_4^5} \right) \right.$$

$$\left. - 5s^2 \left(\frac{u+m}{S_1^7} - \frac{u-n}{S_2^7} - \frac{u+n}{S_3^7} + \frac{u-m}{S_4^7} \right) \right\}$$

$$\left\{ A^2 \left(1 + \frac{T^2}{2A^2} + \frac{T^4}{80A^4} \right) \left(1 + \frac{t^2}{12a^2} \right) \right.$$

$$\left. + a^2 \left(1 + \frac{T^2}{12A^2} \right) \left(1 + \frac{t^2}{2a^2} + \frac{t^4}{80a^4} \right) \right\}$$

$$+ \frac{5}{64} \left\{ 8 \left(\frac{u+m}{S_1^7} - \frac{u-n}{S_2^7} - \frac{u+n}{S_3^7} + \frac{u-m}{S_4^7} \right) \right.$$

$$- 56s^2 \left(\frac{u+m}{S_1^9} - \frac{u-n}{S_2^9} - \frac{u+n}{S_3^9} + \frac{u-m}{S_4^9} \right)$$

$$\left. + 63s^4 \left(\frac{u+m}{S_1^{11}} - \frac{u-n}{S_2^{11}} - \frac{u+n}{S_3^{11}} + \frac{u-m}{S_4^{11}} \right) \right\}$$

$$\left\{ A^4 \left(1 + \frac{5}{4}\frac{T^2}{A^2} + \frac{3}{16}\frac{T^4}{A^4} + \frac{1}{448}\frac{T^6}{A^6} \right) \left(1 + \frac{t^2}{12a^2} \right) \right.$$

$$+ 3A^2a^2 \left(1 + \frac{T^2}{2A^2} + \frac{T^4}{80A^4} \right) \left(1 + \frac{t^2}{2a^2} + \frac{t^4}{80a^4} \right)$$

$$\left. \left. + a^4 \left(1 + \frac{T^2}{12A^2} \right) \left(1 + \frac{5}{4}\frac{t^2}{a^2} + \frac{3}{16}\frac{t^4}{a^4} + \frac{1}{448}\frac{t^6}{a^6} \right) \right\} \right] \quad \text{pounds} \quad (4)$$

In equations (3) and (4), the dimensions are as shown in Fig. 3. A and a are the mean radii of the two coils; B and b are their axial lengths; T and t are their thicknesses.

$$m = \frac{B+b}{2} \qquad n = \frac{B-b}{2}$$
$$S_1 = \{s^2 + (u+m)^2\}^{\frac{1}{2}}$$
$$S_2 = \{s^2 + (u-n)^2\}^{\frac{1}{2}}$$
$$S_3 = \{s^2 + (u+n)^2\}^{\frac{1}{2}}$$
$$S_4 = \{s^2 + (u-m)^2\}^{\frac{1}{2}}$$

N_1 and N_2 are the turns in the two coils, respectively.

If the instantaneous or direct currents in the two coils are i_1 and i_2 amp, multiply the expressions for force by i_1i_2. If the root-mean-square currents in the two coils are I_1 and I_2 and if they have sine wave form and differ in phase by an angle θ, multiply the expressions by $I_1I_2 \cos \theta$ for the average force or the steady push. Since formulas (3) and (4) involve ratios of dimensions, the dimensions may be all in inches or all in centimeters. To express the force in grams, use the constant 981×100 in the denominator instead of 4.45×10^7.

It is desired to make acknowledgment to Mr. F. H. Kierstead of the Transformer Engineering Department of the General Electric Co., Pittsfield, Mass., for his suggestion of this problem and advice regarding it.

Example 3.   Two reactance coils with parallel axes, as shown in Fig. 3. Dimensions in inches. $A = 3.08$, $B = 5.62$, $T = 0.55$, $N_1 = 1,142$, $a = 4.635$, $b = 0.95$, $t = 1.635$, $N_2 = 516$, $s = 12.20$, $u = 2.90$.

$$I_1 = 9.54 \text{ amp}, \qquad I_2 = 2.46 \text{ amp, direct current.}$$

$$F_u = \frac{\pi^2 \times 3.08^2 \times 4.635^2 \times 1,142 \times 516 \times 9.54 \times 2.46}{98,100 \times 5.62 \times 0.95} (3.5 + 1.6 + 0.5$$

$$+ 0.1)10^{-4}$$

$$= 30 \qquad\qquad \text{grams}$$

The fourth term in the bracket is estimated.

This force was measured by fastening one coil to a balance arm and adding weights to balance the force exerted when current was flowing. The measured force was 35 grams.

Example 4.   This example illustrates the use of the formulas with two unequal reactance coils of dimensions such as might be encountered in practical engineering. Dimensions are in inches.

Large coil,

$$A_1 = 26.1, \qquad A_2 = 38.1, \qquad B = 80$$

Small coil,

$$a_1 = 5, \qquad a_2 = 9, \qquad b = 10, \qquad s = 59.5, \qquad u = 31$$

Force perpendicular to the axes,

$$7.9N_1N_2I_1I_2 \times 10^{-10} \qquad\qquad \text{pounds}$$

Force parallel to the axes,

$$10.0N_1N_2I_1I_2 \times 10^{-10} \qquad\qquad \text{pounds}$$

CHAPTER 35

SOME CALCULATIONS FOR MECHANICAL FORCE BETWEEN CYLINDRICAL TRANSFORMER COILS

The mechanical force exerted on power transformer coils is sometimes large. As the structure of the coils and their supports employs insulating materials of necessarily less strength than metals, it is desirable to compute the mechanical force since it can easily cause damage.

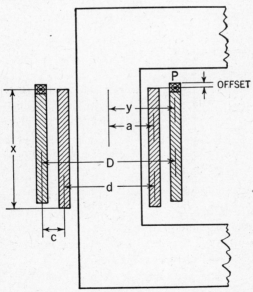

Fig. 1.—One half of concentric-cylinder type, single-phase transformer.

The computation of force may involve several different types of problems. There are transformers of different shapes of core and of winding. There are short circuits outside the transformers and inside, and there are rushes of current in one transformer winding only when it is switched to a power line.

315

In this chapter, a few items are taken up that are connected with the calculation of forces due to external short circuits.

Possibly the most common type of medium and large transformer is the concentric-cylinder type, illustrated in Fig. 1. Computations for the force in an axial direction against the end supports of the winding cylinders depend partly on the number of "tapped-out" turns, if any, near the center of a cylinder and on the amount of axial offset of the high- and low-voltage cylinders due to irregularity in winding or assembly. Formulas for this problem are given in footnotes.[1,2,3]

All the three articles mentioned make use of the same assumptions, namely, the force is computed for the coils without core and the radial thickness of the cylinders is taken as negligible.

For the axial force on coaxial cylindrical coils or portions of coils (see Fig. 2), omitting the effect of the iron core which will be discussed later, formulas (12) to (14), Chap. 33, may be used.

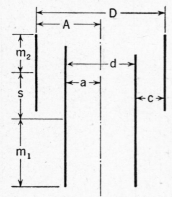

FIG. 2.—Two coaxial cylinders.

The quantity $x_4 = s - m_1 - m_2$ [following equation (12), Chap. 33] is negative in a good many cases, and this results in a negative value of $G_{(x4)}$. Equation (14) is not complete in itself. In almost any practical problem on the coils of a concentric core-type transformer, one of the four values of x is so small that (14) cannot be used, and (13) is required.

In Fig. 3 are shown approximate illustrative curves of the axial thrust against the end supports of the high-voltage or outer cylinder of a 10,000-kva transformer taken as an example. The data for the transformer are as follows:

Single-phase, concentric-cylinder type transformer.

High voltage, 75 kv.

[1] "Kurzschlusskräfte an Transformatoren" (Short-circuit Forces in Transformers), by J. Biermanns, *Bull., Assoc. Suisse Electriciens*, Vol. 14, pp. 212 and 245, 1923.

[2] Mechanical Forces in Transformers, by J. E. Clem, *Trans. A.I.E.E.*, Vol. 46, p. 577, 1927.

[3] Article on transformer forces by A. Korb, *Elek. u Masch.*, 1932, pp. 489 and 505.

Height of stack, 60 in.

Mean diameters of cylinders, 29.6 and 38.4 in.

Turns in high-voltage coil, 3.11 per centimeter of axis.

The transformer is taken to be at a condition of sustained short circuit at the terminals, with equal ampere-turns in high voltage and low voltage. The reactance drop at rated current is taken to be 6.1 per cent of rated voltage for all amounts of tapped-out section of the high-voltage coil up to 20 per cent.

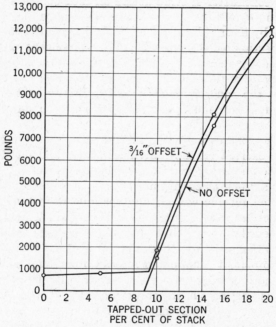

Fig. 3.—Pressure against end support, 10,000 kva transformer. Effect of core not included.

The change in the per cent reactance which would be found for the different taps has not been taken into account, for the sake of simplification of this problem.

When there is a small tapped-out section, less than about 8 per cent of the stack for the sample transformer, the thrust is approximately proportional to the amount of axial offset between the outer and inner cylinders, such as may be caused by irregularities in manufacture and assembly. For a given amount of offset, such as $\frac{3}{16}$ in. for the upper curve of Fig. 3, the thrust

on the end support does not change much until the tapped-out
section becomes large enough for the net compression at the
middle of the cylinder to become zero.   Then the thrust increases
rapidly and reaches 12,100 lb of steady force at the end of the
outer cylinder, for the case of a 20 per cent tapped-out section, in
the sample transformer.

The sharp change in direction in the curve for $\frac{3}{16}$ in. offset
(the upper curve) may be explained as follows.   The force in
dynes per centimeter of strap acting on each copper strap in the
outer cylinder of Fig. 1 is equal to the current in abamperes
multiplied by the resultant magnetic field strength perpendicular
to the direction of the current.   The component of magnetic
field caused by the outer cylinder is in such a direction as to
press the parts of the cylinder together.   The component of field
caused by the inner cylinder is substantially in the opposite
direction and tends to press the parts of the outer cylinder
apart.

Since the magnetic fields partly neutralize each other, the
only force exerted on the individual straps and on the coils is
that due to the difference of the component fields.   However,
the formulas such as equations (13) and (14), Chap. 33, for the
force exerted by one coil on another give what may be called
"components of force" in the two directions.   These are larger
than the resultant force, but it should be remembered that the
only forces that exist are those due to resultant magnetic fields.
Large "component" computed forces do not tend to deform or
move the coils or their supports.   Only resultant forces do so.

The horizontal part of the curve, when the tapped-out sections
are less than about 8 per cent of the stack length, may be computed by equations (12) to (14), Chap. 33.   The result is 770 lb
with no tapped-out section, and very little more with the section
up to 8 per cent.   Over this range, the exploding or separating
component of force is not so great as the attracting component
which tends to press the cylinder together.   All forces discussed
are in an axial direction.   The radial forces are carried by the
metal conductors and represent another computation.   The stack
of coils can be taken to withstand compression and pass on such
forces from part to part of the stack.   With a 5 per cent tap
section in the example described, the computed steady force on a
half of the outer cylinder tending to press it toward the center, is

27,100 lb.   The calculated component of force tending to move the same half cylinder outward is 23,500 lb. for the half which overhangs $\frac{3}{16}$ in.   Neither of these large steady forces exists under short-circuit conditions.   The conductors of this half cylinder are acted on by 27,100 − 23,500 = 3,600 lb. pressing them toward the center of the transformer.   Similarly, the other half cylinder is acted on by 27,100 − 22,700 = 4,400 lb. toward the center.   Since the stack can be taken to withstand compression, the net pressure against the support at the end is

$$4,400 - 3,600 = 800 \text{ lb}$$

as plotted in Fig. 3.   The compressive stress within the cylinder might deform it or crush it, since an assemblage of copper and insulation is not mechanically strong, but the steady value of this stress at the time of a short circuit, as shown by the above values, is much smaller than 27,100 lb, the largest computed component.

The large separate components, such as 27,100 lb in the preceding paragraph, are sometimes taken by engineers to be the actual forces for which provision must be made in the strength of the coils and their supports.   However, only the resultant force should be used, for a correct calculation and, since the materials are weak, a low unit breaking stress and a large factor of safety should be used.

An example illustrating the neutralizing of opposite forces which act on the molecules of a body might be that of a large solid sphere of soft material which is acted on by the attraction of the sun in the east and of the moon in the west.   If the moon is supposed to be near enough to exert a force equal to that of the sun, then the two attractions neutralize each other, molecule by molecule throughout the sphere, and there is no tendency to deformation of the sphere.   On the other hand, forces applied to the surface of the sphere may produce deformation.   For instance, the attraction of the earth, acting on the molecules of the sphere, opposed by the thrust of the floor on which the sphere rests, can produce deformation.

When the tapped-out section of the sample transformer is greater than 8 per cent of the stack, the outward axial forces are greater than the attracting forces.   If the stack be taken to be unable to withstand tension in an axial direction, then the resultant forces on the two halves must be withstood by the end supports of the cylinders, and the amounts will be as shown in Fig. 3.

With a 20 per cent tap section and $\frac{3}{16}$ in. offset, the outward component of steady force on a half section is 27,200 lb and the attractive component is 15,100 lb, giving a net outward force of 12,100 lb as plotted in Fig. 3.

The values of short-circuit force which have been given are the steady or average values and are subject to the usual increases for peak current and for current offset. These would make the instantaneous values of force nearly eight times the steady values, since the forces vary as the square of the current.

When a transformer is switched onto a power line, the current inrush is in one winding only. There is no force of repulsion and therefore no computed force against the end supports and no neutralizing of the compressive force. The current does not have the same value as the short-circuit current. For this compressive force, equations (12) to (14), Chap. 33, may be used, or better, (15) to (17) of that chapter, since they make allowance for the radial thickness of the cylinders.

An alternative, shorter calculation may be given for the horizontal part of the curves of Fig. 3 which gives the same results as the longer method which has been described. Although the force is not nearly so large as in other problems connected with the transformer, yet the calculation is made at times, as is shown by the first three footnotes, and the saving in work compared with their methods is worth while. Further, the alternative calculation is a check on the longer calculations, where it is applicable. It gives a method of computing the effect of the radial thickness of the cylinders and an estimate of the effect of the core on the value of mechanical force, both of which are of interest.

In Fig. 1, taking the coils to have no tapped-out section or a negligibly small one, the components of force tending to press the cylinder together are stronger than those tending to spread it apart, and so the cylinders move as a whole, for the case of the horizontal part of the curves of Fig. 3. It is desired to compute the net vertical thrust on the outer cylinder.

The parts of the cylinders in Fig. 1 which are lightly hatched are symmetrical about a horizontal center line and plainly exert no axial thrust. The entire axial thrust on the outer coil is equal to the repulsion on the doubly cross-hatched part exerted by the current in the inner coil. This repulsion is equal to the force on the doubly hatched part due to its lying in the magnetic field produced by the inner coil. Only the radial component of this field produces axial thrust.

A convenient expression for the radial component of magnetic field strength in absolute electromagnetic units, produced by the inner coil at the point P (Fig. 1) at the center of the doubly hatched part is given by equations (40) and (36) in Chap. 32.

Taking the magnetic field density in lines per square centimeter in air equal to H, the force in dynes is obtained by multiplying H by the number of ampere-conductors in the doubly hatched section, divided by 10, and again multiplying by the circumference through P, measured in centimeters. Using the facts that 981 dynes are equal to 1 gram and that 1 kg equals 2.205 lb, the axial force in pounds is obtained.

The effect of the steel core inside the cylinders of windings should next be estimated, but for the sake of clearness a numerical example of the calculation so far will first be given.

Example. For an illustrative example, the dimensions of the 10,000-kva, 75-kv transformer previously described may be used (see Fig. 1).

Find the steady force during a sustained short circuit at the transformer terminals.

By (36), Chap. 32,

$$H_{r(s)\infty} = \frac{3.11 \times 2,180}{10} \frac{\sqrt{29.6}}{\sqrt{38.4}} [6.85(1 + 0.0128 - 0.0001 + \cdots)$$
$$- 4 - 0.0085 + 0.0001 - \cdots]$$
$$= 1,740$$

By (40), Chap. 32,

$$H_{r(s)} = 1,740 - \frac{3.11 \times 2,180}{10} \times \frac{\pi \times 19.2}{14.8} [0.0130 - 0.0010$$
$$+ 0.0001 \cdots]$$
$$= 1,740 - 30 = 1,710$$

Magnetic field strength at P (Fig. 1) = 1,710 lines/sq cm
Ampere-conductors in doubly hatched section,

$$3.11 \times 0.375 \times 2.54 \times 2,180 = 6,460$$
Mean turn of outer coil = $\pi \times 38.4 \times 2.54 = 306$ cm
Vertical force = $\dfrac{6,460 \times 1,710 \times 306 \times 2.205}{10 \times 981,000}$

$$= 760 \text{ lb, not including the effect of the core.}$$

This checks closely with 770 lb obtained by equations (13) and (14), Chap. 33.

By inspection of equation (36), Chap. 32, it is seen that the force on a turn at the top of the outer coil, due to current in the inner coil, assumed infinitely long, is obtained by multiplying that formula by $\pi DI/10$ and the result is independent of whether D in the result is the diameter of the coil or the turn. For short coils, inspection of (9), Chap. 32, shows the same thing to be true. It must therefore be true also of the coils of finite length represented by equation (40), Chap. 32. In other words, the outer coil exerts the same axial force on the inner coil as the inner coil does on the outer, as would be expected.

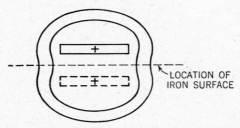

LOCATION OF
IRON SURFACE

Fig. 4.—Conductor and its image behind an iron surface.

When a straight conductor carrying direct current lies parallel to a plane surface of iron of negligible reluctance, the magnetic field around the conductor enters the iron surface always at right angles, as indicated by the cross section in Fig. 4. The shape and strength of the magnetic field around the conductor are just the same as if there were two conductors symmetrically placed, with air instead of the iron. For any line of force, half of the magnetomotive force (mmf) is provided by the conductor and half by the image conductor. This gives the same strength of field around the conductor as if the mmf for the parts of the lines of force below the dotted line in Fig. 4 were made zero by reason of the magnetism going through iron.

The image conductor solution just described applies with alternating current, provided the iron is finely laminated, with the edges of the laminations appearing at the iron surface. If the laminations are parallel to the iron surface, eddy currents will flow in them which will substantially prevent alternating magnetic flux from entering the iron.   The magnetic flux around the conductor will then have to take paths through air and the mmf will be provided entirely by the conductor, without the equivalent effect of an image conductor.

In this problem it is desired to find the magnetic flux caused by the inner coil only, so as to find the repulsion on a relatively small group of conductors at P (Fig. 1).   The coil goes around a core whose section is usually cruciform in shape.   There are two places, one on each side of the core, in which the conductors are parallel to the faces of the laminations instead of their edges, but for the most part the core behaves like finely laminated iron, and an image conductor can be assumed.

The average location of the iron surface can be determined by sketching a circle on the cross section of the core.   This gives a radius of 12 in. in the numerical example.   The image coil then has a mean radius of 9.2 in.   When the computation for field strength at P due to this image coil is carried out, a result $0.79\ n_1 I/10$ is obtained, which is 0.31 times the previous result. For this item, equation (31) in Chap. 32 may be convenient.

Taking $n_1 I/10$ to be the same for the image as for the actual conductor, which is correct for a flat iron surface but an approximation for a cylindrical surface, the computed force becomes $760 \times 1.31 = 1,000$ lb.   The effect of the thickness of the inner coil (in this example 2.4 in.) may be computed by equation (38), Chap. 32, and results in an increase in the force of 1 per cent. The effect of the thickness of the outer coil will be approximately the same.   It does not seem to be worth recommending to make computations for these small corrections.   The percentage of effect of the thickness is somewhat larger in the case of the compressive component of force.

Formula (37), Chap. 32, for the effect of coil thickness, cannot be used in this type of problem because t^2/c^2 is not a very small quantity and so terms in t^4/c^4 which are omitted from the formula, would not be negligible.   Accordingly, (38) should be used.

Since the effect of the coil thickness of 2.4 in. is only 1 per cent of the result and since it is practically the same as averaging the field density over a distance of 2.4 in., then to average the field density over the $\frac{3}{8}$ in. axial length of the doubly hatched section at P will be quite negligible in effect.   There is a certain amount of irregularity in the amount of force as the offset increases, when the winding is made up of disk coils separated by oil spaces, but this variation is also small.

The formulas and calculations for mechanical force in transformers could be checked by actual measurement of the forces. There do not appear to be any published measurements in the electrical engineering literature. Measurements have been published for the force between reactance coils, disconnecting switches, wires at right angles, and closely adjacent bus-bar straps. The measurements have agreed with calculations within about 5 to 10 per cent or less. In the case of transformer coils, the high-low voltage insulation could be removed and the upper half of the outer cylinder separated from the lower half. First one-half and then the other could be supported by cords, and the vertical force due to measured currents could be determined. Current could be taken in to the coils through mercury cups. For a null method, the cords could be suspended from a spiral spring and shot put in a container so that the same coil position be obtained with and without current. The weight of the shot added would give the steady vertical force caused by the current. When the net force between the halves was compression, the halves could be fastened together and the force on the entire cylinder measured. Even the computed components could be measured by removing the primary current, though short-circuit currents imply both primary and secondary currents. All these forces could be measured with and without the core.

Such measurements of forces, combined with the usual oscillographs for currents, should clear up any differences of opinion as to the correctness of formulas or the method of using the formulas.

CHAPTER 36

A PRELIMINARY CALCULATION OF MAGNETIC FORCE OF CURRENT ELEMENTS BY DOPPLER EFFECT

The following calculation is of interest in connection with the computation of magnetic field strength and the force of repulsion due to a current.   A calculation based on sound will be taken up first and then it will be applied to electric currents.

Let two small bodies a and b (Fig. 1) be moving horizontally to the left with velocities v_a and v_b through still air, these velocities being small compared with the speed of sound.   Let b send out sound waves of a constant frequency, which travel through the air with velocity c.   Let the peak of a sound wave start from body

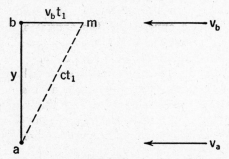

FIG. 1.—Two small bodies in air at time t_1.

b at time 0 and reach a at time t_1 when b is a distance y vertically above a, as in Fig. 1.   Body b will have traveled $v_b t_1$ and the sound will have traversed the path $ma = ct_1$.

If the vibrations sent out by a source of sound are symmetrical in all directions or if they are directional but sent out in directions that are constantly changing in a fortuitous manner, then the effect is uniformly spread over any spherical area whose center is at the source from which the vibrations came.   The effect per square centimeter varies inversely as the area of the sphere, that is, inversely as the square of the distance that the vibrations have traveled.   Then the pressure exerted by the sound on the body a varies inversely as ma^2. Let the intensity of the sound from b be such that the pressure on a is P when the sound has traveled 1 cm, when a and b are stationary. Then because of the inverse square law, the pressure on a (Fig. 1) is to be multiplied by

$$\frac{1}{ma^2} = \frac{1}{c^2 t_1^2}$$

where ma is the distance from m to a. But

$$c^2 t_1^2 = y^2 + v_b^2 t_1^2 \qquad \text{from Fig. 1}$$

$$\frac{1}{t_1^2} = \frac{c^2 - v_b^2}{y^2}$$

$$\frac{1}{c^2 t_1^2} = \frac{1}{y^2}\left(1 - \frac{v_b^2}{c^2}\right) \qquad (1)$$

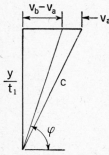

FIG. 2.—Velocity vector diagram.

It is desired to find the vertical component of pressure on body a. This is obtained by multiplying the pressure by $\sin \varphi$ where φ is the angle with the horizontal at which a experiences the arrival of the vibrations. This can be obtained from a velocity vector diagram, as in Fig. 2.

The vibrations travel with velocity c which has the same slope as ma (Fig. 1). But because body a has the velocity v_a to the left, the vibrations appear to approach a at the angle φ with the horizontal, where

$$\sin \varphi = \frac{y}{(y^2 + v^2 t_1^2)^{\frac{1}{2}}} \qquad (\text{where } v = v_b - v_a)$$

$$= 1 - \frac{v^2 t_1^2}{2y^2}$$

But $\qquad t_1^2 = \frac{y^2}{c^2}\left(1 - \frac{v_b^2}{c^2}\right)^{-1} \qquad$ from (1)

Then $\qquad \sin \varphi = 1 - \frac{v^2}{2c^2} \qquad (2)$

omitting terms in $1/c^4$.

As part of the Doppler effect, the motions of a and b change not only the apparent angle φ but also the frequency of the vibrations experienced by the body a.

The peak of the first sound wave, described previously, reached a at time t_1. Let the peak of a second sound wave start from body b at time t and reach body a at time t_2. The frequency of the sound leaving body b is $1/t$ when that body is stationary. Let $v_b - v_a = v$. The time t is much smaller than the time t_1 and the wave length is small compared with y.

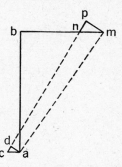

In Fig. 3, ma is the path of the first peak and nc is the path of the second. To a first approximation,

$$mn = v_b t \qquad \text{and} \qquad ac = v_a t$$

FIG. 3.—Path of second impulse.

The distance mn is taken to be a small quantity compared with mb. By similar triangles,

$$\frac{np}{nm} = \frac{mb}{ma} = \frac{v_b t_1}{c t_1} = \frac{v_b}{c}$$

$$\frac{cd}{ca} = \frac{mb}{ma} = \frac{v_b}{c}$$

The path nc is shorter than the path ma by

$$np - cd = \frac{v_b}{c}(nm - ca)$$

$$= \frac{v_b}{c}(v_b - v_a)t$$

If the bodies a and b were stationary, the distance between two adjacent wave peaks would be ct, but this has been shortened by $(np - cd)$ in the neighborhood of a.

The time between successive peaks is decreased in the ratio

$$\frac{\cdot ct - \dfrac{v_b^2 t}{c} + \dfrac{v_a v_b}{c} t}{ct}$$

and therefore the frequency, to a first approximation, is increased in the ratio

$$1 + \frac{v_b^2}{c^2} - \frac{v_a v_b}{c^2} \tag{3}$$

Taking the pressure on a to vary with the square of the frequency of the vibrations experienced at a, as well as to vary with factors (1) and (2), the pressure on a is

$$\frac{P}{y^2}\left(1 - \frac{v_b^2}{c^2}\right)\left(1 - \frac{v^2}{2c^2}\right)\left(1 + \frac{v_b^2}{c^2} - \frac{v_a v_b}{c^2}\right)^2$$

Neglecting terms in $1/c^4$, the downward component of pressure on a is

$$\frac{P}{y^2}\left(1 - \frac{v_b^2}{c^2} - \frac{v_b^2}{2c^2} + \frac{v_a v_b}{c^2} + \frac{v_a^2}{2c^2} + \frac{2v_b^2}{c^2} - \frac{2v_a v_b}{c^2}\right)$$
$$= \frac{P}{y^2}\left(1 + \frac{v_a^2}{2c^2} - \frac{v_a v_b}{c^2} + \frac{v_b^2}{2c^2}\right) \quad (4)$$

The electrostatic force of repulsion between two stationary, concentrated, electric charges q_a and q_b at separation y, is

$$\frac{q_a q_b}{y^2} \qquad\qquad \text{dynes} \quad (5)$$

where q_a and q_b are in absolute electrostatic units. If electrostatic repulsion is taken to be a pressure exerted by vibrations radiated from electric charges and if it is taken to be governed by the same mechanical laws that have been used in the foregoing problem on sound, then the downward repulsion on $-q_a$ caused by $-q_b$ is

$$\frac{q_a q_b}{y^2}\left(1 + \frac{v_a^2}{2c^2} - \frac{v_a v_b}{c^2} + \frac{v_b^2}{2c^2}\right) \quad (6)$$

as in (4), where c is now the speed of light.

Taking an electric current in a short element of wire to consist of stationary positive charges and moving negative charges, with the total positive equal to the total negative, per centimeter of a given wire, and taking the same calculation to apply to attraction as to repulsion, then the downward force of $+q_b$ on $-q_a$ is given by putting $v_b = 0$ in (6) and is

$$-\frac{q_a q_b}{y^2}\left(1 + \frac{v_a^2}{2c^2}\right) \quad (7)$$

For the force of $-q_b$ on $+q_a$, put $v_a = 0$ in (6), with the result

$$-\frac{q_a q_b}{y^2}\left(1 + \frac{v_b^2}{2c^2}\right) \quad (8)$$

The force for the two stationary charges is given by (5).   Adding
these four quantities, the downward force on the lower element
of wire is

$$- \frac{q_a q_b}{y^2} \frac{v_a v_b}{c^2} \tag{9}$$

But

$$\frac{q_a v_a}{c} = i_1 \, ds_1$$

where i_1 is in absolute electromagnetic units and ds_1 is the length
of wire over which the charge q_a is distributed.

Therefore, the force between two short parallel elements of
current flowing in the same direction and placed opposite each
other is an attraction whose amount is the well-known expression

$$\frac{i_1 i_2}{y^2} \, ds_1 \, ds_2 \qquad\qquad \text{dynes} \quad (10)$$

If the positive charges are given velocities to the right, expression (10) is still obtained.

This computation is, of course, of no present value since
attempts to extend it in the above form to current elements
which are not opposite each other or which are not parallel, have
not been successful.   However, it computes a case of magnetism
from electrostatic attraction and repulsion, using merely a
Doppler effect calculation as it might be applied to a purely
mechanical vibration without any magnetic field laws or any
special devices.

CHAPTER 37

REPULSION BETWEEN STRAP CONDUCTORS

The repulsion between two round wires or cables carrying opposing electric currents is very easily computed, being proportional to the product of the currents and inversely proportional to the distance between the centers of the conductors. This computation does not apply to the case of rectangular conductors which are near together. In such a case, the force between two strap conductors in parallel planes may be considerably less than that for two round conductors at the same distance between centers.[1]

Taking two narrow strips of width dx and dy in two equal thin sheets in parallel planes, opposite each other, the force between the two elementary strips is

$$\frac{2i_1i_2 \, dy \, dx}{b^2\{s^2 + (x - y)^2\}} \qquad \text{dynes/cm}$$

where i_1 and i_2 are the currents in the two sheets, b is the width of each sheet, s is the separation, and x and y are measured from the edges of the sheets. Absolute units are used.

By integrating first over one sheet and then over the other, the repulsion on a sheet is found to be

$$F = 4 \frac{i_1i_2}{b} \tan^{-1} \frac{b}{s} - 2 \frac{i_1i_2s}{b^2} \text{logn} \left(1 + \frac{b^2}{s^2}\right) \quad \text{dynes/cm} \quad (1)$$

where logn denotes natural logarithm. The curve for this expression, plotted on a base $(s - a)/(a + b)$, is the lowest curve of Fig. 1.

The repulsion between two solid straps placed opposite each other at an axial distance s, each of cross section $a \times b$, with the

[1] Repulsion between Strap Conductors, by H. B. Dwight, *Elec. World*, Sept. 15, 1917, p. 522.

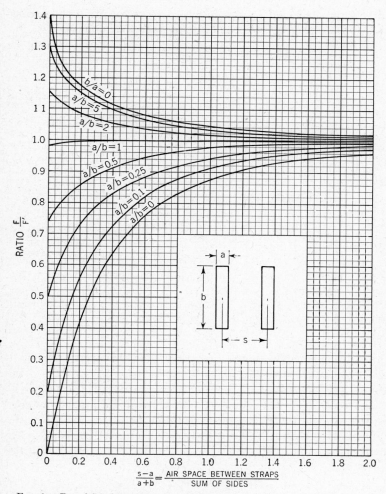

Fig. 1.—Repulsion between strap conductors.

F = repulsion between two equal long parallel straps.

F' = repulsion between two long parallel straight wires.

$$= 5.40 \frac{I_1 I_2 \cos \theta}{s} 10^{-7} \text{ pounds per foot of circuit,}$$

where θ is the phase angle between I_1 and I_2 which are in amperes, and where s is the axial spacing in inches. F and F' are average forces.

dimension a parallel to s, is obtained by integrating the expression for two sheets, over the two cross sections, and is

$$F = \frac{i_1 i_2}{a^2 b^2} \left[2b \left\{ (s + a)^2 - \frac{b^2}{3} \right\} \tan^{-1} \frac{b}{s + a} \right.$$

$$+ 2b \left\{ (s - a)^2 - \frac{b^2}{3} \right\} \tan^{-1} \frac{b}{s - a} - 4b \left(s^2 - \frac{b^2}{3} \right) \tan^{-1} \frac{b}{s}$$

$$+ (s + a) \left\{ b^2 - \frac{(s + a)^2}{3} \right\} \operatorname{logn} \left\{ \frac{b^2 + (s + a)^2}{s^2} \right\}$$

$$+ (s - a) \left\{ b^2 - \frac{(s - a)^2}{3} \right\} \operatorname{logn} \left\{ \frac{b^2 + (s - a)^2}{s^2} \right\}$$

$$- 2s \left(b^2 - \frac{s^2}{3} \right) \operatorname{logn} \left(\frac{b^2 + s^2}{s^2} \right) + \frac{2}{3} (s + a)^3 \operatorname{logn} \left(\frac{s + a}{s} \right)$$

$$\left. + \frac{2}{3} (s - a)^3 \operatorname{logn} \left(\frac{s - a}{s} \right) \right] \quad \text{dynes/cm of strap} \quad (2)$$

Equation (2) gives the intermediate curves of Fig. 1. The upper curve, for two thin sheets of width a placed edge to edge, with axial spacing s, is given by

$$F = \frac{2 i_1 i_2}{a^2} \left[(s + a) \operatorname{logn} \left(\frac{s + a}{s} \right) + (s - a) \operatorname{logn} \left(\frac{s - a}{s} \right) \right] \quad (3)$$

In the calculations described, skin effect has been neglected, and the current density has been assumed uniform over the section of the conductors.

In Fig. 1, the curves show the ratio between the force F between two straps and the force F' between two round conductors at the same axial spacing and with the same currents. In order to use these curves, one computes F' with a slide rule, according to the formula

$$F' = \frac{2 I_1 I_2}{100 s \times 2.54} \times \frac{2.54 \times 12}{981 \times 454} = 5.40 \frac{I_1 I_2}{s} 10^{-7} \quad \text{lb/ft} \quad (4)$$

where I_1 and I_2 are in amperes and s is in inches. If the currents are alternating and are out of phase by an angle θ, the force is multiplied by $\cos \theta$, as indicated below Fig. 1, just as is done in the computation of watts where there is a phase difference of θ between volts and amperes.

It is seen from Fig. 1 that, if the rectangular conductors are far enough apart so that $(s - a)/(a + b)$ is greater than 2, then there is less than 5 per cent error in computing the force if the round-wire formula (4) is used.

In Fig. 2, computed values of force given by equation (2) are compared with measured values published by C. J. Barrow in

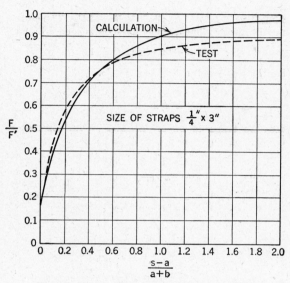

FIG. 2.—Comparison of calculation with test.

Trans. A.I.E.E., 1911, p. 392.   Currents up to 8,000 amp were used in making the measurements.

Example 1.   Find the average repulsion between two copper straps measuring ¼ by 6 in., in parallel planes, with the distance between centers 1¼ in. and with the current in each strap 5,000 amp.

$$F' = \frac{5.40 \times 5{,}000^2 \times 10^7}{1.25} = 10.8 \qquad \text{lb/ft by (4)}$$

From Fig. 1, $F/F' = 0.42$ since $a/b = \tfrac{1}{24}$ and

$$\frac{s - a}{a + b} = \frac{1.25 - 0.25}{0.25 + 6} = \frac{1}{6.25} = 0.16$$

Therefore, $F = 10.8 \times 0.42 = 4.5$ lb/ft

This is the force for 5,000 amp, direct current, and it is the average force if the currents are in-phase, alternating currents, in which case the momentary force changes from zero to twice the average value during every cycle.

Example 2.   Find, by Fig. 1, the average force in the case of two straps $\frac{1}{4}$ by 3 in. in parallel planes, with the distance between centers 6 in. and with a current of 10,000 amp, single phase.   *Ans.* 8.6 lb/ft.

Example 3.   Find the average mechanical force on three-phase bus bars measuring $\frac{1}{4}$ by 3 in. in parallel planes, with an axial spacing of 6 in. and with 10,000 amp per phase.

Let the 3 bus bars in a row be called A, B, and C.   The currents in them are 120° apart in phase.   The average force on A caused by I_B is

$$9.0 \times 0.96 \cos 120° = 4.3 \qquad\qquad \text{lb/ft}$$

In computing the repulsion on A caused by I_C,

$$\frac{s - a}{a + b} = 3.61$$

and F/F' may be taken to be 1.   Then, $F = 4.5 \cos 120° = 2.2$ lb/ft The total average force on A is

$$4.3 + 2.2 = 6.5 \qquad\qquad \text{lb/ft}$$

The force on C is also 6.5 lb/ft.   The middle strap B is under repulsion by both C and A and, although it has a momentary force first in one direction and then in the other, the average force is zero.

CHAPTER 38

MAGNETIC FORCE ON DISCONNECTING SWITCHES[1]

It is a well-known feature connected with short circuits in large electric power systems, that disconnecting switches are sometimes forcibly opened by the magnetic repulsion caused by the large currents flowing. This is recognized by the designers

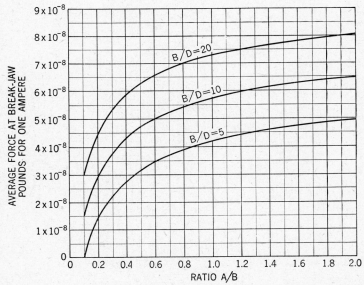

Fig. 1.—Repulsion in disconnecting switches. B = length of blade; D = width of break jaw. The force varies as the square of the current. Force due to return circuit is not included.

of disconnecting switches, who provide the switches subject to heavy duty with latches to hold them closed.

In this chapter are given formulas for the magnetic force acting on a disconnecting switch, which can be applied to the

[1] Calculation of Magnetic Force on Disconnecting Switches, by H. B. Dwight, *Trans. A.I.E.E.*, 1920, p. 1337.

various types of circuits usually used with such switches. Curves are given in Figs. 1 and 2 from which values of magnetic force can be taken without using the formulas. It is believed that the formulas or the curves give the value of the magnetic force

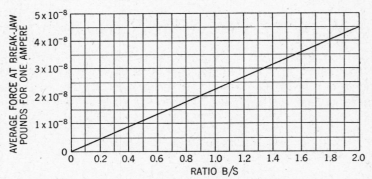

Fig. 2.—Repulsion due to return circuit. B = length of blade; S = distance from blade to return conductor. The force varies as the square of the current.

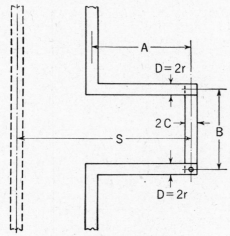

Fig. 3.—Typical circuit.

within a very small percentage. The formulas should be useful not only to the designers of switches who must design the parts so as to withstand the maximum force to be expected, but also for purposes of comparison when circuits are being designed containing disconnecting switches, for it is often desirable to choose a form of circuit that will produce the least possible magnetic force on the switch. The formulas and methods of calculation may also be used for calculating the forces on different parts of circuit breakers and other types of apparatus.

In Fig. 3 there is shown a typical electric circuit which approximates very closely to a disconnecting switch. The jaws are represented by round rods of diameter $D = 2r$, and the blade is a flat strap of width $2C$. This is the nearest to average conditions, and very little difference is made in the result if the calculation is made assuming the jaws to be flat instead of round.

The mechanical force on the blade is proportional to the current in the blade and to the magnetic lines of force cutting it.

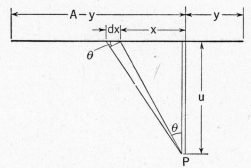

Fig. 4.—Element of blade.

The mechanical force acts in a direction perpendicular to the blade.

The first part calculated will be the force on the part of the blade not inside the break jaw, produced by magnetic lines due to the current in the upper arm of length A. The current in the arm, which tapers off gradually for the distance $2C$ at the jaw, may be assumed to be full strength as far as the middle of the blade. The magnetic field produced by current in a round rod is in circles around it, and the strength of the field is the same, outside the metal, as if the current were concentrated at the axis of the rod. Therefore, if the rear part of the arm is of a smaller diameter than D, the magnetic field at the blade will not be changed on that account.

The flux density at a point P (Fig. 4) caused by a current of I abamp in the element of conductor dx is

$$\frac{I \, dx \, \cos \theta}{u^2 + x^2} \qquad \cdot (1)$$

$$= \frac{Iu \, dx}{(u^2 + x^2)^{\frac{3}{2}}} \qquad \text{lines/sq cm} \quad (2)$$

The flux density at P due to the length $A - y$ is obtained by integrating expression (2) from $x = 0$ to $x = A - y$ and is

$$\frac{I(A - y)}{u \sqrt{u^2 + (A - y)^2}} \qquad \text{lines/sq cm} \quad (3)$$

By adding a similar expression obtained for the length y, the flux density at P due to the conductor of length A is

$$\frac{I(A - y)}{u \sqrt{u^2 + (A - y)^2}} + \frac{Iy}{u \sqrt{u^2 + y^2}} \qquad \text{lines/sq cm} \quad (4)$$

By integrating from $u = r$ to $u = B$, where y is constant, the flux in an elementary strip of the blade is found to be

$$I \left[\operatorname{logn} \left\{ \frac{(A - y) + \sqrt{(A - y)^2 + r^2}}{r} \right\} \right.$$
$$\left. - \operatorname{logn} \left\{ \frac{(A - y) + \sqrt{(A - y)^2 + B^2}}{B} \right\} + \operatorname{logn} \left\{ \frac{y + \sqrt{y^2 + r^2}}{r} \right\} \right.$$
$$\left. - \operatorname{logn} \left\{ \frac{y + \sqrt{y^2 + B^2}}{B} \right\} \right] dy \quad \text{lines} \quad (5)$$

where logn denotes natural logarithm.

This must be integrated from $y = 0$ to $y = C$ to obtain the flux cutting the inner half of the blade, outside of the break jaw.

The flux density at a point in the outer half of the blade is obtained in a somewhat similar manner and is equal to

$$\frac{I(A + y)}{u \sqrt{u^2 + (A + y)^2}} - \frac{Iy}{u \sqrt{u^2 + y^2}} \qquad \text{lines/sq cm} \quad (6)$$

By integrating this from $u = r$ to $u = B$, and then from $y = 0$ to $y = C$, the flux cutting the outer half of the blade is obtained.

Thus, the flux cutting the entire blade outside the break jaw, produced by the conductor of length A is found to be

$$I\left[(A + C) \operatorname{logn} \left\{ \frac{(A + C) + \sqrt{(A + C)^2 + r^2}}{r} \right\} \right.$$

$$- (A + C) \operatorname{logn} \left\{ \frac{(A + C) + \sqrt{(A + C)^2 + B^2}}{B} \right\}$$

$$- (A - C) \operatorname{logn} \left\{ \frac{(A - C) + \sqrt{(A - C)^2 + r^2}}{r} \right\}$$

$$+ (A - C) \operatorname{logn} \left\{ \frac{(A - C) + \sqrt{(A - C)^2 + B^2}}{B} \right\}$$

$$+ \sqrt{(A + C)^2 + B^2} - \sqrt{(A + C)^2 + r^2}$$

$$\left. - \sqrt{(A - C)^2 + B^2} + \sqrt{(A - C)^2 + r^2} \right] \qquad \text{lines} \quad (7)$$

The mechanical force on the blade in dynes, due to this flux is obtained by multiplying expression (7) by $I/(2C)$ where I is the current in abamperes.

Formula (7) is expressed more simply as a convergent series, but different series are required for the two cases in which B is less than A and greater than A. For this purpose, the following series are used:

$$\operatorname{logn}(x + \sqrt{1 + x^2}) = x - \frac{1}{6} x^3 + \frac{1 \cdot 3}{2 \cdot 4 \cdot 5} x^5 - \cdots \quad (8)$$

where x^2 is less than 1, and

$$\operatorname{logn}(x + \sqrt{1 + x^2}) = \operatorname{logn}(2x) + \tfrac{1}{4}u^2 - \tfrac{3}{32}u^4 + \cdots \quad (9)$$

where x^2 is greater than 1 and where $u = 1/x$.

When B is less than A, the force due to the flux outside of the jaw, caused by the conductor of length A, is

$$\frac{I^2}{100} \left[\operatorname{logn} \frac{B}{r} - \frac{1}{4} \frac{B^2}{A^2} + \frac{1}{4} \frac{r^2}{A^2} + \frac{3}{32} \frac{B^4}{A^4} \right.$$
$$\left. - \frac{1}{4} \frac{B^2 C^2}{A^4} + \cdots \right] \qquad \text{dynes} \quad (10)$$

where I is the current in amperes.

When B is greater than A, the above force is

$$\frac{I^2}{100} \left[\operatorname{logn} \frac{2A}{r} - \frac{A}{B} - \frac{1}{6} \frac{C^2}{A^2} + \frac{1}{4} \frac{r^2}{A^2} + \frac{1}{6} \frac{A^3}{B^3} + \frac{1}{6} \frac{AC^2}{B^3} - \frac{3}{40} \frac{A^5}{B^5} \right.$$
$$\left. - \frac{1}{4} \frac{A^3 C^2}{B^5} + \cdots \right] \qquad \text{dynes} \quad (11)$$

The second part of the force to be calculated is that due to the flux cutting the part of the blade inside the jaw of the switch.

The magnetic flux inside the metal of the round rod is in concentric circles around the axis. The flux density at any of the circular paths is that which would be produced by the current inside the circular path, for current outside cannot produce magnetic flux in a path which does not surround the current. Therefore, the flux density at radius u inside the metal is obtained by multiplying expression (4) by u^2/r^2 for the parts G and H of the jaw and by multiplying expression (6) by u^2/r^2 for the parts K and L. Now the flux in the jaw does not produce the full amount of mechanical force on the blade, because the current in the blade tapers off gradually from the full value to zero in

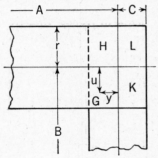
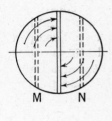

Fig. 5.—Switch jaw.

the distance $2r$ in the jaw. Consequently, the flux in the parts G and K must be multiplied by $(r + u)/(2r)$ to obtain the effective flux, and the flux in the parts H and L must be multiplied by $-(r - u)/(2r)$, since the flux in the parts H and L is in the opposite direction to that in G and K and is such as to tend to hold the blade closed. See Fig. 5.

By integrating the effective flux for each of the four parts of the jaw, the total force on the part of the blade in the jaw is found to be

$$\frac{I^2}{4r^3C} \left[\frac{1}{4}(A - C)^4 \operatorname{logn} \left\{ \frac{r + \sqrt{r^2 + (A - C)^2}}{A - C} \right\} \right.$$
$$- \frac{1}{4}(A + C)^4 \operatorname{logn} \left\{ \frac{r + \sqrt{r^2 + (A + C)^2}}{A + C} \right\}$$
$$+ \frac{r}{4}(A - C)^2 \sqrt{r^2 + (A - C)^2} - \frac{r}{4}(A + C)^2 \sqrt{r^2 + (A + C)^2}$$
$$\left. - \frac{r}{2}\{r^2 + (A - C)^2\}^{3/2} + \frac{r}{2}\{r^2 + (A + C)^2\}^{3/2} \right] \quad \text{dynes} \quad (12)$$

When this is expressed as a convergent series, it becomes

$$A r^2 \left(\frac{1}{3} - \frac{1}{10} \frac{r^2}{A^2} \right) \qquad \text{dynes} \qquad (13)$$

This is, in an ordinary case, about 8 per cent of the total mechanical force on the switch blade. Since the result of this part of the calculation is such a small percentage of the total, the effect of the approximations used in making up the typical circuit will be seen to be small. The fact that the current in the horizontal conductor tapers gradually to zero in the distance $2C$

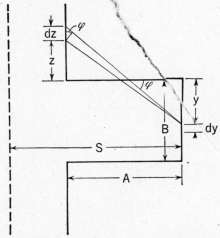

Fig. 6.—Typical circuit for connections parallel to blade.

and the fact that the section of the jaw may be approximately square instead of round will not make an important difference in this small part of the total force. If the blade is made up of two parallel straps, which is often done to make a more rigid structure as indicated by the dotted lines at M and N (Fig. 5), only the outermost lines of force will cut the blade. However, when the integration is carried out for this case, expression (13) is found to be reduced by only one-eighth of itself. This is only 1 per cent of the total force. Accordingly, only one formula is given for the different types of disconnecting switches, and the formula has been calculated on the basis of a single-blade switch.

It is evident that the effective flux inside the metal is calculated quite differently from the method used for calculating self-inductances. Therefore the geometrical mean distance of the section of the conductor should not be used in this problem.

In calculating the force due to the connections parallel to the blade, the flux density at dy (Fig. 6) due to the upper connection is in the opposite direction to the flux previously considered, and is

$$I \int_{z=0}^{z=\infty} \frac{-dz \cos \varphi}{A^2 + (y + z)^2} = I \int_{z=0}^{z=\infty} \frac{-A \, dz}{\{A^2 + (y + z)^2\}^{3/2}}$$

$$= I \left[\frac{-1}{A \sqrt{1 + \frac{A^2}{(y + z)^2}}} \right]_{z=0}^{z=\infty}$$

$$= I \left(-\frac{1}{A} + \frac{y}{A \sqrt{A^2 + y^2}} \right) \quad \text{lines/sq cm} \quad (14)$$

The force on the blade due to the upper connection is

$$I^2 \int_{y=0}^{y=B} \left(-\frac{1}{A} + \frac{y}{A \sqrt{A^2 + y^2}} \right) dy = I^2 \left[-\frac{y}{A} + \frac{\sqrt{A^2 + y^2}}{A} \right]_{y=0}^{y=B} = I^2 \left(-\frac{B}{A} + \frac{\sqrt{A^2 + B^2}}{A} - 1 \right) \quad \text{dynes} \quad (15)$$

I being the current in abamperes.

When this is expanded as a series, it becomes, when B is less than A,

$$\frac{I^2}{100} \left(-\frac{B}{A} + \frac{1}{2} \frac{B^2}{A^2} - \frac{1}{8} \frac{B^4}{A^4} + \cdots \right) \quad \text{dynes} \quad (16)$$

and, when A is less than B,

$$\frac{I^2}{100} \left(-1 + \frac{1}{2} \frac{A}{B} - \frac{1}{8} \frac{A^3}{B^3} + \frac{1}{16} \frac{A^5}{B^5} \right.$$

$$\left. - \frac{1}{8} \frac{AC^2}{B^3} + \cdots \right) \quad \text{dynes} \quad (17)$$

where I is the current in amperes. The term $-\dfrac{1}{8} \dfrac{AC^2}{B^3}$ is obtained by integrating the formula over the blade of width $2C$.

In some cases the return conductor is brought back directly behind the switch at a distance S, as indicated by the dotted lines in Figs. 3 and 6. This adds to the force tending to open the switch. The flux density at dy (Fig. 6) due to the part of the return conductor above the center of the switch is

$$I \int_{z=-\frac{B}{2}}^{z=\infty} \frac{S\,dz}{\{S^2 + (y+z)^2\}^{\frac{3}{2}}} = I \left[\frac{1}{S\sqrt{1 + \frac{S^2}{(y+z)^2}}} \right]_{z=-\frac{B}{2}}^{z=\infty}$$

$$= I \left[\frac{1}{S} - \frac{\left(y - \frac{B}{2}\right)}{S\sqrt{S^2 + \left(y - \frac{B}{2}\right)^2}} \right] \quad \text{lines/sq cm} \quad (18)$$

The force on the blade due to this part of the conductor is

$$I^2 \int_{y=0}^{y=B} \left[\frac{1}{S} - \frac{\left(y - \frac{B}{2}\right)}{S\sqrt{S^2 + \left(y - \frac{B}{2}\right)^2}} \right] dy$$

$$= I^2 \left[\frac{y}{S} - \frac{\sqrt{S^2 + \left(y - \frac{B}{2}\right)^2}}{S} \right]_{y=0}^{y=B} = I^2 \frac{B}{S} \quad \text{dynes} \quad (19)$$

where I is in abamperes.

This is the part of the force supported by the friction of the break jaw, or the latch, and it agrees with the usual formula for the repulsion of two long parallel conductors.

The forces acting on the switch blade are in general symmetrical as regards the two ends of the blade. One-half of the complete total force is supported at the break jaw and one-half at the hinge jaw. Therefore, in calculating the force at the break jaw, an addition is made of the forces acting on the blade due to one horizontal conductor, one vertical connection to the switch, and one-half of the return conductor, if it returns directly behind the switch. In cases where the horizontal connections are of unequal length, a good approximation to the value of the force may be obtained by using their average length for the dimension A in the formulas.

The force at the break jaw, expressed as a series, is, when B is less than A

$$\frac{I^2}{4.45 \times 10^7} \left[2.30 \log_{10}\left(\frac{B}{r}\right) + \frac{1}{3} - \frac{B}{A} + \frac{1}{4}\frac{B^2}{A^2} + \frac{3}{20}\frac{r^2}{A^2} \right.$$

$$\left. - \frac{1}{32}\frac{B^4}{A^4} + \frac{B}{S} \right] \quad \text{pounds} \quad (20)$$

When A is less than B, the force is

$$\frac{I^2}{4.45 \times 10^7} \left[2.30 \log_{10} \left(\frac{2A}{r} \right) - \frac{2}{3} - \frac{1}{2} \frac{A}{B} - \frac{1}{6} \frac{C^2}{A^2} + \frac{3}{20} \frac{r^2}{A^2} \right. $$
$$\left. + \frac{1}{24} \frac{A^3}{B^3} + \frac{1}{24} \frac{AC^2}{B^3} + \frac{B}{S} \right] \quad \text{pounds} \quad (21)$$

where I is in amperes.   If the circuit does not return behind the switch, the term B/S is zero.

The average force in pounds acting along the center line of the break jaw, assuming that the circuit does not return behind the switch, is plotted in Fig. 1.   If the circuit returns directly behind the switch, the force to be added can be taken from Fig. 2. These curves are more convenient for the solution of engineering problems than the formulas.   In the curves, C is taken to equal r.

The dimensions used in the formulas and curves may be all in centimeters or all in inches, since only ratios of dimensions appear.

The force given by the formulas and curves is the average force, or the steady push, exerted by the current, which is measured in effective amperes.   It is the force that would be measured by a spring balance if the blade were free to move.   However, it should not be forgotten that with alternating current the force rises to double the average value every cycle.   This large momentary value of force should be used in some problems, for it is capable of overcoming initial friction or of cracking a latch which holds a switch closed.   If I represents the peak value of the current, the formulas give the maximum momentary value of the force.

Example.   Find the force of repulsion at 30,000 amp, effective, on a disconnecting switch in which $A = 15$ in., $B = 20$ in., width of blade $= 2C$ $= 1.5$ in., and width of jaw $= D = 2r = 1$ in.   There is no return circuit behind the switch.

By formula (21), since A is less than B, the average force at the break jaw is

$$\frac{9 \times 10^8}{4.45 \times 10^7} \ [4.094 - 0.667 - 0.375 + 0.018] = \frac{90}{4.45} \times 3.07 = 62 \quad \text{pounds}$$

Using the curves of Fig. 1, $A/B = 0.75$ and $B/D = 20$, and therefore the average force is $9 \times 10^8 \times 6.9 \times 10^{-8} = 62$ lb.

The maximum momentary force at the peak of the current wave is 124 lb.

CHAPTER 39

LONGITUDINAL FORCE IN A TAPERED CONDUCTOR

When a heavy electric current is carried by a liquid conductor such as the molten metal in the trough of an electric furnace of appropriate shape, a constriction forms in the liquid. This grows until at a certain amperage the conductor separates, leaving an arc between the two parts. This reduces the current and the mechanical force so that the parts of the liquid touch again, and the action is repeated. In an electric furnace, the arc thus formed is quite violent. With a trough of mercury and a current

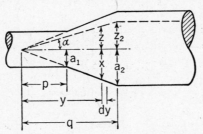

FIG. 1.—Conductor with change in section.

of 1,500 amp in one laboratory, the current was broken several times a second.

A tapered portion of a straight cylindrical conductor[1] is shown in Fig. 1. Assume that the current density is uniform over any given section of the cylinder; that is, skin effect is not taken into account. Also, assume that the flow is along straight lines, as indicated in Fig. 1. The rounding off of the corners of the streamlines is not taken into account.

The current density at distance y where the radius is x, is

$$i = \frac{I}{\pi x^2}$$

[1] See Two Cases of Calculation of Mechanical Forces in Electric Circuits, by H. B. Dwight, *Trans. A.I.E.E.*, 1927, p. 570.

where I is the total current in amperes and the dimensions are in centimeters. The total current inside radius z is

$$\pi i z^2 = I\,\frac{z^2}{x^2} = I\,\frac{z_2{}^2}{a_2{}^2}$$

The magnetic field is in circles around the axis if the return conductor is taken to be very remote. The mmf around the circle of radius z is

$$\frac{4\pi I}{10}\,\frac{z_2{}^2}{a_2{}^2}$$

Then the flux density at radius z is

$$\frac{2I}{10z}\,\frac{z_2{}^2}{a_2{}^2}$$

The dotted line at radius z (Fig. 1) is always at a distance equal to the proportionate part z_2/a_2 of the radius x, and it is almost exactly a line of current flow. A short element of it has a length $dy/\cos\alpha$ where $\tan\alpha = z/y$. A force acts on the short element of the filament, proportional to the current in the filament and the magnetic field in which it lies. It is

$$\frac{2I}{100z}\,\frac{z_2{}^2}{a_2{}^2}\,\frac{dy}{\cos\alpha} \quad \text{dynes/amp of current in the filament} \quad (1)$$

Multiply by $\sin\alpha$ to obtain the component of the force parallel to the axis.

$$\frac{2I}{100z}\,\frac{z_2{}^2}{a_2{}^2}\tan\alpha\,dy = \frac{2I}{100}\,\frac{z_2{}^2}{a_2{}^2}\,\frac{dy}{y}$$

Integrate this from $y = p$ to q. The total force parallel to the axis, acting on the filament, is

$$\frac{2I}{100}\,\frac{z_2{}^2}{a_2{}^2}\log n\,\frac{q}{p} \quad \text{dynes/amp of current in the filament}$$

If the filament be taken to have a radial thickness dz_2 at the radius z_2, then the total cross section of all such filaments at radius z_2 is

$$2\pi z_2\,dz_2$$

and the total current in them is

$$\frac{I}{\pi a_2{}^2}\,2\pi z_2\,dz_2 = \frac{2I}{a_2{}^2}\,z_2\,dz_2$$

The force parallel to the axis acting on the above filaments is

$$\frac{2I}{100}\frac{z_2^2}{a_2^2}\left(\operatorname{logn}\frac{q}{p}\right)\frac{2I}{a_2^2}z_2\,dz_2$$

Integrate this from $z_2 = 0$ to a_2. The total force parallel to the axis is

$$\frac{I^2}{100}\operatorname{logn}\frac{a_2}{a_1} \qquad\qquad \text{dynes} \quad (2)$$

That is,
$$F = \frac{I^2}{100}\operatorname{logn}\frac{a_2}{a_1}$$

where I is in amperes.

The force where the taper is not uniform may be obtained from (2). If the cylinder tapers from a radius a_1 to a radius a_m, the axial force on that part is

$$\frac{I^2}{100}\operatorname{logn}\frac{a_m}{a_1}$$

If the cylinder then tapers at a different rate from radius a_m to a_2, the force on that part is

$$\frac{I^2}{100}\operatorname{logn}\frac{a_2}{a_m}$$

and the total force is

$$\frac{I^2}{100}\operatorname{logn}\frac{a_2}{a_1}$$

This is the same as if the cylinder had tapered uniformly from radius a_1 to a_2 as in Fig. 1. The change in radius can therefore be made by means of a large number of tapers of different angles and the total axial force will depend only on the initial and final radii and will be given by equation (2).

The hydrostatic pressure due to the radial component of force, which has been described and computed by E. F. Northrup and C. Hering, is also of interest in connection with liquid conductors and electric furnaces. It may be computed for a straight cylinder of constant diameter $2a$. The pressure at radius r in the liquid cylinder is[2]

$$\frac{I^2}{100\pi a^4}(a^2 - r^2) \qquad \text{dynes/sq cm} \quad (3)$$

The dimensions are in centimeters and the current is in amperes.

[2] E. F. Northrup, *Phys. Rev.*, Vol. 24, p. 487, 1907.

The total thrust on a vertical cross section, omitting pressure due to gravity, is

$$\frac{I^2}{200} \qquad \qquad \text{dynes} \quad (4)$$

which is independent of the diameter.

Some experiments with several pounds of mercury in a trough about 6 cm in diameter were made by E. H. Dodge in connection with a thesis at Massachusetts Institute of Technology under the supervision of the author. At a heavy current a deep constriction formed, and at 1,450 amp the mercury circuit was repeatedly broken several times a second.

At about 1,000 amp the top surface of the mercury was rounded up, the horizontal column of mercury thus tending to have a circular cross section. At the same current a depression occurred next the vertical metal terminals where they dipped into the mercury. The outwardly directed force at the right-angle turn in the current is similar to the force that opens a disconnecting switch.

The following numerical computed values are based on an assumed cylinder 6 cm in diameter, with a constricted part 2 cm in diameter, and a current of 1,400 amp.

The longitudinal force acting in one direction, due to the taper, is by equation (2),

$$\frac{1,400}{100} \log n \frac{3}{1} = 21,500 \qquad \qquad \text{dynes}$$

The pressure at the center, with a mercury cylinder of 1 cm radius, is by equation (3) 6,200 dynes per sq cm, and where the cylinder has a radius of 3 cm, the pressure at the center is 900 dynes per sq cm. The total thrust on a cross section due to pressure computed by (3) is given by equation (4) and is 9,800 dynes.

The difference in pressure, 6,200 − 900 dynes per sq cm, would start a stream of mercury flowing along the axis away from the constriction and returning in the outer parts. Such a flow was observed and described by E. H. Dodge, in *Trans. A.I.E.E.*, 1927, p. 573. The forces behind such a flow, due to the hydrostatic pressure, are not so great in this example as the longitudinal electromagnetic force given by equation (2).

Index